NATURE CONSERVANCY COUNCIL

British Red Data Books:
2. Insects

Edited by D. B. Shirt

Co-ordinated by
the Insect Red Data Book Committees
in collaboration with
the Institute of Terrestrial Ecology (NERC)
the International Union for Conservation of Nature and Natural Resources
the Joint Committee for the Conservation of British Insects
the Nature Conservancy Council and
the Royal Society for Nature Conservation

1987

Contents

Foreword

In recent years the publication of Red Data Books has been instrumental in drawing attention to the status of the rarest and most threatened animals and plants. Both national and international approaches have been adopted, as each has an important role to play in defining which species are most in need of special conservation measures to ensure their survival. The publication of this Red Data Book for British insects is particularly welcome because previously the information on the status, biology and conservation needs of our insect fauna has been widely scattered in specialist publications or has remained unpublished and known to few entomologists.

The insects, with 22,500 species, comprise the richest part of the British fauna and the diversity of their life cycles and habitat needs naturally poses special problems for conservationists. Often better site protection is needed to safeguard our most threatened insects, and careful work is required to define the appropriate habitat management regimes to sustain their populations. This Red Data Book is an important step in developing the conservation of this fascinating part of our wildlife heritage. If it succeeds in stimulating entomologists and conservationists to find out more about these species and to do more to ensure their survival in Britain, it will have fulfilled two of its most important objectives.

The compilation of this book has been a truly co-operative effort which has involved many amateur as well as professional entomologists and both the governmental and non-governmental conservation organisations. The wide scope of the entries is a tribute to those many naturalists who make the results of their studies available for conservation, and we must take the opportunity presented to ensure that insect conservation is pursued with the same diligence that has done so much to safeguard our vertebrate and botanical heritage.

William Wilkinson.

W H N Wilkinson
Chairman, Nature Conservancy Council

Introduction

This is the first comprehensive statement on the status of the most threatened insects in Great Britain. It has been drawn up by leading specialists and covers most of the major groups of insects, including butterflies, moths, dragonflies, grasshoppers, beetles, flies, caddis-flies, heteropteran bugs, ants, bees and wasps.

The main purpose of this book is to draw attention to those insects whose continued survival in Britain is threatened, including those that have stable populations but occur in only very few sites. Many species could easily become extinct, as much by inappropriate site management as by habitat destruction, so that the special needs of these insects must be given attention. It is a matter of great concern to find that some 1800 species of insects qualify for inclusion in the Red Data Book, representing nearly 15 per cent of species in the groups fully covered (excluding the Microlepidoptera). By way of comparison, the total native British flora (vascular plants) is about 1700 species, of which 20 per cent are listed in *British Red Data Books: 1. Vascular plants* (Perring & Farrell, second edition 1983). The long-standing neglect of insect conservation must be overcome if Britain's fauna is not to suffer further serious declines and losses in the coming decades.

Red Data Books or Red Lists (listed by Burton, 1984) are now an established method of determining priorities in the conservation of individual animal and plant species. Invertebrate animals have only become a matter for concern relatively recently, the first publication being a well-produced Red Book of the Spanish Lepidoptera (mainly butterflies) (Viedma & Gomez-Bustillo, 1976). Many Red Data Books have been produced for very restricted areas, for only a few popular groups, or as simple lists of species. More comprehensive publications include *Threatened Rhopalocera (butterflies) in Europe* (Heath, 1981) and *The IUCN Invertebrate Red Data Book* (Wells, Pyle & Collins, 1983). Heath's work, commissioned by the Council of Europe, has laid a basis for the conservation of the rarest European butterflies. The International Union for Conservation of Nature's Red Data Book is more extensive in its coverage, but makes no claim to be other than a selection of threatened species, communities and phenomena from all invertebrate groups worldwide. More recently, IUCN has produced the first Red Data Book to assess all species in a single insect group. *Threatened swallowtail butterflies of the world: The IUCN Red Data Book* (Collins & Morris, 1985) examines the status of every swallowtail species and shortlists over 70 species that are of conservation concern. All of these works, and their compilers, have made valuable contributions to the present work.

Although other factors have also been important, the idea of a Red Data Book for British insects can be said to have followed from the publication in 1972 of *A code for insect collecting*, which is reproduced in the present book. The code was produced by the Joint Committee for the Conservation of British Insects (JCCBI), on which are represented all the entomological bodies, both amateur and professional, as well as conservation organisations and other interested parties. Whilst in many ways the code stood on its own, the JCCBI was anxious to urge restraint in the collecting of *particular* species. Lists of threatened insects in some of the major orders were published in the interests both of conservation and of gaining more accurate data on the status of the species concerned (Joint Committee for the Conservation of British Insects, 1973a, 1973b, 1974). These lists were used by the late Lord Cranbrook in the early stages of his promotion of the parliamentary Bill that became the Conservation of Wild Creatures and Wild Plants Act 1975.

Groundwork for the insect Red Data Book was done by an RDB Criteria and Species Selection Committee, assisted by a large number of invited specialists. Evaluation of the British fauna and compilation of the draft entries took over five years. An RDB Publication Committee then took over and a full-time Editor (Dr David Shirt) was employed by the Nature Conservancy Council (NCC) for twelve months, bringing the total time scale to nine years. The undertaking has involved a great deal of time and expertise, and has been a collaborative effort between the NCC, the Institute of Terrestrial Ecology, the IUCN Species Monitoring Unit, the JCCBI and the Royal Society for Nature Conservation.

The allocation of conservation categories to species is based upon the criteria established by the IUCN and adopted internationally. Minor adaptations have been made for reviewing the insect fauna of Britain, based partly upon usage in *British Red Data Books: 1. Vascular plants* (Perring & Farrell, 1983). The conservation status of species is constantly being reviewed and the allocation to categories is not rigid, but is undergoing continual reassessment. It is inevitable that publication of this book will reveal much new information.

Publication of the Red Data Book provides a standard reference for assessing faunal lists and evaluating sites. Since the lists were first drafted the Wildlife and Countryside Act 1981 has become law, giving firmer measures for the protection of Sites of Special Scientific Interest (SSSIs). Evaluation of SSSIs can now take into account the presence of Red Data Book species, and the needs of those species can be considered when deciding upon potentially damaging operations. In many instances the new procedures give the opportunity for introducing positive management measures for the flora and fauna. The Red Data Book therefore takes on a level of significance that could not have been foreseen at the outset, quite apart from its wider objectives as they apply to site management generally.

There can be no doubt that continuity of habitat, including appropriate management, is the key to success in species conservation. Whilst the 1981 Act also provides for the protection of species, the number of species that would benefit over and above the habitat protection of SSSIs is small. The broad guideline has been that species would be listed for special protection only if their survival was threatened by collecting. Such a threat actually has very little substance, since extinctions have been due almost entirely to other causes. The Red Data Book Committees urge strongly that the RDB list should not be used as a basis for a legislative list, which would be a very restricted and negative use of the data so diligently gathered and collated. The blanket listing of whole categories of species would cause immense practical problems, not least because many of the species are difficult or impossible to identify in the field. The greatest benefit to the conservation movement will stem from fostering the recording and study of insects: proscribing up to 28 per cent of the species in each order would effectively inhibit further acquisition of data on those very insects on which information is most desperately needed.

This first edition of the insect Red Data Book is a foundation on which to build. Greater clarification is required as to the location of breeding sites, and in many cases the data are old and in need of review. Often the ecological information is scant and requires improvement before it is possible to suggest suitable site management – usually the make or break for survival. Hopefully it will be possible to incorporate into future editions some of the lesser-known orders which have been omitted from the present edition. Publication focuses attention on the gaps in our knowledge and should lead towards a much fuller understanding of what needs to be done to ensure that this list of Britain's threatened insects becomes a list of species 'Out of Danger' through the application of appropriate conservation measures.

Production of the Red Data Book

Area covered The British Red Data Books cover Great Britain and the Isle of Man, but not the Republic of Ireland, Northern Ireland or the Channel Islands. The Irish insect fauna differs in many respects from that of Britain, and the fauna of the Channel Islands is more closely allied to that of mainland Europe. In addition, the executive powers of the NCC are confined to Great Britain, and the RSNC restricts its activities to the United Kingdom.

Categories The categories used here are based upon those developed by the IUCN and do not necessarily correspond with the terms used in the Wildlife and Countryside Act 1981. Their definitions and criteria are given in detail after the photographs. *It is stressed that the species are categorised according to degree of threat, and not degree of rarity.* The general term 'threatened' is used to cover RDB categories 1-3.

The species lists Full listings of the species in all categories follow the category definitions. The sequence and nomenclature are taken from the appropriate part of *A check list of British insects* (Kloet & Hincks, 1964-78), except that species are listed alphabetically within each genus. In some cases the Kloet & Hincks check list has been updated by a more recent publication, in which case details are given in the order introductions. Synonyms are only given for those species not dealt with in detail in the species accounts.

The order introductions Each order or section covered in the species accounts is preceded by a brief introduction. The threatened species are summarised, with general comments on the causes of their decline. This is followed by mention of the principal references for study and identification, concluding with a note on recording schemes, distribution atlases and specialist groups. An account of the parasitic Hymenoptera has been added, as this group has not been dealt with in detail in the present edition.

The species accounts Accounts are provided on all the Endangered and Vulnerable species listed, except for the Diptera (where a representative selection has been so treated). Each account is headed by the currently-accepted scientific name, which should be used in all communications. An English name is added wherever possible. The full name complete with authority and date is given before the text, with the addition of subgenus (in brackets) if this is included in the relevant check list, as this has frequently been used as a generic synonym. Earlier names that have been used for the species (for whatever reason) have also been added if they appear in the quoted references. It is hoped that the inclusion of alternative names may assist the non-specialist to locate records in old published sources, etc., though for a complete list of synonyms the check list should be consulted. The names of authorities have not been abbreviated, except for Linnaeus (L.) and Fabricius (F.).

The text is arranged under a series of sub-headings: the omission of one implies that no information was available on that particular subject. They are as follows:

Identification   Works of identification are inevitably technical in nature, though more popular works are mentioned wherever possible.

Distribution   British distribution is described using modern (1974 in England and Wales, 1975 in Scotland) administrative counties, regions and districts, as these are generally the standard units for conservation purposes and the planning authorities relate to them. In a few cases, reference is made to the Watsonian vice-counties (Dandy, 1969).

Habitat and ecology   The English and scientific names of plants are taken from the current (3rd) edition of *Excursion Flora of the British Isles* (Clapham, Tutin & Warburg, 1981).

Status   This section may include a brief account of the species' recent history, together with any general comments on status. Information has been updated to the end of 1984 wherever possible and to October 1986 in selected cases.

Threats   Events or activities which have affected the species in the past, or may do so in future, are detailed.

Conservation   This section describes both the measures that have been taken and those that are proposed for the future.

Author   The author of the account, with any additional references, is given.

Abbreviations and symbols	AES	Amateur Entomologists' Society
	BM(NH)	British Museum (Natural History)
	BRC	Biological Records Centre (ITE, Monks Wood)
	DoE	Department of the Environment
	FBA	Freshwater Biological Association
	ITE	Institute of Terrestrial Ecology (a component of NERC)
	IUCN	International Union for Conservation of Nature and Natural Resources
	JCCBI	Joint Committee for the Conservation of British Insects
	LNR	Local Nature Reserve
	LRC	Local records centre
	MAFF	Ministry of Agriculture, Fisheries and Food
	NCC	Nature Conservancy Council (formerly the Nature Conservancy)

NCR	*A Nature Conservation Review* (Ratcliffe, 1977)
NERC	Natural Environment Research Council
NNR	National Nature Reserve
RDB	Red Data Book
RESL	Royal Entomological Society of London
RSM	Royal Scottish Museum
RSNC	Royal Society for Nature Conservation
RSPB	Royal Society for the Protection of Birds
SSSI	Site of Special Scientific Interest
+	Category 1 species believed to be extinct
" "	English name as listed in Schedule 5 of the Wildlife and Countryside Act 1981

Symbols used in the species lists:

!	Listed in Schedule 5 of the Wildlife and Countryside Act 1981
>	Category 1 or 2 species with species account (Diptera only)
*	Category 3 status as yet uncertain (recently discovered or recognised)
(5)	Also listed in Category 5 (Endemic)

Red Data Book Committees

The groundwork was carried out by an **RDB Criteria and Species Selection Committee**, which held twenty meetings (1 March 1978 to 14 April 1983). The members were as follows:

Chairman Dr M G Morris, ITE
Secretary J Heath, ITE
P T Harding, ITE (from 5 March 1981)
A J B Rudge, NCC
B Skinner
A E Stubbs, NCC
Dr J A Thomas, ITE

Some meetings of that committee were also attended by P J Chandler, D G Chelmick, G R Else (BM(NH)), Lt Col A M Emmet, Dr M J Ford (NCC), P M Hammond (BM(NH)), Dr I F G McLean (NCC), Dr M R Shaw (RSM), and Dr R C Welch (ITE).

The production and editing were overseen by an **RDB Publication Committee**. This held seventeen meetings (16 May 1983 to 24 October 1986), and the members were as follows:

Chairman Dr M G Morris, ITE
Secretary J Heath (to 16 August 1983)
P T Harding, ITE (from 30 September 1983)
Editor Dr D B Shirt, NCC (from 9 February 1984)
Dr N M Collins, IUCN
A M Heaton, RSNC (from 5 April 1984)
A J B Rudge, NCC (to 30 May 1984)
T S Sands, RSNC (to 7 March 1984)
B Skinner
A E Stubbs, NCC

There were also two meetings of a Coleoptera Panel, attended (in addition to several members of the Publication Committee) by Dr R C Welch (ITE), and one meeting of a Heteroptera Panel, attended in addition by B C Eversham (ITE), Dr P Kirby and Dr B S Nau.

Acknowledgements The species accounts were contributed by the following:

Odonata	R Merritt
Orthoptera	E C M Haes
Heteroptera	B C Eversham, Dr M G Morris
Trichoptera	Dr I D Wallace
Lepidoptera	Lt Col A M Emmet, B Skinner, Dr J A Thomas
Coleoptera	M J D Brendell, Dr M L Cox, Dr G N Foster, P M Hammond, P T Harding, D G Holland, F A Hunter, B Levey, Dr M L Luff, Dr M G Morris, R D Pope, Dr D B Shirt, Dr R C Welch
Hymenoptera	G R Else, Dr M R Shaw, G M Spooner
Diptera	P J Chandler, Dr A G Irwin, Dr I F G McLean, A C Pont, A E Stubbs

For specialist advice and species records, we are also indebted to K N A Alexander, A A Allen, D G Chelmick, J Cooter, Dr R H L Disney, J Heath, P J Hodge, C Johnson, Dr P Kirby, H Mendel, Dr B S Nau and Prof J A Owen. Authors of the species accounts gratefully acknowledge the assistance of D M Ackland, A Amsden, D Appleton, Dr R M Badcock, D B Baker, K Barrett, D Bilton, B Bolton, A Buse, J M Chalmers-Hunt, J H Cole, R Crossley, Dr M C Day, J P Dear, M Denton, G H L Dicker, W R Dolling, A B Drane, M Edwards, G W Elmes, A Eve, R Fairclough, J Felton, J H Flint, E C M d'A Fonseca, M Greenwood, K M Guichard, M L Hall, P D Hiley, C Hobday, I Lorimer, Dr B E Miles, Dr N J Mills, Dr N W Moore, D Morgan, J M Nelson, M Newcombe, Dr C O'Toole, J Parry, Mrs E R Peacock, E C Pelham-Clinton, E G Philp, P Skidmore, K G V Smith, Dr M C D Speight, Dr J H Sudd, A Warne, Dr M S Warren, L S Whicher, G Wildridge and many other entomologists. Finally, thanks are also due to the staff of the NCC for their constructive criticism of the text and for preparing it for publication.

Correspondence The NCC is maintaining data files on all British Red Data Book species and would be pleased to receive modern records and biological information on any of the species dealt with here, as well as views on the inclusion, exclusion or grading of any species. The biology and habitat requirements of many Red Data Book species are insufficiently known. This information is urgently needed to allow the correct management to be assessed and where possible implemented for the conservation of these species. Please address all correspondence to: Red Data Book (Insects), Nature Conservancy Council, Northminster House, Peterborough, PE1 1UA. Records will be passed on to the appropriate BRC recording scheme (or to BRC for groups where there is no recording scheme); thus it would be helpful if records were submitted on BRC record cards. These are available free of charge from: Biological Records Centre, Institute of Terrestrial Ecology, Monks Wood Experimental Station, Abbots Ripton, Huntingdon, PE17 2LS.

Revised editions of this Red Data Book are planned for the future. In the meantime, for readers wishing to be kept up to date with changes in the status of Red Data Book insects, it is intended to issue occasional bulletins. Those wishing to be placed on the mailing list should write to the NCC at the above address.

A code for insect collecting

(This code was published by the Joint Committee for the Conservation of British Insects in 1972. It is reproduced verbatim here, but it is being revised.)

This Committee believes that with the ever-increasing loss of habitats resulting from forestry, agriculture, and industrial, urban and recreational development, the point has been reached where a code for collecting should be considered in the interests of conservation of the British insect fauna, particularly Macrolepidoptera. The Committee considers that in many areas this loss has gone so far that collecting, which at one time would have had a trivial effect, could now affect the survival in them of one or more species if continued without restraint.

The Committee also believes that by subscribing to a code of collecting, entomologists will show themselves to be a concerned and responsible body of naturalists who have a positive contribution to make to the cause of conservation. It asks all entomologists to accept the following Code in principle and to try to observe it in practice.

1 **Collecting – general**

1.1 No more specimens than are strictly required for any purpose should be killed.

1.2 Readily identified insects should not be killed if the object is to 'look them over' for aberrations or other purposes: insects should be examined while alive and then released where they were captured.

1.3 The same species should not be taken in numbers year after year from the same locality.

1.4 Supposed or actual predators and parasites of insects should not be destroyed.

1.5 When collecting leaf-mines, galls and seed heads, never collect all that can be found; leave as many as possible to allow the population to recover.

1.6 Consideration should be given to photography as an alternative to collecting, particularly in the case of butterflies.

1.7 Specimens for exchange, or disposal to other collectors, should be taken sparingly or not at all.

1.8 For commercial purposes insects should be either bred or obtained from old collections. Insect specimens should not be used for the manufacture of 'jewellery'.

2 Collecting – rare and endangered species

2.1 Specimens of Macrolepidoptera listed by this Committee (and published in the entomological journals) should be collected with the greatest restraint. As a guide, the Committee suggests that a pair of specimens is sufficient, but that those species in the greatest danger should not be collected at all. The list may be amended from time to time if this proves to be necessary.

2.2 Specimens of distinct local forms of Macrolepidoptera, particularly butterflies, should likewise be collected with restraint.

2.3 Collectors should attempt to break new ground rather than collect a local or rare species from a well-known and perhaps over-worked locality.

2.4 Previously unknown localities for rare species should be brought to the attention of this Committee, which undertakes to inform other organisations as appropriate and only in the interests of conservation.

3 Collecting – lights and light-traps

3.1 The 'catch' at light, particularly in a trap, should not be killed casually for subsequent examination.

3.2 Live trapping, for instance in traps filled with egg-tray material, is the preferred method of collecting. Anaesthetics are harmful and should not be used.

3.3 After examination of the catch the insects should be kept in cool, shady conditions and released away from the trap site at dusk. If this is not possible the insects should be released in long grass or other cover and not on lawns or bare surfaces.

3.4 Unwanted insects should not be fed to fish or insectivorous birds and mammals.

3.5 If a trap used for scientific purposes is found to be catching rare or local species unnecessarily it should be re-sited.

3.6 Traps and lights should be sited with care so as not to annoy neighbours or cause confusion.

4 Collecting – permission and conditions

4.1 Always seek permission from landowner or occupier when collecting on private land.

4.2 Always comply with any conditions laid down by the granting of permission to collect.

4.3 When collecting on nature reserves or Crown land, or sites of known interest to conservationists, supply a list of species collected to the appropriate authority.

4.4 When collecting on nature reserves it is particularly important to observe the code suggested in section 5.

5 Collecting – damage to the environment

5.1 Do as little damage to the environment as possible. Remember the interests of other naturalists; be careful of nesting birds and vegetation, particularly rare plants.

5.2 When 'beating' for lepidopterous larvae or other insects never thrash trees and bushes so that foliage and twigs are removed. A sharp jarring of branches is both less damaging and more effective.

5.3 Coleopterists and others working dead timber should replace removed bark and worked material to the best of their ability. Not all the dead wood in a locality should be worked.

5.4 Overturned stones and logs should be replaced in their original positions.

5.5 Water weed and moss which has been worked for insects should be replaced in its appropriate habitat. Plant material in litter heaps should be replaced and not scattered about.

5.6 Twigs, small branches and foliage required as foodplants or because they are galled, e.g. by clearwings, should be removed neatly with secateurs or scissors and not broken off.

5.7 'Sugar' should not be applied so that it renders tree-trunks and other vegetation unnecessarily unsightly.

5.8 Exercise particular care when working for rare species, e.g. by searching for larvae rather than beating for them.

5.9 Remember the Country Code!

6 Breeding

6.1 Breeding from a fertilised female or pairing in captivity is preferable to taking a series of specimens in the field.

6.2 Never collect more larvae or other livestock than can be supported by the available supply of foodplant.

6.3 Unwanted insects that have been reared should be released in the original locality, not just anywhere.

6.4 Before attempting to establish new populations or 'reinforce' exisiting ones please consult this Committee.

Legislation to protect insects

The Conservation of Wild Creatures and Wild Plants Act became law in 1975, though only one insect – the Large Blue Butterfly – was listed. A second, the Essex Emerald Moth, was added in 1979. That Act was soon superseded by the **Wildlife and Countryside Act 1981**, which was passed on 30 October of that year (though the provisions relating to insects did not come into effect until September 1982). Fourteen species of insect are specially protected under Section 9: among other things, it is illegal to kill, take or sell them, except under licence. Possession of a specimen of any of these species, whether alive or dead, is also an offence unless it was obtained legally (for example, before the Act came into force). Licences for killing, taking or possessing for scientific or educational purposes, marking and recapture, conservation, protection of zoological collections, or photography are issued by the NCC (Section 16(3), a-e). Licences for killing or taking for the preservation of public health or safety, the prevention of the spread of disease, or the prevention of serious damage are issued by the agriculture Minister (the Minister of Agriculture, Fisheries and Food or the Secretary of State) (Section 16(3), f-h). Licences to sell specimens or to offer or advertise them for sale are issued by the Department of the Environment (DoE) (Section 16(4), b). Eggs, larvae, pupae or other immature stages of protected species are covered by the law as well as adults (Section 27(3)).

The species, as listed in Schedule 5 of the Act, are as follows:

Norfolk Aeshna Dragonfly	*Aeshna isosceles*
Wart-biter Grasshopper	*Decticus verrucivorus*
Field Cricket	*Gryllus campestris*
Mole Cricket	*Gryllotalpa gryllotalpa*
Chequered Skipper Butterfly	*Carterocephalus palaemon*
Swallowtail Butterfly	*Papilio machaon*
Large Blue Butterfly	*Maculinea arion*
Heath Fritillary Butterfly	*Mellicta athalia* (otherwise known as *Melitaea athalia*)
New Forest Burnet Moth	*Zygaena viciae*
Essex Emerald Moth	*Thetidia smaragdaria*
Barberry Carpet Moth	*Pareulype berberata*
Black-veined Moth	*Siona lineata* (otherwise known as *Idaea lineata*)
Reddish Buff Moth	*Acosmetia caliginosa*
Rainbow Leaf Beetle	*Chrysolina cerealis*

As part of its first five-yearly review of Schedule 5 of the Wildlife and Countryside Act 1981, the NCC has proposed that three further species of insect should be given full protection and 22 species of butterfly should be banned from sale except under licence from the DoE; these would include the Chequered Skipper, which the NCC considers no longer requires fuller protection.

Releases and imports

It should be noted that Section 14 of the Act makes it an offence to release or allow to escape into the wild *any* animal which is of a kind which is not ordinarily resident in, and is not a regular visitor to, Great Britain in a wild state. The NCC interprets this to apply to any stock of foreign origin whether obviously genetically different or not, and a licence from the Department of the Environment is required for any such release. The Endangered Species (Import and Export) Act 1976 prohibits import of the Large Blue Butterfly without a licence, which is issued by the DoE.

International Conventions

The United Kingdom has ratified three international agreements concerning species protection – the Convention on the Conservation of European Wildlife and Natural Habitats (the Bern Convention), the Convention on International Trade in Endangered Species (CITES), and the Convention on the Conservation of Migratory Species of Wild Animals (the Bonn Convention). At present no British insects are listed in these Conventions but some are likely to be added in the future, in which case the UK will be required to add them to the list of protected species.

Biological recording schemes

Many of the insects in this book are covered by national recording schemes. Further information may be obtained from the Biological Records Centre, Monks Wood Experimental Station, Abbots Ripton, Huntingdon, Cambs PE17 2LS.

The following insect schemes are currently in operation:

Ephemeroptera (mayflies)

Odonata (dragonflies and damselflies)

Orthoptera, Phasmida, Dermaptera and Dictyoptera (grasshoppers, crickets, stick-insects, earwigs and cockroaches)

Hemiptera
- Terrestrial Heteroptera (land bugs)
- Aquatic Heteroptera (water bugs)
- Auchenorrhyncha (leafhoppers and froghoppers)

Neuroptera, Mecoptera and Megaloptera (lacewings, scorpion-flies, alderflies and snake-flies)

Trichoptera (caddis flies)

Lepidoptera
- Micropterigidae and Eriocraniidae (micro-moths)
- Incurvariidae and Heliozelidae (micro-moths)
- Oecophoridae (micro-moths)
- Rhopalocera (butterflies)

Coleoptera
- Carabidae (ground beetles)
- Aquatic Coleoptera (water beetles)
- Atomariinae and Ptiliidae (featherwing beetles, etc)
- Staphylinidae (rove beetles)
- Scarabaeoidea (stag and dung beetles, chafers, etc)
- Elmidae (riffle beetles)
- Buprestoidea and Cantharoidea (jewel beetles, soldier beetles, etc)
- Elateroidea (click beetles, etc)
- Cleroidea, Lymexyloidea and Heteromera
- Coccinellidae (ladybirds)
- Cerambycidae (longhorn beetles)
- Chrysomelidae and Bruchidae (leaf and pulse beetles)
- Nemonychidae to Apionidae (orthocerous weevils)
- Elm Scolytidae (elm bark beetles)

Hymenoptera - Aculeata (ants, wasps and bees) .

Diptera   - Tipuloidea and Ptychopteridae (craneflies)
                 - Dixidae (meniscus midges)
                 - Culicidae (mosquitoes)
                 - Larger Brachycera (including horseflies, robberflies, beeflies and soldierflies)
                 - Syrphidae (hoverflies)
                 - Conopidae
                 - Sepsidae
                 - Sciomyzidae (snail-killing flies)

Siphonaptera (fleas)

Useful addresses

AMATEUR ENTOMO-LOGISTS' SOCIETY
355 Hounslow Road
Hanworth
Feltham
Middlesex
TW13 5JH

BALFOUR-BROWNE CLUB
Dr G N Foster
20 Angus Avenue
Prestwick
Ayrshire
KA9 2HZ

BIOLOGICAL RECORDS CENTRE
Monks Wood Experimental Station
Abbots Ripton
Huntingdon
Cambs
PE17 2LS

BRITISH BUTTERFLY CONSERVATION SOCIETY
Mrs M N Tatham
Tudor House
102 Chaveney Road
Quorn
Loughborough
Leics
LE12 8AD

BRITISH DRAGONFLY SOCIETY
R H Dunn
4 Peakland View
Darley Dale
Matlock
Derbyshire
DE4 2GF

BRITISH ENTOMO-LOGICAL & NATURAL HISTORY SOCIETY
c/o The Alpine Club
74 South Audley Street
London
W1Y 5FF

BRITISH MUSEUM (NATURAL HISTORY)
Department of Entomology
Cromwell Road
London
SW7 5BD

DEPARTMENT OF THE ENVIRONMENT
Wildlife Division
Tollgate House
Houlton Street
Bristol
BS12 9DJ

FIELD STUDIES COUNCIL
Information Office
Preston Montford
Montford Bridge
Shrewsbury
SY4 1HW

FRESHWATER BIO-LOGICAL ASSOCIATION
The Ferry House
Ambleside
Cumbria
LA22 OLP

INSTITUTE OF TERRES-TRIAL ECOLOGY
Monks Wood Experimental Station
Abbots Ripton
Huntingdon
Cambs
PE17 2LS

INTERNATIONAL UNION FOR CONSERVATION OF NATURE & NATURAL RESOURCES
Species Conservation Monitoring Unit
219c Huntingdon Road
Cambridge
CB3 ODL

JOINT COMMITTEE FOR THE CONSERVATION OF BRITISH INSECTS
c/o Royal Entomological Society
41 Queen's Gate
London
SW7 5HU

MINISTRY OF AGRICUL-TURE, FISHERIES & FOOD
Infestation Control Branch
Great Westminster House
Horseferry Road
London
SW1P 2AE

NATURE CONSERVANCY COUNCIL
Northminster House
Peterborough
PE1 1UA

ROYAL ENTOMOLOGICAL SOCIETY OF LONDON
41 Queen's Gate
London
SW7 5HU

ROYAL SOCIETY FOR NATURE CONSERVATION
The Green
Nettleham
Lincoln
LN2 2NR

Habitats of Red Data Book insects

Photographs 1 to 18 illustrate a selection of habitats of particular importance for their insect fauna, including Red Data Book species. The following text draws attention to some of the habitat features exploited by insects and outlines their management requirements. In some cases threats to the insect fauna are also mentioned. Because the majority of insects have annual life cycles, suitable conditions for their reproduction and development must be present every year within the area occupied by each population. Therefore it is necessary to maintain continuity of, for example, foodplants growing in appropriate situations or resources such as dead wood, if rare insects are to be successfully conserved. This continuity is often best achieved through the perpetuation of traditional, long-established ways of managing land such as coppicing woodland or rotational cutting of fens.

1 **Woodland – high forest**

Bramshaw Wood, New Forest, Hampshire. Oak and beech with holly understorey.

Ancient forest supports a larger number of threatened British insects than any other habitat. The majority of this fauna is dependent upon ancient decaying trees, dead wood and fungi, so it is essential to maintain these resources in abundance. The beetles and flies are particularly rich in species and they are best represented in the New Forest and in Windsor Forest, Berkshire.

2 **Woodland – coppice with standards**

Felshamhall Wood, Suffolk. Freshly cut and regrowing coppice.

The considerable decline in coppicing of woodland this century is thought to be the principal cause of the decline in many woodland insects such as the Heath Fritillary Butterfly. The traditional annual cutting of small areas encourages a rich vernal flora, and many insects exploit foodplants in the open conditions during the years immediately after coppicing, before shade increases through regrowth of the understorey.

3 **Woodland – Caledonian pine forest**

Abernethy Forest, Badenoch and Strathspey. Mature pine forest grading into open moorland.

Many of the rare insects of ancient pine forest develop in decaying trees, dead wood or fungi. Open glades are also important for these and other insects, providing nectar-bearing flowers and warm suntraps. Such features as ancient trees, dead wood and sunny glades tend to be absent in the conifer plantations which have replaced many of the original native forests.

4 Parkland		Windsor, Berkshire. Ancient oaks, grassland and scrub.

Mainly oaks, but also other trees such as beech, were traditionally pollarded in parks where deer and other animals were grazed. This allowed elements of the old forest fauna (especially beetles) to survive in association with the ancient trees. Windsor has the richest insect fauna of this habitat type. Many parks are in need of a new generation of trees to be planted and pollarded to ensure the future continuity of both the distinctive parkland landscape and the presence of mature timber to support the insects.

5 Wetland – fenland   Woodbastwick, Norfolk. Dyke bordering reed fen which grades into carr.

The East Anglian fens are renowned for the richness and diversity of their insect fauna, which requires for its conservation the maintenance of a high water-table and frequently the continuation of traditional patterns of rotational cutting. Fens elsewhere in England, and in Scotland and Wales, also support important insect communities dependent upon open swamp and carr habitats.

6 Wetland – acid bog   West of Loch Caluim, Dorrery, Caithness. Blanket bog flow with dubh lochan and swamp.

Britain has some of the best examples of this habitat, and where well developed pool systems occur, the dragonflies and water beetles are well represented. Afforestation has been the major threat in recent years, especially in Scotland.

7 Wetland – grazing marsh   Southlake Moor, Somerset. Ditch (or rhyne) with rich emergent vegetation.

Much of the considerable entomological importance resides in the fauna of the ditches and their margins, and it is dependent upon the maintenance of high, stable water levels and the continuation of a traditional ditch clearance regime on a rotational basis. Ditches managed in this manner can support scarce dragonflies and diverse fly and water beetle communities. The change in land-use from grazing stock to arable farming (with the associated over-deepening and reprofiling of ditches) is the main threat to this habitat.

8 Aquatic – lowland river   The Stour/Moors River confluence, Dorset. Open and wooded river banks.

Absence of pollution is a major factor determining the quality and nature of the riverine insect fauna. The presence of riffles and pools, the underlying geology and the type of vegetation along the banks also significantly affect the aquatic and water-margin fauna.

9 Aquatic – river shingle River Spey, Aviemore, Badenoch and Strathspey. Shingle bank with developing scrub community.

Where rivers flowing from upland areas deposit extensive beds of shingle, sand and mud, a distinctive insect community occurs which includes many species with very restricted distributions in Britain. The larger and more stabilised banks, where alder or sallow scrub develops, and stands of wetland grasses on finer deposits are typical situations where many of the threatened insects are found.

10 Aquatic – lowland pond Bolder Mere, Wisley, Surrey. Pond margin with emergent vegetation and bare mud.

There has been a substantial loss and degradation of lowland ponds in Britain this century, which has resulted in declines of some freshwater insects. In addition to the maintenance of an adequate depth of unpolluted water, ponds may need to be occasionally cleared of vegetation and silt to retain sufficient open water. This should be done carefully over a two- to three-year period to ensure that the fragile marginal vegetation is not trampled or otherwise destroyed.

11 Chalk grassland Old Winchester Hill, Hampshire. Short and long grassland with patches of scrub.

The traditional grazing of chalk grassland by sheep gave rise to a rich and specialised insect fauna. Some species, with a mainly southern distribution in Europe, are confined in Britain to south-facing slopes of chalk grassland where short turf results in a hot summer microclimate. Well-planned and sophisticated management is needed to conserve this fauna together with those species which require long grassland or scrub.

12 Heathland Cavenham Heath, Suffolk. Transition from *Calluna* heath to grassland.

Burning and grazing have played a vital role in maintaining the characteristic early successional stages of heathland vegetation with associated bare ground, which are the conditions required by many heathland insects. Heaths have been greatly reduced and fragmented in recent years by forestry, agricultural reclamation and urban expansion. These losses, coupled with insufficient management of many remaining heaths, have caused declines of many heathland insects.

13 Heathland Weeting Heath, Norfolk. Dry, rabbit-grazed heath with lichens, grasses and bare ground.

The bleak appearance and sparse vegetation cover of some of the remaining Breckland short heaths belies their significance for a specialised insect fauna dependent upon heavily grazed conditions. Some other insects exploit disturbed ground which is not cultivated for crops, conditions which used to be much more widespread when less intensive agriculture was typical in this area.

14 Saltmarsh Stiffkey, Norfolk. Mature saltmarsh with sea lavender and pools.

The highly specialised and distinctive insect fauna of saltmarshes is best represented on the larger sites with well-developed vegetation zonation and extensive creek systems. The construction of sea walls for coastal defences and agricultural reclamation has caused significant loss and degradation of saltmarshes and consequent declines of some insects, especially those associated with the more species-rich upper saltmarsh zones and those transitional to other habitats such as dunes.

15 Sand dunes Newborough Warren, Anglesey. A system of slacks in semi-stable dunes.

The development of a wide range of vegetation types from fore-dunes through to stabilised hummocks and hollows (including extensive wet slacks) and a moderate level of grazing on calcareous dunes (less grazing is required on acid dunes) are the major factors which favour a rich insect fauna on coastal dunes.

16 Soft rock coastal cliffs Axmouth to Lyme Regis undercliffs, Devon. Bare ground, ruderal communities and scrub.

The slumping of soft rock cliffs creates a continually changing mosaic of pioneer communities and scrub. This is exploited by many insect species, particularly bees, wasps, beetles and flies, including several species treated in this Red Data Book.

17 Coastal shingle Dungeness, Kent. Shingle ridges with prostrate broom in the foreground.

Dungeness has the best developed coastal shingle insect fauna in Britain, including distinctive pale-coloured subspecies of some moths. Gravel extraction, a military training area and competing development interests have caused significant damage to Dungeness, which nevertheless still remains of international importance. Similar threats pose problems for other coastal shingle sites.

18 Upland Feith Buidhe, Ben Macdui, Moray. Late snow hollow with *Nardus stricta* snowbed communities.

Harsh upland habitats support a highly specialised insect fauna, including boreo-alpine species which have remained perched on mountain tops after the glacial retreat at the end of the last ice age. This fragile habitat is easily damaged by trampling or skiing developments.

1 Woodland – high forest. Bramshaw Wood, New Forest, Hampshire.

2   Woodland – coppice with standards. Felshamhall Wood, Suffolk.

3 Woodland — Caledonian pine forest. Abernethy Forest, Badenoch and Strathspey.

4   Parkland – Windsor, Berkshire.

5 Wetland – fenland. Woodbastwick, Norfolk.

6 Wetland – acid bog. West of Loch Caluim, Dorrery, Caithness.

7 Wetland – grazing marsh. Southlake Moor, Somerset.

8   Aquatic – lowland river. The Stour/Moors River confluence, Dorset.

9 Aquatic — river shingle. River Spey, Aviemore, Badenoch and Strathspey.

10 Aquatic – lowland pond. Bolder Mere, Wisley, Surrey.

11 Chalk grassland – Old Winchester Hill, Hampshire.

12   Heathland – Cavenham Heath, Suffolk.

13 Heathland – Weeting Heath, Norfolk.

14 Saltmarsh – Stiffkey, Norfolk.

15 Sand dunes – Newborough Warren, Anglesey.

16 Soft rock coastal cliffs – Axmouth to Lyme Regis undercliffs, Devon.

17 Coastal shingle – Dungeness, Kent.

18 Upland — Feith Buidhe, Ben Macdui, Moray.

Category definitions and criteria

These categories are based on degree of **threat**, and not on degree of rarity.

Category 1
ENDANGERED

Definition Taxa in danger of extinction and whose survival is unlikely if the causal factors continue operating.

Included are taxa whose numbers have been reduced to a critical level or whose habitats have been so dramatically reduced that they are deemed to be in immediate danger of extinction. Also included are taxa that are believed to be extinct.

Criteria Species which are known as only a single population within one 10km square of the National Grid.

Species which only occur in habitats known to be especially vulnerable.

Species which have shown a rapid and continuous decline over the last twenty years and now exist in five or fewer 10km squares.

Species which are believed extinct but which if rediscovered would need protection.

Category 2
VULNERABLE

Definition Taxa believed likely to move into the Endangered category in the near future if the causal factors continue operating.

Included are taxa of which most or all of the populations are **decreasing** because of over-exploitation, extensive destruction of habitat or other environmental disturbance; taxa with populations that have been seriously **depleted** and whose ultimate security is not yet assured; and taxa with populations that are still abundant but are under **threat** from serious adverse factors throughout their range.

Criteria Species declining throughout their range.

Species in vulnerable habitats.

Species whose populations are low.

Category 3
RARE

Definition Taxa with small populations that are not at present Endangered or Vulnerable, but are at risk.

These taxa are usually localised within restricted geographical areas or habitats or are thinly scattered over a more extensive range.

This category also includes taxa which are believed to be rare but are too recently discovered or recognised to be certain of placing (designated 3*).

Criteria Species which exist in only fifteen or fewer 10km squares.

1

Category 4	Taxa formerly meeting the criteria of one of the above
OUT OF DANGER	categories, but which are now considered relatively secure because effective conservation measures have been taken or the previous threat to their survival has been removed.
Category 5	Taxa which are not known to occur naturally outside Britain.
ENDEMIC	Taxa within this category may also be in any of Categories 1-4.
APPENDIX	Taxa which were formerly native to Britain but have not been recorded since 1900. (This definition is slightly modified for the Lepidoptera.)

Summary of species numbers

Order	No. of British species	Endangered	Vulnerable	Rare	Out of danger	Endemic	Appendix	No. of RDB species	% in RDB of total no.
ODONATA	41	4	2	3	–	–	–	9	22.0
ORTHOPTERA	30	3	2	1	–	–	–	6	20.0
HETEROPTERA	540	14	6	53*	–	1*	6	79*	14.6
TRICHOPTERA	199	9	4	18	–	–	2	33	16.6
LEPIDOPTERA									
Butterflies	56	2	3	2	2	2*	3	12	21.4
Macro-moths	c.900	21*	12*	53	–	1*	13	99*	11.0
Micro-moths	c.1500	4	7	–	–	–	–	11	0.7
COLEOPTERA	c.3900	142	84	266	–	6	54	546	14.0
HYMENOPTERA									
Aculeata	580	37	12	97	–	–	18	164	28.3
DIPTERA	c.6000	270	226	328	–	–	3	827	13.8
TOTAL	c.13,746	506*	358*	821*	2	10*	99	1786*	14.5**
Species accounts in RDB	452	274	179	–	2				

* Includes subspecies.   ** Excludes Micro-moths.

Odonata – Dragonflies

Category 1 **ENDANGERED**	**Coenagriidae** +*Coenagrion armatum* (Charpentier) +*Coenagrion scitulum* (Rambur)	Norfolk Coenagrion, Norfolk Damselfly Dainty Coenagrion, Dainty Damselfly
	Aeshnidae !*Aeshna isosceles* (Mueller)	"Norfolk Aeshna Dragonfly", Norfolk Hawker
	Corduliidae +*Oxygastra curtisii* (Dale)	Orange-spotted Emerald
Category 2 **VULNERABLE**	**Coenagriidae** *Coenagrion hastulatum* (Charpentier)	Northern Coenagrion, Northern Damselfly
	Lestidae *Lestes dryas* Kirby	Scarce Green Lestes, Scarce Emerald Damselfly
Category 3 **RARE**	**Coenagriidae** *Coenagrion mercuriale* (Charpentier)	Southern Coenagrion, Southern Damselfly
	Corduliidae *Somatochlora arctica* (Zetterstedt)	Northern Emerald
	Libellulidae *Libellula fulva* Mueller	Scarce Libellula, Scarce Chaser

Orthoptera – Grasshoppers & Crickets

Category 1 ENDANGERED	**Gryllidae**	
	!*Gryllus campestris* L.	"Field Cricket"
	Mogoplistidae	
	Mogoplistes squamiger (Fischer)	Scaly Cricket
	Gryllotalpidae	
	!*Gryllotalpa gryllotalpa* (L.)	"Mole Cricket"
Category 2 VULNERABLE	**Tettigoniidae**	
	!*Decticus verrucivorus* (L.)	Wart-biter, "Wart-biter Grasshopper"
	Acrididae	
	Stethophyma grossum (L.)	Large Marsh Grasshopper
Category 3 RARE	**Acrididae**	
	Chorthippus vagans (Eversmann)	Heath Grasshopper

Hemiptera: Heteroptera – Bugs

Category 1
ENDANGERED

Cydnidae
Geotomus punctulatus (Costa)

Scutelleridae
+*Eurygaster austriaca*
(Schrank)

Coreidae
Gonocerus acuteangulatus
(Goeze)

Pyrrhocoridae
Pyrrhocoris apterus (L.)

Lygaeidae
Macroplax preyssleri
(Fieber)
Ischnodemus quadratus
Fieber
Peritrechus gracilicornis
Puton
Eremocoris fenestratus
(Herrich-Schaeffer)

Tingidae
Physatocheila harwoodi
China

Miridae
Placochilus seladonicus
(Fallen)
Pilophorus confusus
(Kirschbaum)
Halticus macrocephalus
Fieber
Polymerus vulneratus (Wolff)

Hydrometridae
Hydrometra gracilenta
Horvath

Category 2
VULNERABLE

Pentatomidae
Eysarcoris aeneus (Scopoli)

Coreidae
Arenocoris waltli (Herrich-
Schaeffer)

Lygaeidae
Henestaris halophilus
(Burmeister)

Tingidae
Lasiacantha capucina Germar

Miridae
Tuponia carayoni Wagner

Saldidae
Saldula setulosa (Puton)

Category 3
RARE

Aradidae
Aradus aterrimus Fieber
Aradus betulae (L.)
Aradus corticalis (L.)

Scutelleridae
Odontoscelis fuliginosa (L.)

Pentatomidae
Holcostethus vernalis (Wolff)

Lygaeidae
Heterogaster artemisiae
Schilling
*Nysius graminicola Kolenati

Nysius helveticus (Herrich-
Schaeffer)
Ortholomus punctipennis
(Herrich-Schaeffer)
Pachybrachius luridus (Hahn)
*Megalonotus sabulicola
(Thomson)
Trapezonotus ullrichi (Fieber)
Pterotmetus staphyliniformis
(Schilling)
Pionosomus varius (Wolff)

Emblethis verbasci (F.)
Acompus pallipes (Herrich-Schaeffer)
Drymus pilipes Fieber
Drymus pumilio Puton
Eremocoris abietis (L.)
*Eremocoris plebejus (Fallen)
Taphropeltus hamulatus (Thomson)
Taphropeltus limbatus (Fieber)

Berytinidae
Cymus obliquus Horvath

Piesmatidae
(5)*Piesma quadratum spergulariae* Woodroffe

Tingidae
Tingis angustata Herrich-Schaeffer

Reduviidae
Empicoris baerensprungi (Dohrn)
Pygolampis bidentata (Goeze)

Nabidae
Nabis brevis Scholtz
Nabis pseudoferus Remane

Acanthocoridae
**Temnostethus tibialis* Reuter
**Anthocoris amplicollis* Horvath
*Anthocoris minki Dohrn

Cimicidae
Cimex columbarius Jenyns

Miridae
Chlamydatus evanescens (Boheman)
Chlamydatus pulicarius (Fallen)
**Monosynamma bohemani* (Fallen)
**Monosynamma maritima* Wagner
Hallodapus montandoni (Reuter)
Orthotylus virens Fallen
Myrmecoris gracilis (Sahlberg)
*Lygus pratensis (L.)
**Charagochilus weberi* Wagner
Adelphocoris seticornis (F.)
Phytocoris insignis Reuter
Capsus wagneri Remane
**Teratocoris caricis* Kirkaldy

Saldidae
Saldula fucicola (Sahlberg)
Saldula opacula (Zetterstedt)
Micracanthia marginalis (Fallen)

Veliidae
Microvelia pygmaea (Dufour)
Microvelia umbricola Wroblewski

Corixidae
Micronecta minutissima (L.)
Sigara striata (L.)

Category 5
ENDEMIC

Piesmatidae
Piesma quadratum spergulariae Woodroffe
(Category 3)

APPENDIX
No post-1900 records

Acanthosomatidae
Elasmucha ferrugata (F.)

Pentatomidae
Chlorochroa juniperina (L.)
(= *Pitedia juniperina*)

Rhopalidae
Stictopleurus abutilon Butler

Stictopleurus punctato-nervosus (Goeze)

Nabidae
Prostemma guttula (F.)

Miridae
Hadrodemus m-flavum (Goeze)

Trichoptera – Caddis Flies

Category 1 ENDANGERED

Polycentropodidae
Cyrnus insolutus McLachlan

Hydropsychidae
+*Hydropsyche bulgaroma-norum* Malicky
+*Hydropsyche exocellata* Dufour
Hydropsyche saxonica McLachlan

Phryganeidae
Agrypnia crassicornis (McLachlan)

Hagenella clathrata (Kolenati)

Limnephilidae
Grammotaulius nitidus (Mueller)
Limnephilus pati O'Connor

Leptoceridae
Leptocerus lusitanicus (McLachlan)

Category 2 VULNERABLE

Hydroptilidae
Hydroptila lotensis Mosely

Psychomyiidae
Tinodes pallidulus McLachlan

Limnephilidae
Ironoquia dubia (Stephens)
Limnephilus tauricus Schmid

Category 3 RARE

Rhyacophilidae
Rhyacophila septentrionis McLachlan

Glossosomatidae
Glossosoma intermedium (Klapalek)

Hydroptilidae
Oxyethira mirabilis Morton
(= *Oxytrichia mirabilis*)
Oxyethira sagittifera Ris
Tricholeiochiton fagesii (Guinard)

Polycentropodidae
Plectrocnemia brevis McLachlan

Hydropsychidae
Hydropsyche fulvipes (Curtis)

Limnephilidae
Enoicyla pusilla (Burmeister)

Mesophylax aspersus (Rambur)
*Nemotaulius punctatolinea-tus (Retzius)

Leptoceridae
Leptocerus interruptus (F.)
Adicella filicornis (Pictet)
Erotesis baltica McLachlan
Ylodes reuteri (McLachlan)
(= *Triaenodes reuteri*)
Oecetis notata (Rambur)
Setodes argentipunctellus McLachlan
Setodes punctatus (F.)

Beraeidae
Ernodes articularis (Pictet)

APPENDIX No post-1900 records

Hydroptilidae
Hydroptila tigurina Ris

Phryganeidae
Agrypnia picta Kolenati

Lepidoptera I – Butterflies

Category 1 **ENDANGERED**	**Lycaenidae** + !*Maculinea arion* (L.)	"Large Blue Butterfly"
	Nymphalidae *Nymphalis polychloros* (L.)	Large Tortoiseshell
Category 2 **VULNERABLE**	**Papilionidae** !*Papilio machaon* L.	"Swallowtail Butterfly"
	Nymphalidae *Argynnis adippe* (Denis & Schiffermueller)	High Brown Fritillary
	!*Mellicta athalia* (Rottemburg)	"Heath Fritillary Butterfly"
Category 3 **RARE**	**Hesperiidae** *Hesperia comma* (L.)	Silver-spotted Skipper
	Nymphalidae *Melitaea cinxia* (L.)	Glanville Fritillary
Category 4 **OUT OF** **DANGER**	**Hesperiidae** !*Carterocephalus palaemon* (Pallas)	"Chequered Skipper Butterfly"
	Lycaenidae *Strymonidia pruni* (L.)	Black Hairstreak

Category 5
ENDEMIC

Numerous local races of Lepidoptera have been named, many of them of doubtful status as subspecies. Those listed here are well-known endemic races which have been confirmed as major subspecies.

Lycaenidae *Plebejus argus caernensis* Thompson	Silver-studded Blue (not threatened)
Satyridae *Hipparchia semele thyone* Thompson	Grayling (not threatened)

APPENDIX
Believed extinct

As the Lepidoptera are relatively well-known this list includes two post-1900 species, and the last confirmed date as resident. (Sporadic migrants have occurred at later dates.) The list does not include transitory residents.

Pieridae

Aporia crataegi (L.)	Black-veined White	1925

Lycaenidae

Lycaena dispar dispar (Haworth)	Large Copper	1865
Cyaniris semiargus (Rottemburg)	Mazarine Blue	1906 or 1920

Lepidoptera II – Moths

**Category 1
ENDANGERED**

Zygaenidae
+*Zygaena purpuralis segontii*   Transparent Burnet
  Tremewan
!*Zygaena viciae* (Denis &   "New Forest Burnet Moth"
  Schiffermueller)

Lyonetiidae
Paraleucoptera sinuella   –
  (Reutti)

Sesiidae
Bembecia chrysidiformis   Fiery Clearwing
  (Esper)

Oecophoridae
Hypercallia citrinalis (Scopoli) –

Tortricidae
Pristerognatha penthinana   –
  (Guenee)
Cydia leguminana (Lienig   –
  & Zeller)

Geometridae
!*Thetidia smaragdaria* (F.)   "Essex Emerald Moth"
Thalera fimbrialis (Scopoli)   Sussex Emerald
+*Scopula immorata* (L.)   Lewes Wave
!*Pareulype berberata* (Denis   "Barberry Carpet Moth"
  & Schiffermueller)
!*Siona lineata* (Scopoli)   "Black-veined Moth"

Notodontidae
Clostera anachoreta (Denis   Scarce Chocolate-tip
  & Schiffermueller)

Arctiidae
Pelosia obtusa (Herrich-   Small Dotted Footman
  Schaeffer)

Noctuidae
Eugraphe subrosea   Rosy Marsh Moth
  (Stephens)
+*Pachetra sagittigera*   Feathered Ear
  (Hufnagel)
Hadena irregularis (Hufnagel)   Viper's Bugloss
Cucullia gnaphalii (Huebner)   The Cudweed, Cudweed
                        Shark
Acronicta strigosa (Denis &   Marsh Dagger
  Schiffermueller)
Photedes morrisii bondii   Bond's Wainscot
  (Knaggs)

Luperina nickerlii leechi Goater	Sandhill Rustic
+*Sedina buettneri* (Hering)	Blair's Wainscot
!*Acosmetia caliginosa* (Huebner)	"Reddish Buff Moth"
+*Emmelia trabealis* (Scopoli)	Spotted Sulphur
Colobochyla salicalis (Denis & Schiffermueller)	Lesser Belle

Category 2 **VULNERABLE**	**Nepticulidae** *Stigmella torminalis* (Wood)	–
	Cossidae *Phragmataecia castaneae* (Huebner)	Reed Leopard
	Psychidae *Pachythelia villosella* (Ochsenheimer)	–
	Phyllocnistidae *Phyllocnistis xenia* Hering	–
	Coleophoridae *Coleophora leucapennella* (Huebner)	–
	Gelechiidae *Syncopacma vinella* (Bankes)	–
	Cochylidae *Aethes margarotana* (Duponchel)	–
	Pterophoridae *Stenoptilia graphodactyla* (Treitschke)	–
	Lasiocampidae *Eriogaster lanestris* (L.)	Small Eggar
	Geometridae *Scopula nigropunctata* (Hufnagel)	Sub-angled Wave
	Eustroma reticulatum (Denis & Schiffermueller)	Netted Carpet
	Perizoma sagittata (F.)	Marsh Carpet
	Lymantriidae *Orgyia recens* (Huebner)	Scarce Vapourer
	Arctiidae *Coscinia cribraria* (L.)	Speckled Footman
	Noctuidae *Photedes morrisii morrisii* (Dale)	Morris's Wainscot
	Luperina nickerlii gueneei Doubleday	Sandhill Rustic

Gortyna borelii Pierret	Fisher's Estuarine Moth
Deltote bankiana (F.)	Silver Barred
Tyta luctuosa (Denis & Schiffermueller)	The Four-spotted

Category 3 RARE

Zygaenidae

Adscita globulariae (Huebner)	Scarce Forester
(5)*Zygaena exulans* (Hohenwarth)	Scotch Burnet
Zygaena loti (Denis & Schiffermueller)	Slender Scotch Burnet

Limacodidae

Heterogenea asella (Denis & Schiffermueller)	The Triangle

Sesiidae

Synanthedon scoliaeformis (Borkhausen) (= *Conopia scoliaeformis*)	Welsh Clearwing

Lasiocampidae

Malacosoma castrensis (L.)	Ground Lackey
Phyllodesma ilicifolia (L.)	Small Lappet

Endromidae

Endromis versicolora (L.)	Kentish Glory

Drepanidae

Sabra harpagula (Esper) (= *Palaeodrepana harpagula*)	Scarce Hook-tip

Geometridae

Aplasta ononaria (Fuessly)	Rest Harrow
Cyclophora pendularia (Clerck)	Dingy Mocha
Scopula rubiginata (Hufnagel)	Tawny Wave
Idaea degeneraria (Huebner)	Portland Ribbon Wave
Idaea dilutaria (Huebner)	Silky Wave
Idaea ochrata (Scopoli)	Bright Wave
Xanthorhoe biriviata (Borkhausen)	Balsam Carpet
Eupithecia abietaria (Goeze)	Cloaked Pug
Eupithecia egenaria (Herrich-Schaeffer)	Pauper Pug
Eupithecia extensaria (Freyer)	Scarce Pug
Lithostege griseata (Denis & Schiffermueller)	Grey Carpet
Semiothisa carbonaria (Clerck)	Netted Mountain Moth
Epione paralellaria (Denis & Schiffermueller)	Dark Bordered Beauty
Lycia lapponaria (Boisduval)	Rannoch Brindled Beauty

Lycia zonaria (Denis & Schiffermueller)	Belted Beauty
*Peribatodes secundaria (Esper)	Feathered Beauty
Psodos coracina (Esper)	Black Mountain Moth

Arctiidae

Pelosia muscerda (Hufnagel)	Dotted Footman
Eilema pygmaeola (Doubleday)	Pigmy Footman
Eilema sericea (Gregson)	Northern Footman

Noctuidae

Anarta cordigera (Thunberg)	Small Dark Yellow Underwing
Hadena albimacula (Borkhausen)	White Spot
Hadena caesia (Denis & Schiffermueller)	The Grey
*Eriopygodes imbecilla (F.)	The Silurian
Senta flammea (Curtis)	Flame Wainscot
Calophasia lunula (Hufnagel)	Toadflax Brocade
Leucochlaena oditis (Huebner)	Beautiful Gothic
Brachionycha nubeculosa (Esper)	Rannoch Sprawler
Jodia croceago (Denis & Schiffermueller)	Orange Upperwing
Moma alpium (Osbeck)	Scarce Merveille du Jour
Photedes brevilinea (Fenn)	Fenn's Wainscot
Photedes captiuncula (Treitschke)	Least Minor
Photedes extrema (Huebner)	The Concolorous
Hydraecia osseola (Staudinger)	Giant Ear or Marsh Mallow Moth
Archanara algae (Esper)	Rush Wainscot
Archanara neurica (Huebner)	White-mantled Wainscot
Athetis pallustris (Huebner)	Marsh Moth
Heliothis maritima Graslin	Shoulder-striped Clover
Heliothis viriplaca (Hufnagel)	Marbled Clover
Catocala promissa (Denis & Schiffermueller)	Light Crimson Underwing
Catocala sponsa (L.)	Dark Crimson Underwing
Lygephila craccae (Denis & Schiffermueller)	Scarce Blackneck
Herminia tarsicrinalis (Knoch) (= *Polypogon tarsicrinalis*)	Shaded Fan-foot
Trisateles emortualis (Denis & Schiffermueller)	Olive Crescent

Category 5
ENDEMIC

Numerous local races of Lepidoptera have been named, many of them of doubtful status as subspecies. The one listed here is a well-known endemic race which has been confirmed as a major subspecies.

Zygaenidae
Zygaena exulans   Scotch Burnet (Category 3)
    subochracea White

APPENDIX
Believed extinct

As the Lepidoptera are relatively well-known this list includes some post-1900 species, and the last confirmed date as resident. The list does not include transitory residents. (Sporadic migrants have occurred at later dates.)

Geometridae
Idaea humiliata (Hufnagel)	Isle of Wight Wave	1931
Costaconvexa polygrammata (Borkhausen)	The Many-lined	c.1875
Isturgia limbaria (F.)	Frosted Yellow	1914
Fagivorina arenaria (Hufnagel)	Speckled Beauty	1885

Notodontidae
Leucodonta bicoloria (Denis & Schiffermueller)	White Prominent	1865

Lymantriidae
Laelia coenosa (Huebner)	Reed Tussock	1875
Lymantria dispar (L.)	Gypsy Moth	1907

Nolidae
Nola aerugula (Huebner)	Scarce Black Arches	1898

Noctuidae
Hecatera dysodea (Denis & Schiffermueller)	Small Ranunculus	1937
Lithophane furcifera suffusa (Tutt)	The Conformist	c.1880
Trigonophora flammea (Esper)	Flame Brocade	1919
Trachea atriplicis (L.)	Orache Moth	1915
Apamea pabulatricula (Brahm)	Union Rustic	1919

Coleoptera – Beetles

**Category 1
ENDANGERED**

Carabidae
Omophron limbatum (F.)
Carabus intricatus L.
Dyschirius obscurus
  (Gyllenhal)
Trechus rivularis (Gyllenhal)
Trechus subnotatus Dejean
Bembidion humerale Sturm
Bembidion virens Gyllenhal
Pterostichus aterrimus
  (Herbst)
+*Agonum sahlbergi* (Chaudoir)
Harpalus cupreus Dejean
+*Harpalus honestus*
  (Duftschmid)
+*Scybalicus oblongiusculus*
  (Dejean)
Acupalpus elegans (Dejean)
Chlaenius nitidulus (Schrank)
Chlaenius tristis (Schaller)
Callistus lunatus (F.)
Lebia cruxminor (L.)
Drypta dentata (Rossi)

Haliplidae
+*Haliplus furcatus* Seidlitz

Dytiscidae
Bidessus unistriatus (Schrank)
+*Rhantus aberratus* Gem-
  minger & von Harold
+*Graphoderus bilineatus*
  (Degeer)
Graphoderus zonatus (Hoppe)

Hydrophilidae
+*Spercheus emarginatus*
  (Schaller)
Paracymus aeneus (Germar)
Hydrochara caraboides (L.)

Histeridae
+*Teretrius fabricii* Mazur
Paromalus parallelepipedus
  (Herbst)

Hydraenidae
+*Ochthebius aeneus* Stephens

Ptiliidae
Ptilium affine Erichson
Micridium halidaii (Matthews)
Microptilium palustre Kuntzen
Microptilium pulchellum
  (Allibert)
Ptinella limbata (Heer)

Leiodidae
(5)*Aglyptinus agathidioides*
  Blair

Silphidae
Silpha carinata Herbst

Scydmaenidae
Eutheia linearis Mulsant
Euconnus pragensis
  (Machulka)

Scaphidiidae
Scaphium immaculatum
  (Olivier)

Staphylinidae
Olophrum assimile (Paykull)
Orochares angustatus
  (Erichson)
Xylodromus testaceus
  (Erichson)
Eudectus whitei Sharp
Bledius filipes Sharp
Bledius furcatus (Olivier)
Carpelimus schneideri
  (Ganglbauer)
Stenus fossulatus Erichson
Stenus glacialis Heer
Scopaeus laevigatus
  (Gyllenhal)
Astenus subditus (Mulsant &
  Rey)
Cafius cicatricosus (Erichson)
Emus hirtus (L.)
Velleius dilatatus (F.)
Quedius balticus Korge
Acylophorus glaberrimus
  (Herbst)

Euryusa sinuata Erichson
Tachyusida gracilis
(Erichson)
Amarochara bonnairei
(Fauvel)

Pselaphidae
Plectophloeus nitidus
(Fairmaire)
Batrisodes buqueti (Aube)
Batrisodes delaporti (Aube)
Claviger longicornis Mueller

Trogidae
Trox perlatus Goeze

Scarabaeidae
Aegialia rufa (F.)
Aphodius brevis Erichson
Aphodius niger (Panzer)
+*Psammodius porcicollis*
(Illiger)
Copris lunaris (L.)
Gnorimus variabilis (L.)

Byrrhidae
Curimopsis nigrita (Palm)

Buprestidae
Anthaxia nitidula (L.)

Elateridae
Lacon querceus (Herbst)
Ampedus nigerrimus
(Lacordaire)
Ampedus ruficeps (Mulsant
& Guillebeau)
Megapenthes lugens
(Redtenbacher)
Limoniscus violaceus
(Mueller)
Anostirus castaneus (L.)
Elater ferrugineus L.

Eucnemidae
Eucnemis capucina Ahrens
Hylis cariniceps (Reitter)

Lampyridae
Phosphaenus hemipterus
(Goeze)

Lycidae
Platycis cosnardi (Chevrolat)

Dermestidae
Globicornis nigripes (F.)

Anobiidae
Gastrallus immarginatus
(Mueller)
Dorcatoma dresdensis Herbst
Caenocara affinis (Sturm)

Peltidae
Ostoma ferrugineum (L.)

Melyridae
Hypebaeus flavipes (F.)

Rhizophagidae
Rhizophagus oblongicollis
Blatch & Horner

Cucujidae
Laemophloeus monilis (F.)

Cryptophagidae
Cryptophagus falcozi Roubal
Cryptophagus labilis Erichson
Atomaria reitteri Loevendal

Coccinellidae
Clitostethus arcuatus (Rossi)

Lathridiidae
Corticarina latipennis
(Sahlberg)

Colydiidae
Teredus cylindricus (Olivier)

Tenebrionidae
Platydema violaceum (F.)
Omophlus rufitarsis (Leske)

Melandryidae
Abdera affinis (Paykull)
Melandrya barbata (F.)

Scraptiidae
Anaspis schilskyana Csiki

Oedemeridae
Chrysanthia nigricornis
Westhoff

Meloidae
Apalus muralis (Forster)

Cerambycidae
Acmaeops collaris (L.)
Oberea oculata (L.)

Chrysomelidae

Zeugophora flavicollis
(Marsham)
Labidostomis tridentata (L.)
Gynandrophthalma affinis
(Illiger)
Cryptocephalus coryli (L.)
Cryptocephalus exiguus
Schneider
Cryptocephalus nitidulus F.
Cryptocephalus primarius
Harold
Bromius obscurus (L.)
! *Chrysolina cerealis* (L.)
"Rainbow Leaf Beetle"
Chrysomela tremula F.
Galeruca interrupta Illiger
Longitarsus nigerrimus
(Gyllenhal)
Dibolia cynoglossi (Koch)
Psylliodes hyoscyami (L.)
(5) *Psylliodes luridipennis*
Kutschera

Curculionidae

Otiorhynchus auropunctatus
Cyllenhal
Cathormiocerus attaphilus
Brisout

Cathormiocerus britannicus
Blair
Sitona gemellatus Gyllenhal
Lixus algirus (L.)
Lixus paraplecticus (L.)
Lixus vilis (Rossi)
Hypera pastinacae (Rossi)
Dryophthorus corticalis
(Paykull)
Bagous binodulus (Herbst)
Bagous brevis Gyllenhal
Bagous czwalinai Seidlitz
Bagous diglyptus Boheman
Bagous frit (Herbst)
Bagous longitarsis Thomson
Bagous nodulosus Gyllenhal
Bagous puncticollis Boheman
Pachytychius haematocephalus (Gyllenhal)
Ceutorhynchus insularis
Dieckmann
Rhinoncus albicinctus
Gyllenhal
Baris analis (Olivier)

Scolytidae

Ernoporus caucasicus
Lindemann

Category 2
VULNERABLE

Carabidae

Amara fusca Dejean
Panagaeus cruxmajor (L.)
Dromius longiceps Dejean
Dromius sigma (Rossi)
Polystichus connexus
(Fourcroy)

Dytiscidae

Laccophilus obsoletus
Westhoff
Hydroporus rufifrons
(Mueller)
Hydroporus scalesianus
Stephens
Graptodytes flavipes (Olivier)
Agabus brunneus (F.)
Agabus striolatus (Gyllenhal)
Agabus undulatus (Schrank)

Hydrophilidae

Helophorus laticollis Thomson

Histeridae

Hypocaccus metallicus
(Herbst)
Hypocaccus rugiceps
(Duftschmid)
Hister quadrimaculatus L.
Paralister obscurus
(Kugelann)

Hydraenidae

Ochthebius lenensis Poppius
Hydraena palustris Erichson

Scydmaenidae

Eutheia formicetorum Reitter
Neuraphes carinatus
(Mulsant)
Microscydmus minimus
(Chaudoir)

Staphylinidae

Phyllodrepa nigra
(Gravenhorst)
Manda mandibularis
(Gyllenhal)

Planeustomus flavicollis
Fauvel
Bledius crassicollis Boisduval
& Lacordaire
Bledius dissimilis Erichson
(5)*Thinobius newberyi*
Scheerpeltz
Lathrobium rufipenne
Gyllenhal
Scopaeus minimus (Erichson)
Scopaeus minutus Erichson
Philonthus dimidiatipennis
Erichson
Tachinus bipustulatus (F.)
Euryusa optabilis Heer
Stichoglossa semirufa
(Erichson)
Haploglossa picipennis
(Gyllenhal)
Aleochara inconspicua Aube
Aleochara maculata Brisout
Aleochara moesta
Gravenhorst
Aleochara villosa
Mannerheim

Pselaphidae
Bibloplectus tenebrosus
(Reitter)

Scarabaeidae
Diastictus vulneratus (Sturm)

Elmidae (Elminthidae)
Normandia nitens (Mueller)
Stenelmis canaliculata
(Gyllenhal)

Buprestidae
Agrilus pannonicus (Piller &
Mitterpacher)
Agrilus sinuatus (Olivier)
Agrilus viridis (L.)

Elateridae
Ampedus cardinalis
(Schioedte)
Ampedus rufipennis
(Stephens)
Procraerus tibialis (Boisduval
& Lacordaire)

Melyridae
Axinotarsus pulicarius (F.)

Lymexylidae
Lymexylon navale (L.)

Cucujidae
Uleiota planata (L.)
Leptophloeus clematidis
(Erichson)

Cryptophagidae
Cryptophagus badius Sturm
Cryptophagus lapponicus
Gyllenhal

Coccinellidae
Nephus quadrimaculatus
(Herbst)

Endomychidae
Lycoperdina succincta (L.)

Lathridiidae
Enicmus rugosus (Herbst)
Corticaria fagi Wollaston

Tenebrionidae
Diaperis boleti (L.)
Prionychus melanarius
(Germar)

Melandryidae
Hypulus quercinus (Quensel)

Oedemeridae
Ischnomera cinerascens
(Pandelle)

Cerambycidae
Pyrrhidium sanguineum (L.)
Lamia textor (L.)

Chrysomelidae
Donacia obscura Gyllenhal
Cryptocephalus biguttatus
(Scopoli)
*Cryptocephalus decemma-
culatus* (L.)
Cryptocephalus querceti
Suffrian
Cryptocephalus sexpunctatus
(L.)
Chrysolina latecincta
(Demaison)
Longitarsus rutilus (Illiger)

Curculionidae
Otiorhynchus ligustici (L.)
Cathormiocerus socius
Boheman
Limobius mixtus (Boheman)
Liparus germanus (L.)

Anchonidium unguiculare
(Aube)
Bagous argillaceus Gyllenhal
Bagous cylindrus (Paykull)
Dorytomus affinis (Paykull)

Ceutorhynchus pilosellus
Gyllenhal
Ceutorhynchus querceti
(Gyllenhal)
Tychius quinquepunctatus (L.)

Category 3
RARE

Carabidae
Cicindela germanica L.
Cicindela hybrida L.
Leistus montanus Stephens
Nebria nivalis (Paykull)
Dyschirius angustatus
(Ahrens)
Dyschirius extensus Putzeys
(5)*Tachys edmondsi* Moore
Tachys micros (von
Waldheim)
Tachys scutellaris Stephens
Amara alpina (Paykull)
Bradycellus csikii Laczo
Dromius quadrisignatus
Dejean
Lionychus quadrillum
(Duftschmid)

Haliplidae
Haliplus mucronatus Stephens
Haliplus variegatus Sturm
*Haliplus varius Nicolai

Dytiscidae
Hydrovatus clypealis Sharp
Bidessus minutissimus
(Germar)
*Coelambus nigrolineatus (von
Steven)
(= *C. lautus* Schaum)
Hydroporus elongatulus
Sturm
Hydroporus glabriusculus
Aube
Graptodytes bilineatus
(Sturm)
*Oreodytes alpinus (Paykull)
Graphoderus cinereus (L.)

Hydrophilidae
Hydrochus brevis (Herbst)
Hydrochus carinatus Germar
Hydrochus elongatus
(Schaller)
Hydrochus ignicollis
Motschulsky
Hydrochus nitidicollis Mulsant

Helophorus dorsalis
(Marsham)
Helophorus longitarsis
Wollaston
Helophorus tuberculatus
Gyllenhal
Cercyon bifenestratus
Kuester
*Cercyon granarius Erichson
*Laccobius simulator
d'Orchymont
*Helochares obscurus
(Mueller)
*Enochrus isotae Hebauer
Hydrophilus piceus (L.)
Berosus spinosus (von
Steven)

Sphaeritidae
Sphaerites glabratus (F.)

Histeridae
Aeletes atomarius (Aube)
Acritus homoeopathicus
Wollaston
*Epierus comptus (Erichson)
Hetaerius ferrugineus
(Olivier)

Hydraenidae
Ochthebius poweri Rye
Hydraena pygmaea
Waterhouse
*Limnebius crinifer Rey

Ptiliidae
Ptenidium gressneri Erichson

Leiodidae
Agathidium badium Erichson
Agathidium confusum Brisout
Catops nigriclavis Gerhardt

Silphidae
Thanatophilus dispar (Herbst)
Aclypea undata (Mueller)

Scydmaenidae
Euconnus maeklini
(Mannerheim)

Staphylinidae

Olophrum consimile (Gyllenhal)
Eusphalerum sorbicola (Kangas)
Phyllodrepa salicis (Gyllenhal)
Hypopycna rufula (Erichson)
Planeustomus palpalis (Erichson)
Bledius diota Schioedte
Bledius erraticus Erichson
Bledius occidentalis Bondroit
Carpelimus halophilus (Kiesenwetter)
(= *C. despectus* sensu auct. Brit.)
**Carpelimus lindrothi* (Palm)
Carpelimus obesus (Kiesenwetter)
Carpelimus subtilis (Erichson)
Thinobius brevipennis Kiesenwetter
Thinobius major Kraatz
Anotylus fairmairei (Pandelle)
Stenus asphaltinus Erichson
**Stenus calcaratus* Scriba
Stenus incanus Erichson
Stenus kiesenwetteri Rosenhauer
Stenus opticus Gravenhorst
Stenus proditor Erichson
Stenus subdepressus Mulsant & Rey
Paederus caligatus Erichson
Lathrobium dilutum Erichson
Lathrobium fennicum Renkonen
Lathrobium pallidum von Nordmann
Ochthephilum jaquelini (Boieldieu)
Medon piceus (Kraatz)
Medon pocoferus (Peyson)
Scopaeus gracilis (Sperk)
Astenus procerus (Gravenhorst)
Gabrius astutoides Strand
Gabrius exiguus (von Nordmann)
Gabrius scoticus (Joy & Tomlin)
(= *Philonthus scoticus*)

Staphylinus caesareus Cederhjelm
Staphylinus nero Faldermann
Staphylinus ophthalmicus Scopoli
Quedius riparius Kellner
Bryoporus cernuus (Gravenhorst)
Bryoporus crassicornis (Maeklin)
Tachyporus quadriscopulatus Pandelle
Brachida exigua (Heer)
Arena tabida (Kiesenwetter)
Rhopalocerina clavigera (Scriba)
Borboropora kraatzi Fuss
Schistoglossa viduata (Erichson)
Zyras haworthi Stephens
Zyras plicatus (Erichson)
Lomechusoides strumosa (F.)
Lomechusa paradoxa Gravenhorst
Phloeodroma concolor Kraatz
Ilyobates propinquus (Aube)
Calodera uliginosa Erichson
Ityocara rubens (Erichson)
Amarochara forticornis Boisduval & Lacordaire
*Meotica lohsei Benick
Ocyusa hibernica (Rye)
Ocyusa nigrata (Fairmaire & Laboulbene)
**Ocyusa nitidiventris* Fagel
Hygropora cunctans (Erichson)
Oxypoda nigrocincta Mulsant & Rey
Oxypoda riparia Fairmaire
Homoeusa acuminata (Maerkel)
Aleochara discipennis Mulsant & Rey
Aleochara sanguinea (L.)

Pselaphidae

Bibloporus minutus Raffray
Euplectus brunneus (Grimmer)
Trichonyx sulcicollis (Reichenbach)
Amauronyx maerkeli (Aube)

21

Batrisodes venustus
(Reichenbach)
Tychobythinus glabratus
(Rye)

Geotrupidae
Odontaeus armiger (Scopoli)

Scarabaeidae
Colobopterus subterraneus
(L.) (= *Aphodius*
subterraneus)
Aphodius lividus (Olivier)
Aphodius quadrimaculatus
(L.)
Aphodius sus (Herbst)
(= *Heptaulacus sus*)
Aphodius testudinarius (F.)
(= *Heptaulacus*
testudinarius)
Gnorimus nobilis (L.)

Eucinetidae
Eucinetus meridionalis
(Castelnau)

Scirtidae
Elodes elongata (Tournier)
Cyphon pubescens (F.)
Prionocyphon serricornis
(Mueller)
Scirtes orbicularis (Panzer)

Byrrhidae
Simplocaria maculosa
Erichson

Psephenidae
Eubria palustris Germar

Heteroceridae
Heterocerus hispidulus
Kiesenwetter

Dryopidae
Dryops anglicanus Edwards
Dryops griseus (Erichson)
(not *D. griseus* sensu auct.
Brit.)

Elmidae (Elminthidae)
Macronychus quadri-
tuberculatus Mueller
Oulimnius major (Rey)

Elateridae
Ampedus cinnabarinus
(Eschscholtz)

Ampedus tristis (L.)
Negastrius pulchellus (L.)
Negastrius sabulicola
(Boheman)
Melanotus punctolineatus
(Pelerin)
Harminius undulatus (Degeer)
Athous subfuscus (Mueller)
Selatosomus angustulus
(Kiesenwetter)
Synaptus filiformis (F.)

Throscidae
Trixagus brevicollis (de
Bonvouloir)

Eucnemidae
Dirhagus pygmaeus (F.)
Hylis olexai (Palm)

Cantharidae
Malthodes brevicollis
(Paykull)
Malthodes crassicornis
(Maeklin)

Lycidae
Pyropterus nigroruber
(Degeer)

Dermestidae
Trinodes hirtus (F.)

Anobiidae
Ernobius gigas (Mulsant &
Rey)

Bostrichidae
Bostrichus capucinus (L.)

Trogossitidae
Nemozoma elongatum (L.)

Melyridae
Malachius aeneus (L.)
Malachius barnevillei Puton
Malachius vulneratus Abeille

Rhizophagidae
Rhizophagus parvulus
(Paykull)
Rhizophagus picipes (Olivier)
Cyanostolus aeneus (Richter)
Monotoma angusticollis
Gyllenhal
Monotoma quadrifoveolata
Aube

Cucujidae
Notolaemus unifasciatus
(Latreille)

Silvanidae
Silvanus bidentatus (F.)
Silvanoprus fagi (Guerin-
Meneville)

Cryptophagidae
Cryptophagus micaceus Rey
Atomaria lohsei Johnson &
Strand

Erotylidae
Triplax lacordairii Crotch
Triplax scutellaris
Charpentier

Corylophidae
Orthoperus brunnipes
(Gyllenhal)
Rypobius ruficollis (du Val)

Coccinellidae
*Hippodamia tredecim-
punctata* (L.)
Coccinella distincta
Faldermann
Coccinella quinquepunctata
L.

Cisidae
Cis coluber Abeille

Colydiidae
Synchita separanda (Reitter)
Colydium elongatum (F.)
Oxylaemus variolosus
(Dufour)

Tenebrionidae
Bolitophagus reticulatus (L.)
Corticeus unicolor Piller &
Mitterpacher

Pyrochroidae
Schizotus pectinicornis (L.)

Melandryidae
Anisoxya fuscula (Illiger)
Osphya bipunctata (F.)

Scraptiidae
Anaspis melanostoma Costa

Mordellidae
Tomoxia biguttata (Gyllenhal)

Oedemeridae
Oedemera virescens (L.)

Meloidae
Meloe autumnalis Olivier
Meloe brevicollis Panzer
Meloe cicatricosus Leach
Meloe rugosus Marsham
Meloe variegatus Donovan

Aderidae
Aderus brevicornis (Perris)

Cerambycidae
Tetropium castaneum (L.)
Grammoptera ustulata
(Schaller)
Leptura rubra L.
Leptura sexguttata F.
Strangalia revestita (L.)
Callidium violaceum (L.)
Mesosa nebulosa (F.)

Chrysomelidae
Macroplea appendiculata
(Panzer)
Macroplea mutica (F.)
Oulema erichsoni Suffrian
Hydrothassa hannoveriana
(F.)
Phyllodecta polaris Schneider
Longitarsus quadriguttatus
(Pontoppidan)
Chaetocnema conducta
(Motschulsky)
Psylliodes sophiae
Heikertinger
Cassida denticollis Suffrian

Anthribidae
Tropideres niveirostris (F.)
Tropideres sepicola (F.)
*Bruchela rufipes (Olivier)

Apionidae
Apion brunnipes Boheman
*Apion dispar Germar
Apion lemoroi Brisout

Curculionidae
Otiorhynchus morio (F.)
Cathormiocerus maritimus
Rye
*Cathormiocerus myrmeco-
philus* (Seidlitz)
Omias mollinus Boheman

Brachysomus hirtus
  (Boheman)
Strophosomus curvipes
  Thomson
Chromoderus affinis
  (Schrank)
Hypera diversipunctata
  (Schrank)
Hypera meles (F.)
Hylobius transversovittatus
  (Goeze)
Leiosoma pyrenaeum Brisout
Syagrius intrudens
  Waterhouse
Pissodes validirostris
  (Sahlberg)
* *Magdalis memnonia*
  (Gyllenhal)
Bagous arduus Sharp
Procas armillatus (F.)
Smicronyx coecus (Reich)
Ceutorhynchus arquatus
  (Herbst)
Ceutorhynchus moelleri
  Thomson
Ceutorhynchus parvulus
  Brisout
Ceutorhynchus pectoralis
  Weise
Ceutorhynchus syrites
  Germar

* *Phytobius olssoni* (Israelson)
Phytobius quadrinodosus
  (Gyllenhal)
Baris scolopacea Germar
* *Tychius crassirostris* Kirsch
Tychius polylineatus
  (Germar)
Miarus degorsi Abeille
Miarus micros (Germar)
Rhynchaenus decoratus
  (Germar)

Scolytidae
Tomicus minor (Hartig)
Dryocoetinus alni (Georg)
Lymantor coryli (Perris)
Xyloterus signatum (F.)
Cryphalus abietis (Ratzeburg)
Ernoporus tiliae (Panzer)
Trypophloeus asperatus
  (Gyllenhal)
Xyleborus dispar (F.)
Pityophthorus lichtensteini
  (Ratzeburg)
Pityogenes chalcographus
  (L.)
Pityogenes quadridens
  (Hartig)
Pityogenes trepanatus
  (Noerdlinger)

Platypodidae
Platypus cylindrus (F.)

Category 5
ENDEMIC

Carabidae
Tachys edmondsi Moore
  (Category 3)

Leiodidae
Aglyptinus agathidioides
  Blair (Category 1)

Staphylinidae
Thinobius newberyi
  Scheerpeltz (Category 2)

Meotica anglica Bewick
  (not threatened)

Chrysomelidae
Psylliodes luridipennis
  Kutschera (Category 1)

Apionidae
Apion ryei Blackburn
  (not threatened)

APPENDIX
No post-1900
records

Carabidae
Bembidion octomaculatum
  (Goeze)
Diachromus germanus (L.)
Lebia marginata (Fourcroy)
Lebia scapularis (Fourcroy)

Dytiscidae
Cybister lateralimarginalis
  (Degeer)

Sphaeriidae
Sphaerius acaroides Waltl

Histeridae
Saprinus subnitescens
  Bickhardt
Hister illigeri Duftschmid
Hister quadrinotatus Scriba

Ptiliidae
Oligella intermedia Besuchet
Ptilium caesum Erichson

Staphylinidae
Paederus rubrothoracicus
  (Goeze)
Bolitobius formosus
  (Gravenhorst)

Lucanidae
Platycerus caraboides (L.)

Scarabaeidae
Aphodius scrofa (F.)
Rhyssemus germanus (L.)
Pleurophorus caesus
  (Creutzer)
Onthophagus nutans (F.)
Polyphylla fullo (L.)

Elateridae
Ampedus sanguineus (L.)
Cardiophorus gramineus
  (Scopoli)
Cardiophorus ruficollis (L.)
Selatosomus cruciatus (L.)

Cleridae
Tilloidea unifasciatus (F.)
  (= *Tillus unifasciatus*)
Trichodes alvearius (F.)
Trichodes apiarius (L.)
Tarsostenus univittatus (Rossi)

Melyridae
Ebaeus pedicularius (L.)

Corylophidae
Orthoperus atomarius (Heer)

Coccinellidae
Nephus bisignatus (Boheman)
Vibidia duodecimguttata
  (Poda)

Colydiidae
Endophloeus markovichianus
  (Piller & Mitterpacher)
Oxylaemus cylindricus
  (Panzer)

Tenebrionidae
Blaps mortisaga (L.)

Mycteridae
Mycterus curculioides (F.)

Cerambycidae
Strangalia attenuata (L.)
Obrium cantharinum (L.)
Plagionotus arcuatus (L.)

Chrysomelidae
Clytra laeviuscula Ratzeburg
Agelastica alni (L.)
Hypocassida subferruginea
  (Schrank)

Attelabidae
Rhynchites auratus (Scopoli)
Rhynchites bacchus (L.)
Rhynchites sericeus Herbst

Curculionidae
Peritelus sphaeroides Germar
Polydrusus prasinus (Olivier)
Coniocleonus hollbergi
  (Fahraeus)
  (= *Cleonus hollbergi*)
Hypera arundinis (Paykull)
Lepyrus capucinus (Schaller)
Rhyncolus gracilis
  Rosenhauer
Bagous petro (Herbst)
Procas granulicollis Walton
Sibinia pellucens (Scopoli)

Scolytidae
Trypophloeus granulatus
  (Ratzeburg)

Hymenoptera : Aculeata – Ants, bees and wasps

**Category 1
ENDANGERED**

Chrysididae
Omalus truncatus (Dahlbom)
Chrysis fulgida L.

Formicidae
Formica pratensis Retzius
Formica transkaucasica
Nasonov

Pompilidae
Arachnospila rufa (Haupt)
Evagetes pectinipes (L.)
Homonotus sanguinolentus
(F.)
Ceropales variegata (F.)

Eumenidae
+*Odynerus reniformis* (Gmelin)
+*Odynerus simillimus*
Morawitz

Sphecidae
Crossocerus vagabundus
(Panzer)
+*Mellinus crabroneus*
(Thunberg)
Cerceris quadricincta
(Panzer)

Andrenidae
Andrena ferox Smith
Andrena floricola Eversmann
Andrena gravida Imhoff

Andrena lathyri Alfken
Andrena lepida Schenck
Andrena nana (Kirby)
+*Andrena polita* Smith
Andrena tridentata (Kirby)
Andrena vaga Panzer

Halictidae
+*Halictus eurygnathus*
Bluethgen
+*Halictus maculatus* Smith
Dufourea minuta Lepeletier
Dufourea vulgaris Schenck

Melittidae
Melitta dimidiata Morawitz

Megachilidae
Stelis breviuscula (Nylander)
Osmia xanthomelana (Kirby)

Anthophoridae
Nomada armata Herrich-
Schaeffer
Nomada errans Lepeletier
Nomada guttulata Schenck
Nomada sexfasciata Panzer
Nomada xanthosticta (Kirby)
+*Eucera tuberculata* (F.)
Melecta luctuosa (Scopoli)

Apidae
+*Bombus cullumanus* (Kirby)

**Category 2
VULNERABLE**

Chrysididae
Chrysogona gracillima
(Foerster)
Chrysura hirsuta
(Gerstaecker)

Eumenidae
Pseudepipona herrichii
(Saussure)

Sphecidae
Miscophus ater Lepeletier
Rhopalum gracile Wesmael

Psen atratinus (Morawitz)
Passaloecus clypealis Faester
Philanthus triangulum (F.)

Andrenidae
Andrena hattorfiana (F.)

Halictidae
Lasioglossum laticeps
(Schenck)

Megachilidae
Osmia inermis (Zetterstedt)
Osmia uncinata Gerstaecker

**Category 3
RARE**

Chrysididae
Omalus puncticollis
(Mocsary)
Hedychridium coriaceum
(Dahlbom)
Chrysis longula Abeille de
Perrin
Chrysis pseudobrevitarsis
Linsenmaier
Cleptes nitidulus (F.)

Formicidae
Myrmica hirsuta Elmes
Myrmica specioides Bondroit
Sifolinia karavajevi (Arnoldi)
Leptothorax interruptus
(Schenck)
Leptothorax tuberum (F.)
Anergates atratulus (Schenck)
Strongylognathus testaceus
(Schenck)
Solenopsis fugax (Latreille)
Formica exsecta Nylander
Formica rufibarbis F.

Pompilidae
Dipogon bifasciatus
(Geoffroy)
Cryptocheilus notatus
(Rossius)
Priocnemis cordivalvata
Haupt
Priocnemis gracilis Haupt
Arachnospila consobrina
(Dahlbom)
Arachnospila wesmaeli
(Thomson)

Eumenidae
Euodynerus quadrifasciatus
(F.)
Ancistrocerus antilope
(Panzer)
Ancistrocerus quadratus
(Panzer)
Symmorphus connexus
(Curtis)
Symmorphus crassicornis
(Panzer)

Vespidae
*Dolichovespula media Retzius

Sphecidae
*Nitela borealis Valkeila
*Nitela spinolae Latreille
Crossocerus distinguendus
(Morawitz)
Crossocerus exiguus (Vander
Linden)
Crossocerus leucostoma (L.)
Ectemnius borealis
(Zetterstedt)
Ectemnius ruficornis
(Zetterstedt)
Psen bicolor Jurine
Psen littoralis (Bondroit)
Psen spooneri (Richards)
Psen unicolor (Vander
Linden)
Psenulus schencki (Tournier)
Spilomena vagans Bluethgen
Pemphredon clypealis
Thomson
Pemphredon enslini
(Wagner)
Pemphredon morio Vander
Linden
Pemphredon mortifer
Valkeila
Pemphredon wesmaeli
(Morawitz)
Diodontus insidiosus Spooner
Passaloecus eremita Kohl
Podalonia affinis (Kirby)
Nysson interruptus (F.)
Alysson lunicornis (F.)
Gorytes laticinctus
(Lepeletier)
Argogorytes fargei
(Shuckard)
Cerceris quinquefasciata
(Rossius)

Colletidae
Colletes cunicularius (L.)
Colletes marginatus Smith
Hylaeus cornutus Curtis
Hylaeus euryscapus Foerster
Hylaeus gibbus Saunders

Andrenidae
Andrena alfkenella Perkins
Andrena bucephala Stephens
Andrena congruens
Schmiedeknecht

Andrena falsifica Perkins
Andrena florea F.
Andrena fulvago (Christ)
Andrena labiata F.
Andrena nitidiusculus
Schenck
Andrena niveata Friese
Andrena proxima (Kirby)
Andrena rosae Panzer
Andrena ruficrus Nylander
Andrena simillima Smith
Andrena tibialis (Kirby)

Halictidae
Halictus confusus Smith
Lasioglossum aeratum (Kirby)
Lasioglossum angusticeps
(Perkins)
Lasioglossum brevicorne
(Schenck)
Lasioglossum pauperatum
(Brulle)
Sphecodes niger Sichel
Sphecodes reticulatus
Thomson
Sphecodes scabricollis
Wesmael
Sphecodes spinulosus von
Hagens

Melittidae
Macropis europaea Warncke

Megachilidae
Stelis ornatula (Klug)
Stelis phaeoptera (Kirby)
Heriades truncorum (L.)
Osmia parietina Curtis
Osmia pilicornis Smith
Coelioxys mandibularis
Nylander
Coelioxys quadridentata (L.)

Anthophoridae
Nomada conjugens
Herrich-Schaeffer
Nomada fulvicornis F.
Nomada hirtipes Perez
Nomada lathburiana (Kirby)
Nomada signata Jurine
Nomada tormentillae Alfken
Anthophora retusa (L.)

Xylocopidae
Ceratina cyanea (Kirby)

**APPENDIX
No post-1900
records**

Chrysididae
Hedychrum rutilans Dahlbom

Pompilidae
Priocnemis propinqua
(Lepeletier)

Sphecidae
Dinetus pictus (F.)
Tachysphex obscuripennis
(Schenck)
Lestica clypeata (Schreber)
Psen ater (Olivier)
Cerceris sabulosa (Panzer)

Colletidae
Hylaeus punctulatissima Smith

Andrenidae
Andrena nanula Nylander

Halictidae
Halictus subauratus (Rossius)
Lasioglossum laeve (Kirby)
Lasioglossum sexnotatum
(Kirby)
Rophites quinquespinosus
Spinola

Megachilidae
Hoplitis leucomelana (Kirby)
Chalicodoma ericetorum
Lepeletier
Megachile lapponica
Thomson
Coelioxys afra Lepeletier

Apidae
Bombus pomorum (Panzer)

Diptera – Flies

Only those species with the symbol > have accounts included in the Red Data Book.

Category 1
ENDANGERED

Tipulidae
Prionocera pubescens Loew
Prionocera subserricornis (Zetterstedt)
>Ctenophora flaveolata (F.)
Ctenophora ornata Meigen
>Nephrotoma sullingtonensis Edwards
Tipula mutila Wahlgren
Tipula sarajevensis Strobl
Tipula serrulifera Alexander
Tipula siebkei Zetterstedt
>Limonia aperta (Wahlgren)
Limonia frontalis (Staeger)
Elliptera omissa Schiner
>Limnophila fasciata (L.)
Limnophila heterogyna Bergroth
Limnophila pictipennis (Meigen)
Gonomyia bradleyi Edwards
Gonomyia connexa Loew
Gonomyia limbata (von Roeser)
>Gonomyia sexguttata (Dale)
Lipsothrix nigristigma Edwards
>Erioptera pusilla (Schiner)
Arctoconopa melampodia (Loew)
Tasiocera collini Freeman
Tasiocera jenkinsoni Freeman

Culicidae
Aedes communis (Degeer)
Aedes leucomelas (Meigen)
Culiseta longiareolata (Macquart)

Mycetophilidae
Bolitophila fumida Edwards
Diadocidia valida Mik
Macrocera fastuosa Loew
Macrocera longibrachiata Landrock
Macrocera propleuralis Edwards
Macrocera zetterstedti Lundstroem
Cerotelion humeralis (Zetterstedt)
Orfelia macrocera (Edwards)
Orfelia ruficornis (Zetterstedt)
Mycomya britteni Kidd
Mycomya pectinifera Edwards
Mycomya punctata (Meigen)
Mycomya rosalba Hutson
Mycomya wrzesniowskii (Dziedzicki)
>Neoempheria lineola (Meigen)
Eudicrana nigriceps Lundstroem
Syntemna stylata Hutson
Sciophila adamsi Edwards
Sciophila cliftoni Edwards
Sciophila fridolini Stackelberg
Sciophila geniculata Zetterstedt
Sciophila interrupta (Winnertz)
Sciophila limbatella Zetterstedt
>Sciophila ochracea Walker
Sciophila plurisetosa Edwards
Sciophila quadriterga Hutson
Sciophila varia (Winnertz)
Acnemia amoena Winnertz
Palaeodocosia flava (Edwards)
Gnoriste longirostris Siebke
Boletina pectinunguis Edwards
Boletina silvatica Dziedzicki
Ectrepesthoneura pubescens (Zetterstedt)
Manota unifurcata Lundstroem
Anatella lenis Dziedzicki

Anatella pseudogibba
Plassmann
Pseudorymosia fovea
(Dziedzicki)
Exechia dizona Edwards
Exechia lucidula (Zetterstedt)
Exechia lundstroemi
Landrock
Exechiopsis dryaspagensis
Chandler
Pseudexechia parallela
(Edwards)
Allodia angulata Lundstroem
Brevicornu fennicum
(Landrock)
Brevicornu griseolum
(Zetterstedt)
Trichonta bicolor Landrock
Trichonta flavicauda
Lundstroem
Trichonta fusca Landrock
Trichonta nigritula Edwards
Mycetophila autumnalis
Lundstroem
Mycetophila bohemica
(Lastovka)
Mycetophila lubomirskii
Dziedzicki
Mycetophila mitis (Johannsen)
Mycetophila scotica Edwards
Mycetophila strigatoides
(Landrock)
Sceptonia tenuis Edwards

Stratiomyidae
>*Odontomyia angulata*
(Panzer)
>*Stratiomys chamaeleon* (L.)

Xylophagidae
>*Xylophagus junki* Szilady

Rhagionidae
>*Chrysopilus laetus*
(Zetterstedt)

Tabanidae
>*Atylotus plebeius* (Fallen)
>*Atylotus rusticus* (L.)
>*Hybomitra expollicata*
(Pandelle)

Asilidae
>*Epitriptus arthriticus* (Zeller)

>*Neoitamus cothurnatus*
(Meigen)
>*Laphria gilva* (L.)

Therevidae
>*Psilocephala melaleuca*
(Loew)

Empididae
Tachypeza heeri Zetterstedt
Tachypeza truncorum
(Fallen)
Tachydromia acklandi
(Chvala)
Tachydromia halidayi (Collin)
Tachydromia woodi (Collin)
Platypalpus alter (Collin)
Platypalpus analis (Meigen)
Platypalpus carteri (Collin)
Platypalpus excisus (Becker)
Platypalpus inexpectatus
Smith & Chvala
Platypalpus infectus (Collin)
Platypalpus ingenuus (Collin)
Platypalpus longimanus
(Corti)
Platypalpus mikii (Becker)
Platypalpus niveiseta
Zetterstedt
Platypalpus ochrocera
(Collin)
Platypalpus pygialis Chvala
Platypalpus subtilis (Collin)
Platypalpus tonsus (Collin)
Platypalpus unicus Collin
Symballophthalmus pictipes
(Becker)
Syndyas nigripes (Zetterstedt)
>*Syneches muscarius* (F.)
Leptopeza borealis
Zetterstedt
Oedalea oriunda Collin
Rhamphomyia aethiops
Zetterstedt
Rhamphomyia albidiventris
Strobl
Rhamphomyia breviventris
Frey
Rhamphomyia ignobilis
Zetterstedt
Rhamphomyia marginata (F.)
Rhamphomyia physoprocta
Frey

Rhamphomyia plumipes
(Meigen)
Rhamphomyia trigemina
(Oldenberg)
Rhamphomyia vesiculosa
(Fallen)
Empis limata Collin
Empis melaena Bezzi
Hilara aeronetha Mik
Hilara gallica (Meigen)
Hilara merula Collin
Hilara pilosopectinata Strobl
Hilara setosa Collin
Chelifera astigma Collin
Weidemannia impudica Mik
Weidemannia lamellata
(Loew)

Dolichopodidae
Sciapus heteropygus Parent
Dolichopus laticola Verrall
Dolichopus lineatocornis
Zetterstedt
Dolichopus melanopus
Meigen
Dolichopus nigripes Fallen
Dolichopus plumitarsis Fallen
Dolichopus signifer Haliday
Hercostomus sahlbergi
(Zetterstedt)
Poecilobothrus majesticus
Fonseca
Thrypticus cuneatus (Becker)
Cyrturella albosetosa (Strobl)
Rhaphium pectinatum (Loew)
Syntormon macula Parent
Neurigona abdominalis
(Fallen)
Diaphorus hoffmannseggii
Meigen
Diaphorus winthemi Meigen
Acropsilus niger (Loew)
Telmaturgus tumidulus
(Raddatz)

Phoridae
Aenigmatias brevifrons
Schmitz
Aenigmatias franzi Schmitz
Aenigmatias lubbocki
(Verrall)
Plectanocnema nudipes
(Becker)

Woodiphora retroversa
(Wood)
Phora obscura (Zetterstedt)
Phora praepandens Schmitz
Triphleba excisa (Lundbeck)
Triphleba flexipalpis Schmitz
Triphleba smithi Disney

Pipunculidae
>*Nephrocerus scutellatus*
Macquart
Dorylomorpha clavifemora
Coe
Cephalops curtifrons Coe
Eudorylas dissimilis Coe
Eudorylas restrictus Coe

Syrphidae
>*Parasyrphus nigritarsis*
(Zetterstedt)
>*Didea alneti* (Fallen)
>*Chrysotoxum vernale* Loew
>*Chamaesyrphus*
caledonicus Collin
>*Myolepta potens* (Harris)
>*Hammerschmidtia ferruginea*
(Fallen)
>*Callicera rufa* Schummel
>*Callicera spinolae* Rondani
>*Calliprobola speciosa* (Rossi)
>*Blera fallax* (L.)

Conopidae
Myopa vicaria Walker
Sicus abdominalis Kroeber

Tephritidae
Chetostoma curvinervis
Rondani
Trypeta wiedemanni
(Hendel)
Acinia corniculata
(Zetterstedt)
Paroxyna lhommei Hering
Paroxyna praecox (Loew)

Otitidae
Homalocephala albitarsis
Zetterstedt
Homalocephala bipunctata
(Loew)

Micropezidae
>*Rainieria calceata* (Fallen)

Tanypezidae
Strongylophthalmyia ustulata
(Zetterstedt)

Chamaemyiidae
Parochthiphila coronata
(Loew)
Parochthiphila spectabilis
(Loew)

Heleomyzidae
Borboropsis puberella
(Zetterstedt)
Oldenbergiella brumalis
Czerny
Schroederella iners (Meigen)

Chyromyidae
Aphaniosoma propinquans
Collin
Aphaniosoma socium Collin

Sciomyzidae
Dichetophora finlandica
Verbeke

Pallopteridae
Eurygnathomyia bicolor
(Zetterstedt)

Piophilidae
>*Centrophlebomyia furcata*
(F.)

Opomyzidae
Geomyza angustipennis
Zetterstedt

Clusiidae
Heteromeringia nigrimana
(Loew)

Odiniidae
Odinia pomona Cogan
Odinia xanthocera Collin

Periscelididae
Periscelis annulipes Loew
Periscelis nigra (Zetterstedt)
Periscelis winnertzi Egger

Aulacigastridae
Stenomicra cogani Irwin
Stenomicra delicata (Collin)

Anthomyzidae
Anagnota collini Czerny

Ephydridae
Nostima semialata (Collin)
>*Ochthera schembrii* Rondani
Scatella callosicosta Bezzi
Teichomyza fusca Macquart

Drosophilidae
Amiota basdeni Fonseca
Chymomyza distincta (Egger)

Agromyzidae
Metopomyza ornata (Meigen)
Phytomyza orobanchia
Kaltenbach

Oestridae
Cephenemyia trompe
(Modeer)

Tachinidae
Gymnosoma globosum (F.)
Gymnosoma nitens (Meigen)
Cylindromyia brassicaria (F.)
Phania thoracica (Meigen)
Dionaea aurifrons (Meigen)
Labigastera forcipata
(Meigen)
Litophasia hyalipennis
(Fallen)
Estheria bohemani Rondani
Periscepsia prunaria
(Rondani)
Nemoraea pellucida
(Meigen)
Germaria ruficeps (Fallen)
Leskia aurea (Fallen)
Chrysosomopsis auratus
(Fallen)
Peleteria rubescens
Robineau-Desvoidy
Actia exoleta (Meigen)
Ceromya silacea (Meigen)
Trichopareia seria (Meigen)
Belida angelicae (Meigen)
Hemimacquartia paradoxa
Brauer & Bergenstamm
Staurochaeta albocingulata
(Fallen)
Rhaphiochaeta breviseta
(Zetterstedt)
Clemelis pullata (Meigen)
Eurysthaea scutellaris
(Robineau-Desvoidy)
Carcelia excisa (Fallen)

Carcelia intermedia (Herting)
Huebneria affinis (Fallen)
Phebellia stulta (Zetterstedt)
Xylotachina diluta (Meigen)

Rhinophoridae
Angioneura acerba (Meigen)

Sarcophagidae
Angiometopa ruralis (Fallen)
Agria affinis (Fallen)
Sarcophaga exuberans
    Pandelle

Scathophagidae
Cordilura hyalinipennis
    Ringdahl
Cosmetopus dentimanus
    (Zetterstedt)

Anthomyiidae
>*Chirosia montana* Pokorny
Pegohylemyia apiciseta
    (Ringdahl)

Pegohylemyia flavisquama
    (Stein)
Phorbia longipilis (Pandelle)
Phorbia nuditibia Fonseca
Delia caledonica Fonseca
Delia hirtitibia (Stein)

Fanniidae
Fannia hirundinis Ringdahl
Fannia novalis Pont
Fannia pseudonorvegica
    Fonseca

Muscidae
Dendrophaonia setifemur
    (Stein)
Phaonia apicalis Stein
Phaonia gracilis Stein
Helina cilipes (Schnabl &
    Dziedzicki)
Coenosia dubiosa Hennig

Category 2
VULNERABLE

Tipulidae
Ctenophora atrata (L.)
Tipula bistilata Lundstroem
Tipula dilatata Schummel
Tipula gimmerthali
    Lackschewitz
Tipula selene Meigen
Triogma trisulcata
    (Schummel)
>*Limonia bezzii* (Alexander &
    Leonard)
Limonia ctenophora (Loew)
Limonia danica (Kuntze)
>*Limonia omissinervis*
    (de Meijere)
Limonia uniseriata (Schiner)
Limnophila abdominalis
    Staeger
Limnophila glabricula
    (Meigen)
Gonomyia abbreviata Loew
>*Gonomyia punctata* Edwards
Lipsothrix ecucullata
    Edwards
>*Erioptera bivittata* (Loew)
>*Erioptera limbata* Loew
Erioptera meijerei Edwards

Culicidae
Aedes flavescens (Mueller)

Ceratopogonidae
>*Dasyhelea lithotelmatica*
    Strenzke

Mycetophilidae
Macrocera aterrima
    Stackelberg
Macrocera bipunctata
    Edwards
Macrocera fascipennis
    Staeger
>*Asindulum nigrum* Latreille
Orfelia biumbrata (Edwards)
Mycomya clavigera
    (Lundstroem)
Mycomya collini Edwards
Mycomya digitifera Edwards
Mycomya kingi Edwards
Sciophila buxtoni Freeman
Boletina digitata Lundstroem
Boletina nigrofusca Dziedzicki
Ectrepesthoneura colyeri
    Chandler
Anatella dampfi Landrock
Rymosia affinis Winnertz
Rymosia armata Lackschewitz
Exechia sororcula
    Lackschewitz

Exechiopsis furcata
(Lundstroem)
Exechiopsis magnicauda
(Lundstroem)
Allodia czernyi (Landrock)
Brevicornu kingi (Edwards)
Brevicornu serenum Winnertz
Brachypeza armata Winnertz
Dynatosoma cochleare Strobl
Dynatosoma nigromaculatum
Lundstroem
Mycetophila caudata Staeger
Mycetophila confusa
Dziedzicki
Mycetophila hetschkoi
Landrock
Mycetophila morosa Winnertz
Sceptonia humerella Edwards

Stratiomyidae
Oxycera analis Meigen
>*Oxycera dives* Loew
Oxycera fallenii Staeger
Oxycera morrisii Curtis
>*Oxycera pardalina* Meigen
>*Oxycera terminata* Meigen
>*Odontomyia argentata* (F.)
>*Odontomyia ornata* (Meigen)
>*Stratiomys longicornis*
(Scopoli)

Xylomyiidae
>*Xylomyia maculata* (Meigen)
Xylomyia marginata (Meigen)

Rhagionidae
>*Chrysopilus erythroph-
thalmus* Loew

Tabanidae
>*Chrysops sepulcralis* (F.)

Asilidae
>*Epitriptus cowini* Hobby
>*Eutolmus rufibarbis* (Meigen)
Machimus rusticus (Meigen)

Bombyliidae
>*Villa cingulata* (Meigen)
>*Villa circumdata* (Meigen)

Empididae
Platypalpus aeneus
(Macquart)

Platypalpus albicornis
(Zetterstedt)
Platypalpus divisus Walker
Platypalpus luteolus (Collin)
Platypalpus pallidicoxa Frey
Platypalpus stabilis (Collin)
Platypalpus stigma (Collin)
Hormopeza obliterata
Zetterstedt
Rhamphomyia murina Collin
Empis laetabilis Collin
Empis volucris Meigen
Hilara barbipes Frey
Hilara germanica Engel
Hilara hirta Strobl
Hilara medeteriformis Collin
Hilara submaura Collin
Hemerodromia melangyna
Collin

Dolichopodidae
Dolichopus agilis Meigen
Dolichopus caligatus
Wahlberg
Dolichopus cilifemoratus
Macquart
Dolichopus maculipennis
Zetterstedt
Dolichopus mediicornis
Verrall
Hercostomus angustifrons
(Staeger)
Hercostomus fulvicaudis
(Haliday)
>*Poecilobothrus ducalis*
(Loew)
Hydrophorus rufibarbis
Gerstaecker
Rhaphium penicillatum Loew
Syntormon mikii Strobl
Nematoproctus distendens
(Meigen)
Melanostolus melancholicus
(Loew)
Argyra auricollis (Meigen)
Argyra grata Loew

Lonchopteridae
Lonchoptera meijeri Collin

Platypezidae
>*Callomyia elegans* Meigen
Agathomyia collini Verrall
Agathomyia falleni
(Zetterstedt)

Seri obscuripennis
(Oldenberg)

Pipunculidae
>*Cephalops perspicuus*
(de Meijere)
Eudorylas ruralis (Meigen)
Eudorylas terminalis
(Thomson)

Syrphidae
>*Doros conopseus* (F.)
>*Sphaerophoria loewi*
Zetterstedt
>*Chrysotoxum octomaculatum*
Curtis
Xanthandrus comtus (Harris)
>*Rhingia rostrata* (L.)
>*Ferdinandea ruficornis* (F.)
>*Brachyopa bicolor* (Fallen)
>*Callicera aenea* (F.)
>*Microdon devius* (L.)
>*Chalcosyrphus eunotus*
(Loew)
>*Pocota personata* (Harris)
>*Psilota anthracina* Meigen
>*Anasimyia interpuncta*
(Harris)
>*Lejops vittata* (Meigen)
>*Parhelophilus consimilis*
(Malm)
Mallota cimbiciformis (Fallen)
>*Eristalis cryptarum* (F.)

Conopidae
Leopoldius brevirostris
(Germar)
Zodion notatum Meigen
Myopa occulta Wiedemann

Tephritidae
Platyparella discoidea (F.)
Campiglossa argyrocephala
(Loew)
Campiglossa grandinata
(Rondani)

Otitidae
Myennis octopunctata
(Coquebert)

Tanypezidae
Tanypeza longimana (Fallen)

Psilidae
Loxocera nigrifrons Macquart

Chamaemyiidae
Chamaemyia paludosa Collin
>*Acrometopia wahlbergi*
(Zetterstedt)

Lauxaniidae
Minettia dissimilis Collin
Lyciella laeta (Zetterstedt)
Homoneura limnea (Becker)

Heleomyzidae
Suillia oxyphora (Mik)
Eccoptomera ornata Loew
Eccoptomera pallescens
(Meigen)

Sepsidae
Themira gracilis (Zetterstedt)

Sciomyzidae
>*Salticella fasciata* (Meigen)
Colobaea pectoralis
(Zetterstedt)
Pherbellia argyra Verbeke
Pteromicra glabricula (Fallen)
Pteromicra leucopeza
(Meigen)
Pteromicra pectorosa
(Hendel)
>*Sciomyza dryomyzina*
Zetterstedt
Antichaeta analis (Meigen)
Antichaeta brevipennis
(Zetterstedt)
Psacadina vittigera (Schiner)
Psacadina zernyi Mayer

Pallopteridae
Palloptera laetabilis Loew

Neottiophilidae
Actenoptera hilarella
(Zetterstedt)

Piophilidae
Piophila signata (Fallen)

Opomyzidae
Opomyza punctella Fallen

Clusiidae
>*Paraclusia tigrina* (Fallen)

Odiniidae
Odinia hendeli Collin
Odinia maculata (Meigen)

Acartophthalmidae
Acartophthalmus bicolor Oldenberg

Anthomyzidae
>*Anthomyza bifasciata* Wood

Asteiidae
Asteia elegantula Zetterstedt
Astiosoma rufifrons Duda

Ephydridae
Parydroptera discomyzina Collin
Scatella crassicosta Becker

Drosophilidae
Amiota variegata (Fallen)

Milichidae
Madiza britannica Hennig

Chloropidae
Lipara similis Schiner
Aphanotrigonum meijerei (Duda)
Platycephala umbraculata (F.)
Eurina lurida Meigen

Oestridae
Hypoderma bovis (L.)
Hypoderma diana Brauer
Hypoderma lineatum (Villers)

Tachinidae
Gymnosoma rotundatum (L.)
Evibrissa vittata (Meigen)
Lophosia fasciata Meigen
Anthomyiopsis nigrisquama (Zetterstedt)
Freraea gagatea Robineau-Desvoidy
Wagneria costata (Fallen)
Germaria angustata (Zetterstedt)
Redtenbacheria insignis Egger
Rhinotachina modesta (Meigen)
Ernestia puparum (F.)
Eloceria delecta (Meigen)
Actia nudibasis Stein
Asiphona verralli (Wainwright)
Ceromya monstrosicornis (Stein)

Meigenia majuscula (Rondani)
Policheta unicolor (Fallen)
Exorista glossatorum (Rondani)
Parasetigena silvestris (Robineau-Desvoidy)
Stomatomyia acuminata (Rondani)
Elodia ambulatoria (Meigen)
Gonia capitata (Degeer)
Erycia furibunda (Zetterstedt)
Phebellia nigripalpis (Robineau-Desvoidy)

Rhinophoridae
Angioneura cyrtoneurina (Zetterstedt)

Scathophagidae
>*Ernoneura argus* (Zetterstedt)
Scathophaga pictipennis Oldenberg
Scathophaga tinctinervis (Becker)
>*Parallelomma paridis* Hering

Anthomyiidae
>*Pseudomyopina moriens* (Zetterstedt)

Fanniidae
Piezura boletorum (Rondani)
Fannia collini Fonseca
Fannia latipalpis (Stein)

Muscidae
Polietes steinii (Ringdahl)
Hydrotaea meridionalis Portschinsky
Hydrotaea velutina Robineau-Desvoidy
Phaonia crinipes Ringdahl
Phaonia nitida (Macquart)
Phaonia rufiseta (Zetterstedt)
Phaonia umbraticola Fonseca
Helina crinita Collin
Helina intermedia (Villeneuve)
Spilogona scutulata (Zetterstedt)
Neolimnophora maritima (Roeder)
Lispe consanguinea Loew

Orchisia costata (Meigen)
>*Lispocephala rubricornis*
(Zetterstedt)

Coenosia albatella
(Zetterstedt)
Coenosia stigmatica Wood
Coenosia vibrissata Collin

Category 3
RARE

Trichoceridae
Trichocera maculipennis
Meigen

Tipulidae
Ctenophora nigricornis
Meigen
Nephrotoma aculeata (Loew)
Nephrotoma crocata (L.)
Nephrotoma lunulicornis
(Schummel)
Nephrotoma quadristriata
(Schummel)
Tipula alpina Loew
Tipula cheethami Edwards
Tipula coerulescens
Lackschewitz
Tipula grisescens Zetterstedt
Tipula holoptera Edwards
Tipula hortorum L.
Tipula limbata Zetterstedt
Tipula livida Wulp
Tipula luridirostris Schummel
Tipula marginata Meigen
Tipula nodicornis Meigen
(= *T. juncea* Meigen)
Tipula peliostigma Schummel
Tipula truncorum Meigen
Phalacrocera replicata (L.)
Limonia annulata (L.)
Limonia consimilis
(Zetterstedt)
Limonia goriticnsis (Mik)
Limonia masoni (Edwards)
Limonia ornata (Meigen)
Limonia rufiventris (Strobl)
Limonia stylifera
(Lackschewitz)
Limonia ventralis (Schummel)
Orimarga juvenilis
(Zetterstedt)
Orimarga virgo (Zetterstedt)
Pedicia lucidipennis
(Edwards)
Dicranota gracilipes
Wahlgren
Dicranota robusta
Lundstroem

Dicranota simulans
Lackschewitz
Paradelphomyia ecalcarata
(Edwards)
Paradelphomyia fuscula
(Loew)
Paradelphomyia nielseni
(Kuntze)
Dactylolabis sexmaculata
(Macquart)
Pilaria meridiana (Staeger)
Gnophomyia viridipennis
(Gimmerthal)
Gonomyia bifida Tonnoir
Gonomyia conoviensis Barnes
Rhabdomastix hilaris
Edwards
Rhabdomastix inclinata
Edwards
Erioptera meigeni
(Zetterstedt)
Erioptera nielseni de Meijere
Erioptera nigripalpis
Goetghebuer
Erioptera sordida Zetterstedt
Ormosia aciculata Edwards
Ormosia bicornis (de
Meijere)
Scleroprocta pentagonalis
(Loew)
Scleroprocta sororcula
(Zetterstedt)
Molophilus czizeki
Lackschewitz
Molophilus lackschewitzianus
Alexander

Dixidae
Dixa maculata Meigen
Dixella attica Pandazis
Dixella filicornis Edwards
Dixella obscura Loew
Dixella serotina Meigen

Culicidae
Aedes dorsalis (Meigen)
Aedes sticticus (Meigen)

Thaumaleidae
Thaumalea truncata Edwards

Anisopodidae
Mycetobia pallipes Meigen

Mycetophilidae
Bolitophila rossica Landrock
Macrocera crassicornis Winnertz
Macrocera estonica Landrock
Macrocera pusilla Meigen
Keroplatus testaceus Dalman
Orfelia atriceps (Edwards)
Orfelia perpusilla (Edwards)
Mycomya fuscata (Winnertz)
Mycomya lambi Edwards
Mycomya melanoceras Edwards
Mycomya ornata (Meigen)
Mycomya parva (Dziedzicki)
Mycomya trivittata (Zetterstedt)
Syntemna nitidula Edwards
Sciophila fenestella Curtis
Sciophila nigronitida Landrock
Sciophila nonnisilva Hutson
Sciophila rufa Meigen
Coelosia silvatica Landrock
Dziedzickia marginata (Dziedzicki)
Gnoriste bilineata Zetterstedt
Grzegorzekia collaris (Meigen)
Boletina groenlandica Staeger
Boletina villosa Landrock
Megophthalmidia crassicornis (Curtis)
Rymosia britteni Edwards
Rymosia connexa Winnertz
Rymosia spinipes Winnertz
Rymosia winnertzi Barendrecht
Tarnania tarnanii (Dziedzicki)
Allodiopsis ingeniosa Kidd
Allodiopsis rufilatera (Edwards)
Exechiopsis crucigera (Lundstroem)
Exechiopsis dumitrescae Burghele-Balacesco

Exechiopsis fimbriata (Lundstroem)
Exechiopsis pollicata (Edwards)
Pseudexechia aurivernica Chandler
Allodia barbata (Lundstroem)
Trichonta vulcani (Dziedzicki)
Phronia interstincta Dziedzicki
Mycetophila bialorussica Dziedzicki
Mycetophila freyi Lundstroem
Mycetophila immaculata (Dziedzicki)
Mycetophila signata Meigen
Sceptonia flavipuncta Edwards
Sceptonia fuscipalpis Edwards

Rhagionidae
Atrichops crassipes (Meigen)
Rhagio annulatus (Degeer)
Rhagio strigosus (Meigen)

Tabanidae
Haematopota bigoti Gobert
Haematopota grandis Meigen
Atylotus latistriatus (Brauer)
Hybomitra ciureai (Seguy) (= *H. schineri* Lyneborg)

Asilidae
Laphria flava (L.)

Therevidae
Psilocephala rustica (Panzer)
Thereva handlirschi Kroeber
Thereva inornata Verrall
Thereva lunulata Zetterstedt
Thereva strigata F.
Thereva valida Loew

Bombyliidae
Thyridanthrax fenestratus (Fallen)

Empididae
Platypalpus articulatus Macquart
Platypalpus aurantiacus (Collin)

Platypalpus confinis
(Zetterstedt)
Platypalpus interpolus (Collin)
Platypalpus pseudociliaris
Strobl
Platypalpus rapidus (Meigen)
Platypalpus sylvicola (Collin)
Ocydromia melanopleura
Loew
Oedalea apicalis Loew
Rhamphomyia albosegmentata Zetterstedt
Rhamphomyia hirtula
Zetterstedt
Empis prodromus Loew
Empis woodi Collin
Hilara media Collin
Hilara recedens Walker
Dolichocephala ocellata
(Costa)
Clinocera nivalis (Zetterstedt)
(= *Hydrodromia nivalis*)

Dolichopodidae
Dolichopus andalusiacus
Strobl
Dolichopus arbustorum
Stannius
Dolichopus linearis Meigen
Dolichopus migrans
Zetterstedt
Hercostomus plagiatus
(Loew)
Hydrophorus viridis (Meigen)
Schoenophilus versutus
(Haliday)
Aphrosylus mitis Verrall
Medetera cuspidata Collin
Medetera excellens Frey
Medetera infumata Loew
Medetera inspissata Collin
Medetera melancholica
Lundbeck
Medetera oscillans Allen
Medetera pinicola Kowarz
Medetera striata Parent
Medetera unisetosa Collin
Thrypticus divisus (Strobl)
Thrypticus nigricauda Wood
Thrypticus tarsalis Parent
Systenus pallipes (von Roser)
Systenus tener Loew
Campsicnemus compeditus
Loew

Campsicnemus magius
(Loew)
Campsicnemus pectinulatus
Loew

Lonchopteridae
Lonchoptera nitidifrons Strobl
Lonchoptera scutellata Stein

Platypezidae
Microsania straeleni Collart
Callomyia dives Zetterstedt
Platypeza hirticeps Verrall

Pipunculidae
Tomosvaryella cilitarsis
(Strobl)
Tomosvaryella minima
(Becker)
Pipunculus fonsecai Coe

Syrphidae
Epistrophella euchroma
(Kowarz)
Melangyna guttata (Fallen)
Chrysotoxum elegans Loew
Platycheirus melanopsis
Loew
Platycheirus perpallidus
Verrall
Paragus albifrons (Fallen)
Pipizella maculipennis
(Meigen)
Cheilosia carbonaria Egger
Cheilosia cynocephala Loew
Cheilosia mutabilis (Fallen)
Cheilosia nebulosa Verrall
Cheilosia nigripes (Meigen)
Cheilosia pubera (Zetterstedt)
Cheilosia sahlbergi Becker
Cheilosia velutina Loew
* *Cheilosia* 'Species B'
sensu Stubbs & Falk
Chamaesyrphus scaevoides
(Fallen)
Myolepta luteola (Gmelin)
Chrysogaster macquarti
Loew
Orthonevra brevicornis Loew
Orthonevra geniculata
Meigen
Brachyopa pilosa Collin
Neoascia obliqua Coe
Pelecocera tricincta Meigen
Eumerus sabulonum (Fallen)

Microdon eggeri Mik
Microdon mutabilis (L.)
Brachypalpus laphriformis
  (Fallen)
  (= *B. bimaculatus*
  (Macquart))
Helophilus groenlandicus (F.)

Conopidae
Physocephala nigra (Degeer)
Myopa curtirostris Kroeber
Myopa extricata Collin
Myopa strandi Duda

Tephritidae
Rhacochlaena toxoneura
  (Loew)
Trypeta cornuta (Scopoli)
Trypeta spinifrons Schroeder
Orellia vectensis Collin
Urophora spoliata (Haliday)
Myopites blotii Brebisson
Myopites frauenfeldi Schiner

Otitidae
Ulidia erythrophthalma
  Meigen
Dorycera graminum (F.)

Micropezidae
Micropeza lateralis Meigen

Psilidae
Psila clunalis Collin
Psila luteola Collin
Chyliza extenuatum (Rossi)
Chyliza fuscipennis
  (Robineau-Desvoidy)
Chyliza nova Collin

Chamaemyiidae
Leucopis griseola (Fallen)

Lauxaniidae
Minettia flaviventris (Costa)
Sapromyza albiceps Fallen
Sapromyza bipunctata
  Meigen
Sapromyza zetterstedti
  Hendel
Cnemacantha muscaria
  (Fallen)
Homoneura interstincta
  (Fallen)

Heleomyzidae
Ornitholeria nidicola Frey

Morpholeria dudai (Czerny)
Chaetomus flavotestaceus
  (Zetterstedt)
Scoliocentra scutellaris
  (Zetterstedt)

Sepsidae
Themira nigricornis (Meigen)

Sciomyzidae
Pelidnoptera nigripennis (F.)
Colobaea bifasciella (Fallen)
Colobaea distincta (Meigen)
Pherbellia brunnipes Meigen
Pherbellia dorsata
  (Zetterstedt)
Pherbellia griseola (Fallen)
Pherbellia grisescens
  (Meigen)
Sciomyza simplex Fallen
Ectinocera borealis
  (Zetterstedt)
Tetanocera freyi Stackelberg

Pallopteridae
Palloptera ambusta (Meigen)
Palloptera usta (Meigen)

Carniidae
Meonura freta Collin
Meonura lacteipennis (Fallen)
Meonura minutissima
  (Zetterstedt)
Meonura neglecta Collin
Meonura prima Becker
Meonura triangularis Collin

Periscelididae
Periscelis annulata (Fallen)

Aulacigastridae
Aulacigaster leucopeza
  (Meigen)

Drosophilidae
Acletoxenus formosus (Loew)

Tethinidae
Tethina incisuralis (Macquart)
Tethina simplex (Collin)

Chloropidae
Calamoncosis aspistylina
  Duda
Polyodaspis sulcicollis
  (Meigen)
Siphunculina aenea
  (Macquart)

Crassivenula brachyptera
Thalhammer
Gaurax britannicus Deeming
(= *Botanobia britannicus*)
Gaurax niger Czerny
(= *Mimogaurax niger*)
Elachiptera rufifrons Duda
Chlorops citrinella
(Zetterstedt)

Tachinidae
Opesia cana (Meigen)
Subclytia rotundiventris
(Fallen)
Leucostoma simplex (Fallen)
Rondania fasciata (Macquart)
Wagneria gagatea
Robineau-Desvoidy
Zophomyia temula (Scopoli)
Linnaemya comta (Fallen)
Hyalurgus lucidus (Meigen)
Graphogaster brunnescens
Villeneuve
Goniocera versicolor (Fallen)
Peribaea fissicornis (Strobl)
Brachicheta strigata (Meigen)
Erynnia ocypterata (Fallen)
Frontina laeta (Meigen)
Bactromyia aurulenta
(Meigen)
Tlephusa diligens
(Zetterstedt)

Sarcophagidae
Miltogramma germari
Meigen
Macronychia griseola (Fallen)
Macronychia polyodon
(Meigen)
Blaesoxipha rossica
Villeneuve
Sarcophaga cruenta Meigen
Sarcophaga ebrachiata
Pandelle

Calliphoridae
Calliphora alpina (Zetterstedt)
Calliphora uralensis
Villeneuve
Eggisops pecchiolii Rondani

Scathophagidae
Norellia spinipes (Meigen)
Cordilura similis Siebke

Gonatherus planiceps
(Fallen)
Nanna brevifrons
(Zetterstedt)
Microprosopa pallidicauda
(Zetterstedt)
Acanthocnema glaucescens
(Loew)
Acanthocnema nigrimana
(Zetterstedt)
Parallelomma vittatum
(Meigen)

Anthomyiidae
Paraprosalpia albipennis
(Ringdahl)
Hydrophoria spiniclunis
(Pandelle)

Fanniidae
Fannia coracula Collin
Fannia speciosa (Villeneuve)
Fannia tuberculata
(Zetterstedt)

Muscidae
Pyrellia ignita Robineau-
Desvoidy
Hydrotaea pilitibia Stein
Dialytina atriceps (Loew)
Phaonia canescens Stein
Phaonia fusca (Meade)
Helina concolor (Czerny)
Helina parcepilosa (Stein)
Helina pubescens (Stein)
Helina quadrinotata (Meigen)
Mydaea maculiventris
(Zetterstedt)
Spilogona alpica (Zetterstedt)
Spilogona biseriata (Stein)
Spilogona depressiuscula
(Zetterstedt)
Spilogona griseola (Collin)
Spilogona longipes (Ringdahl)
Spilogona septemnotata
(Zetterstedt)
Spilogona triangulifera
(Zetterstedt)
Neolimnophora virgo
(Villeneuve)
Limnophora scrupulosa
(Zetterstedt)
Lispocephala falculata Collin
Dexiopsis lacustris Karl

Dexiopsis minutalis
(Zetterstedt)
Coenosia paludis Tiensuu

Coenosia pudorosa Collin
Coenosia pygmaea
(Zetterstedt)

APPENDIX
No post-1900
records

Stratiomyidae
Clitellaria ephippium (F.)

Asilidae
Dasypogon diadema F.

Oestridae
Pharyngomyia picta (Meigen)

ODONATA

The Dragonflies

The British Odonata are divided into two suborders, the slender Zygoptera or damselflies, and the more robust Anisoptera or true dragonflies. 41 species have bred regularly in Britain until recent years. They are a well-studied group, mostly easy to identify in the hand, and their large size and attractive colours make them popular subjects for amateur photography. Their behaviour makes an interesting study, the males being territorial.

The Red Data Book includes four Endangered, two Vulnerable and three Rare species, together amounting to 22% of the British dragonfly fauna. Of the Endangered species, three probably became extinct in the 1950s; another, the Scarce Green Lestes, was also thought to be extinct, but was rediscovered in 1983. The fifth Endangered species, the Norfolk Aeshna, is on Schedule 5 of the Wildlife and Countryside Act 1981.

All the Odonata have aquatic, carnivorous larvae (nymphs), which spend one to three years in the larval stage. The more conspicuous adults are useful for assessing certain types of freshwater habitat, as their abundance reflects to some degree the state of the aquatic fauna in general. Small lakes and ponds in lowland areas support the greatest diversity of species, but such sites are being lost. The species frequenting river and canal systems are particularly vulnerable to pollution, dredging and bank-clearance. Most of these, including such species as the Scarce Libellula, cannot tolerate increased rates of water flow. The once-excellent Norfolk Broads are almost destroyed by eutrophication and other pollution, and the Norfolk Aeshna now survives in only a few ditch systems. By far the most vulnerable species are those which live in very shallow, well-vegetated water, such as the Southern Coenagrion and the Scarce Green Lestes, which are threatened by quite small reductions in water level caused by drainage ditching. The Northern Coenagrion occurs in the Highlands in shallow lochs and bogs, which are vulnerable to drainage and to shading-out by afforestation.

The principal reference for identification is *The dragonflies of Great Britain and Ireland* by Hammond (2nd edition, 1983). Of earlier books on the natural history of dragonflies, Corbet, Longfield & Moore's *Dragonflies* (1960) and Corbet's *A biology of dragonflies* (1962) have both been reprinted recently. The AES has published a booklet on *Collecting and studying dragonflies (Odonata)* (Keen, 1977), and NCC has published a booklet on *The conservation of dragonflies* (Chelmick et al, 1980).

There is an Odonata Recording Scheme organised by the author of these data sheets. A provisional atlas has been published (Chelmick, 1979), but more up-to-date maps appear in the 2nd edition of Hammond's book. The British Dragonfly Society was formed in April 1983, and produces a journal and newsletter.

Coenagrion armatum	Norfolk Coenagrion or Norfolk Damselfly	**ENDANGERED +**
	Order **Odonata**	Family **Coenagriidae**

Coenagrion armatum (Charpentier, 1840).

Identification	Hammond (1983), p.70 and pl.20:1-3.
Distribution	Considered to be extinct. Formerly known only from one small area in the Norfolk Broads. For map see Hammond (1983), map 4. It has a scattered and very local distribution in north-western Europe, extending to Siberia and Asia Minor.
Habitat and ecology	Small marshy pools with abundant emergent vegetation. The adults fly from late May to the end of July. The eggs are laid in the floating leaves/submerged stems of aquatic plants, including frog-bit *Hydrocharis morsus-ranae*, and hatch after several weeks. The larvae are aquatic and carnivorous, and the duration of larval life is believed to be one year.
Status	This species, first discovered in Britain in 1902, was last reported in the 1950s. NCC surveys in 1974, 1975 and 1976 found its former sites to be entirely unsuitable – lacking in macrophytes other than reed *Phragmites*, overgrown with sallow and alder carr, or completely dried up.
Author	R. Merritt.

Coenagrion hastulatum	Northern Coenagrion or Northern Damselfly	**VULNERABLE**
	Order **Odonata**	Family **Coenagriidae**

Coenagrion hastulatum (Charpentier, 1825).

Identification	Hammond (1983), p.66 and pl.18: 1-5.
Distribution	Confined to a few sites in Highland (Inverness-shire), Tayside (Perthshire), and Grampian (Aberdeenshire). For map see Hammond (1983), map 5. This boreo-alpine species is found in north and central Europe, east to Turkestan and Mongolia.
Habitat and ecology	The marshy margins of shallow reedy lochs, especially those sheltered by nearby woodland. It also frequents sheltered bogs where little open water is present. The adults fly from early June to early August. The eggs are laid in the submerged tissues of aquatic plants, including pondweeds (*Potamogeton* species), and hatch after a couple of weeks. The larvae are aquatic and carnivorous, and the duration of larval life is one year.

Status	Not uncommon at its known sites, the population appears to be fairly stable. However, being known from only fifteen sites (localised in three areas), its status must be considered highly vulnerable to adverse environmental changes.
Threats	Drainage for the purpose of reafforestation.
Conservation	Present on two NNRs.
Author	R. Merritt.

Coenagrion scitulum

Dainty Coenagrion or Dainty Damselfly

ENDANGERED +

Order **Odonata**

Family **Coenagriidae**

Coenagrion scitulum (Rambur, 1842).

Identification	Hammond (1983), p.70 and pl.20: 4-8.
Distribution	Considered to be extinct. Formerly known from only one site in Essex. For map see Hammond (1983), map 10. A Mediterranean species, extending from Belgium to Asia Minor, and very local and scattered throughout its range.
Habitat and ecology	The only known British site was a small pond with abundant aquatic vegetation, near a saltmarsh. On the Continent this species is also known from dykes, canals, and occasionally rivers. The adults fly from approximately mid-June to the end of July. The eggs are laid in the tissues of aquatic plants, including whorled water-milfoil *Myriophyllum verticillatum*. The larvae are aquatic and carnivorous. The life-cycle is usually completed in one year.
Status	First discovered in 1946 by Cynthia Longfield and E.B. Penniger, the colony flourished until 1953 when sea flooding wiped out the population.
Author	R. Merritt.

Lestes dryas

Scarce Green Lestes or Scarce Emerald Damselfly

VULNERABLE

Order **Odonata**

Family **Lestidae**

Lestes dryas Kirby, 1890.

Identification	Hammond (1983), p.58 and pl.14:1-6.
Distribution	Recently rediscovered (1983) in Britain in Essex and Kent, and subsequently Norfolk, after a gap in records of over a decade. Formerly occurred, very locally, in eastern England from Humberside to Sussex. For map see Hammond (1983), map 15. This circumboreal species has a scattered distribution in Europe.

Habitat and ecology	Marshes, shallow pools and dykes, particularly near the sea, containing abundant emergent vegetation, often including sea club-rush *Scirpus maritimus*, water horsetail *Equisetum fluviatile*, and water plantain *Alisma plantago-aquatica*. The adults fly from mid-June to the end of August. The eggs are laid in the stems of emergent vegetation above and/or below water level, and hatch the following spring. The aquatic carnivorous larvae then undergo a period of very rapid growth. The life-cycle is completed in one year.
Status	This species has undoubtedly been on the decline in Britain during the past few decades, having been lost from many former sites. The reasons for the decline are various: loss of habitat as a result of agricultural and urban development, natural causes (marshland representing the final stage of a hydrosere), periods of drought, and small population numbers. Now known to occur at several sites in Essex, Kent and Norfolk, the species had probably been overlooked in these areas.
Threats	Drainage and pollution.
Author	R. Merritt.

Aeshna isosceles

"Norfolk Acshna Dragonfly" or Norfolk Hawker

Order **Odonata**

ENDANGERED

Family **Aeshnidae**

Aeshna isosceles (Mueller, 1767).

Identification	Hammond (1983), p.34 and pl.2:4-6.
Distribution	Confined to the Norfolk Broads area. Though still fairly common at several of its sites, the overall population is low and declining. For map see Hammond (1983), map 24. It has a scattered distribution abroad, centred mainly on the Mediterranean area.
Habitat and ecology	Grazing-marsh dykes and broads with plenty of emergent and aquatic (macrophytic) vegetation, especially the local water soldier *Stratiotes aloides*. The adults fly from approximately early June to mid-July. The eggs are laid in the submerged stems and leaves of certain plants, including *S. aloides*, and hatch after a number of weeks. The larvae are aquatic and carnivorous, and the duration of larval life is usually two years.
Status	Breeding confirmed from only half-a-dozen sites. The overall population appears to have declined in recent years. The species is in danger of extinction in Britain without effective protection and careful management of its known sites.

Threats	Pollution from herbicides, insecticides, and in particular nitrogenous fertilisers which leak into the waterways causing eutrophication. Also, lowering of the water-table for purposes of agricultural improvement.
Conservation	Listed on Schedule 5 of the Wildlife and Countryside Act 1981. Breeds on at least one, possibly two, NNRs.
Author	R. Merritt.

Oxygastra curtisii

Orange-spotted Emerald   **ENDANGERED +**

Order **Odonata**   Family **Corduliidae**

Oxygastra curtisii (Dale, 1834).

Identification	Hammond (1983), p.42 and pl.6: 4-10.
Distribution	Considered to be extinct. Formerly known from a river in south Hampshire. For map see Hammond (1983), map 32. On the Continent, this species is abundant on many of the rivers of southern France and parts of Spain.
Habitat and ecology	Sluggish streams and rivers, and those in which fast gravelly sections alternate with slow muddy sections. The adults fly from approximately early June to mid/late July. The eggs are deposited directly into the water, and hatch after several weeks. The larvae are aquatic, carnivorous and mud-dwelling, and the duration of larval life is usually two to three years.
Status	First discovered in 1820, it was reported for many years from its known locality, but has not been seen since the 1950s. It was reported from north Devon in 1830, and in 1946 three individuals were recorded from a south Devon/Cornwall river but were never seen again despite extensive searches. Pollution (within permitted levels) by a sewage treatment plant appears to have caused the extinction of this species.
Author	R. Merritt, using additional information from D.G. Chelmick (pers. comm.).

ORTHOPTERA

The Crickets and Grasshoppers

In addition to the grasshoppers and true crickets, this group includes the bush-crickets, mole crickets and ground-hoppers. They are a well-studied and popular group with about thirty British species. Most of them are easily identified in the hand, and their characteristic stridulation provides an additional aid to identification in the field.

The Red Data Book includes three Endangered, two Vulnerable and one Rare species, together amounting to 20% of the British fauna. Three of them, Field Cricket, Mole Cricket and Wart-biter, are on Schedule 5 of the Wildlife and Countryside Act 1981, and are reduced to extremely low numbers and very few sites. The Scaly Cricket may at first sight seem a strange inclusion, but it is otherwise known only on the coasts of the Mediterranean and on Madeira.

The five Endangered and Vulnerable species occur in a variety of habitats, with three of them favouring either dry or damp grassland. Consequently, most of the threats are those that reduce the area of unimproved grassland, such as arable crop cultivation, 'improvement' of pasture, drainage of damp meadows, and fire. The height of the vegetation can be critically important: the turf can be too long for the Field Cricket, or too short for the Wart-biter. The Large Marsh Grasshopper is confined to wet 'quaking bogs' on southern heathlands; the Heath Grasshopper (Rare) occurs on the drier heaths.

The principal reference is *Grasshoppers, crickets and cockroaches of the British Isles* (Ragge, 1965), but it is unfortunately out of print and difficult to obtain. However, *Grasshoppers* by Brown (1983) is available and provides much interesting information as well as enabling the identification of most species.

There is an Orthoptera Recording Scheme organised by the author of these data sheets, and a newsletter is produced. A provisional atlas (Haes, 1979) has been published.

Decticus verrucivorus	Wart-biter or "Wart-biter Grasshopper"	**VULNERABLE**
	Order **Orthoptera**	Family **Tettigoniidae**

Decticus verrucivorus (L., 1758).

Identification Ragge (1965), p.103 and pl.4:3.

Distribution There are colonies on chalk downland in East Sussex and Wiltshire as well as smaller downland colonies in East Sussex and Kent, and at least one small heathland colony in Dorset. For map see Haes (1979), map 4. There are a hundred or more adults in the largest East Sussex colony and perhaps in the Wiltshire colony in most years. Twenty or less adults in the other colonies in most years, but exact numbers are not known.

Habitat and ecology Downland or heathland with coarse ground-level vegetation. Food: grasshoppers and probably other insects; nettles, knapweed and probably other plants.

Status The Wart-biter, despite its large size, is easily overlooked. It was unknown in East Sussex until 1955 and in Wiltshire until 1971. It has been known in Dorset and Kent for many years and because of its secretive nature may yet persist in the Isle of Wight and New Forest area of Hampshire, although not seen in the latter area since the end of the last century.

Threats Destruction of habitat by heath or grass fires in summer or by arable cultivation. The Kent colony may have been severely reduced by deliberate attempts to reduce coarse herbage in its downland habitat, in order to encourage downland Lepidoptera and choicer flowering plants. The Wiltshire colony may have been decimated by recent heavy grazing.

Conservation Listed on Schedule 5 of the Wildlife and Countryside Act 1981. Most known colonies are in established nature reserves. Grazing should be curtailed at the Wiltshire site.

Author E.C.M. Haes.

Gryllus campestris	"Field Cricket"	**ENDANGERED**
	Order **Orthoptera**	Family **Gryllidae**

Gryllus campestris L., 1758.

Identification Ragge (1965), p.138 and pl.9:4-5.

Distribution Now reduced to one quite extensive colony on lower greensand and one small colony on chalk in West Sussex. For map see Haes (1979), map 12. The larger colony can produce over one hundred singing males in a good year such as 1976 or 1979 but less than thirty in a cold year such as 1977. In captivity, broods produce about three males to two females. Thus in a good year the larger Sussex colony may contain 150-200 adults. The smaller colony has not been monitored.

Habitat and ecology Close-growing turf in porous sandy or chalky soil in hot, sheltered sites with full sun. Food: grasses, especially *Holcus* species and fescues (*Festuca* species).

Status Precarious. The species was always very local. The famous Selborne (Hampshire) site is now occupied by mature beech trees. The long-known site by Southampton Water is now occupied by Fawley Oil Refinery. The last known Surrey site survived until 1964, but was eventually swamped by the spread of scrubland. At Christchurch several colonies were built over in the 1920s and the recorded Isle of Wight site has been under arable cultivation for about twenty years. Details of the extent and fate of colonies in other counties seem to be unrecorded, but it is doubtful if any survived into the 1950s. There may, however, have been a colony near Salisbury in Wiltshire up to the end of the 1960s.

Threats Almost certainly the loss of short turf, which is normally maintained by grazing mammals (particularly rabbits) in the relatively few localities suitable for the species in this country.

Conservation Listed on Schedule 5 of the Wildlife and Countryside Act 1981. In response to a request by the Sussex Trust for Nature Conservation the owner of the land occupied by the larger colony arranges for much of the occupied terrain to be gang-mown in July or autumn to check scrub and coarse herbage. The smaller colony is on a cricket ground which is mown anyway. Attempts have been made to introduce the native strain to three seemingly suitable protected sites, including an NNR, but these have been unsuccessful. Further attempts to introduce it to potentially suitable protected sites where rabbit and sheep grazing can be assured may be worthwhile, but the native strain is clearly not adaptable.

Author E.C.M. Haes.

Mogoplistes squamiger

Scaly Cricket   **ENDANGERED**

Order **Orthoptera**   Family **Mogoplistidae**

Mogoplistes squamiger (Fischer, 1853).

Identification Ragge (1965), p.147 and pl.9:6.

Distribution Low density at the eastern end of Chesil Beach, Dorset. The population size is not known.

Habitat and ecology	Seashore above and below high tide mark, under rocks, large stones or concrete fragments. Food unrecorded.
Status	Probably introduced via the nearby Portland Naval Base during the Second World War (mid 1940s). If truly native, it is a relict species with a remarkable history, for it is otherwise now restricted to the Mediterranean littoral and Madeira.
Threats	Probably sea floods, as in December 1978, or tidying-up of habitat.
Author	E.C.M. Haes.

Gryllotalpa gryllotalpa

"Mole Cricket" **ENDANGERED**

Order **Orthoptera** Family **Gryllotalpidae**

Gryllotalpa gryllotalpa (L., 1758).

Identification	Ragge (1965), p.150 and pl.20:4.
Distribution	At extremely low density in Wiltshire, Hampshire, Isle of Wight, East Sussex and perhaps the north Midlands. For map see Haes (1979), map 15. Nowhere numerous.
Habitat and ecology	Undrained, grassy swamps and natural pasture in flood plains. Food: probably subterranean worms and arthropods, and perhaps succulent roots.
Status	Widespread until about the 1920s. It was once familiar enough to have such vernacular names as 'Eve-churr' and 'Jarr-worm'. It is now an extreme and elusive rarity.
Threats	Almost certainly land drainage and pasture improvement.
Conservation	Listed on Schedule 5 of the Wildlife and Countryside Act 1981.
Author	E.C.M. Haes.

Stethophyma grossum

Large Marsh Grasshopper **VULNERABLE**

Order **Orthoptera** Family **Acrididae**

Stethophyma grossum (L., 1758).

Identification	Ragge (1965), p.175 and pl.10.
Distribution	Low density, localised populations in the New Forest, east Dorset, Somerset (fenland) and Surrey. A record from east Cornwall has been discounted. For map see Haes (1979), map 19.

Habitat and ecology	Quaking bogs on lowland heaths.
Status	Now apparently extinct in the East Anglian fens and Norfolk Broads, and threatened by drainage and peat extraction in Somerset. Still well-established in east Dorset and the New Forest. An apparently natural colony was discovered in Surrey in 1982, so that it is now present in two Surrey sites.
Threats	Drainage, and the shading of habitat by afforestation.
Conservation	The species has been introduced to an NNR in Surrey. Some Hampshire and Dorset colonies are already within nature reserves being managed for the conservation of the wetland habitat.
Author	E.C.M. Haes.

HEMIPTERA: HETEROPTERA

The True Bugs

The Heteroptera are the smaller of two suborders that make up the Hemiptera, with about 540 species in Britain. They all have sucking mouthparts, and most feed on plant juices. They are not the most popular of groups, suffering from the lack of a currently available and comprehensive identification guide. A few are easy to identify, but many require microscopic examination, and several critical groups require expert assistance. Aquatic species are perhaps better known, as they are noted by many freshwater biologists.

The Red Data Book includes 14 Endangered, six Vulnerable and 53 Rare species. At least one Endangered species is believed to be extinct, and a further six species are listed in the Appendix as having become extinct before 1900. Eleven Rare species are designated Category 3* (recently discovered or recognised), and one Rare subspecies is also listed in Category 5 (Endemic). The total number listed here amounts to 79, representing 14.6% of the British heteropteran fauna.

The Heteroptera occur in all habitats, but most are associated with low vegetation or are ground-living. Of the 20 Endangered and Vulnerable species, six occur on grass or herbs, six occur on sand-dunes or sandy soil or are ground-living, five occur on shrubs or trees, two are littoral or saltmarsh species, and one is aquatic. All but the last are plant-feeders. It is notable that about 60% of the species discussed are coastal in occurrence; most of these are confined to very few sites in the extreme south of England and are on the edge of their European range. Coastal habitats are naturally unstable, maintaining a habitat which is attractive to many species, but they are also vulnerable to disturbance by man in the form of coastal defences and development for tourism.

The main identification guide is *Land and water bugs of the British Isles* by Southwood & Leston (1959). Unfortunately it is now out of print and not easy to obtain except from libraries. The Heteroptera Study Group (see below) issues keys, etc., which bring Southwood & Leston up to date. Aquatic species are, however, covered comprehensively in Macan's *A key to British water bugs* (1965).

There are now two BRC recording schemes, covering the aquatic and terrestrial species respectively. They are coordinated by the Heteroptera Study Group, which is based at the Biological Records Centre, Monks Wood Experimental Station. Newsletters are issued along with much other useful information.

Geotomus punctulatus	A shieldbug	**ENDANGERED**
	Order **Hemiptera: Heteroptera**	Family **Cydnidae**

Geotomus punctulatus (Costa, 1847).

Identification	Southwood & Leston (1959), pp.28-29 and fig.17.
Distribution	Widely distributed in the southern Palaearctic from England to Japan. In Britain it is only known from Whitesand Bay (Sennen Cove), Cornwall and, formerly, from Cowbridge, South Glamorgan. The population size is not known, but is probably numbered in hundreds rather than thousands.
Habitat and ecology	Sand dunes; a ground-living bug. It is phytophagous, though the host-plants are not known with accuracy.
Status	Extremely local in Britain, but widely distributed elsewhere in its range. It was present at Whitesand Bay in May 1962 "in considerable numbers" (Woodroffe, 1962), and was again numerous there on 31 May 1982 (P. Hodge, pers. comm.).
Threats	Vulnerable to development of the site as a pleasure beach (bathing, etc).
Conservation	Listed by the Joint Committee for the Conservation of British Insects (1974) as a species to be collected with restraint.
Author	M. G. Morris, using additional information from Stichel (1955-62), 4: 695-696.

Eurygaster austriaca	A tortoise bug	**ENDANGERED +**
	Order **Hemiptera: Heteroptera**	Family **Scutelleridae**

Eurygaster austriaca (Schrank, 1776).

Identification	Southwood & Leston (1959), pp.32-33.
Distribution	On the Kent coast, at Folkestone, Deal and Margate. It has not been found for many years despite careful searching.
Habitat and ecology	Probably feeds on grasses (Gramineae). It is migratory in the Mediterranean area (Brown, 1965, p.94).
Status	Possibly extinct.
Threats	The development of coastal habitats for recreation.
Conservation	If the species is re-found, its sites would probably need protection.
Author	B. C. Eversham, using additional information from W. R. Dolling and E. G. Philp (pers. comms).

Eysarcoris aeneus	A shieldbug	**VULNERABLE**
	Order **Hemiptera: Heteroptera**	Family **Pentatomidae**

Eysarcoris aeneus (Scopoli, 1763).

Identification   Southwood & Leston (1959), pp.39-41.

Distribution   Throughout Europe and eastwards to Siberia. In Britain it is very local; it is best known from the New Forest but has also been reported from single localities in Kent, Sussex, Bedfordshire and Ceredigion (Dyfed).

Habitat and ecology   Rather damp rides and grassland. It is said to feed on the seeds of slender St John's wort *Hypericum pulchrum*, but probably also on other plants.

Status   Further information is needed on sites other than the New Forest.

Threats   Overgrazing by ponies (in the New Forest).

Conservation   Grazing should be controlled: stock should be excluded from some areas on a rotational basis.

Author   M. G. Morris, using additional information from Stichel (1955-62), 4: 564-565.

Gonocerus acuteangulatus	A squashbug	**ENDANGERED**
	Order **Hemiptera: Heteroptera**	Family **Coreidae**

Gonocerus acuteangulatus (Goeze, 1778).

Identification   Southwood & Leston (1959), pp.57-58 and pl.11:3.

Distribution   Restricted to Box Hill, Surrey, and the vicinity, in Britain. It is not known from other sites with box. Widely distributed in southern and central Europe from Portugal to southern Russia and Iran. The bug is usually scarce as well as extremely localised.

Habitat and ecology   Phytophagous. In Britain it has been found solely on box *Buxus sempervirens*, but it occurs on other trees and shrubs abroad.

Status   This species was last seen by the author in 1967, but has not been looked for since. The restriction to box in Britain is very curious: Stichel (1955-62), 4: 367, does not mention the shrub, though he gives a long list of other Continental hosts.

Conservation   Listed by the Joint Committee for the Conservation of British Insects (1974) as a species which should be collected with restraint. Box Hill is owned by the National Trust.

Author   M. G. Morris, using additional information from Butler (1923), pp.95-96.

Arenocoris waltli

A squashbug   **VULNERABLE**

Order **Hemiptera: Heteroptera**   Family **Coreidae**

Arenocoris waltli (Herrich-Schaeffer, 1834).

Identification   Southwood & Leston (1959), pp.62-63.

Distribution   Widely distributed in Europe from the Netherlands and Portugal eastwards to southern USSR and Turkestan. In Britain it is now confined to a small area of the East Anglian Breckland, apart from a single Kent record which may be a misidentification.

Habitat and ecology   Sandy soil, sparsely vegetated. A ground-living insect.

Status   No recent information: the sites are not identified.

Threats   Agriculture and forestry.

Author   M. G. Morris, using additional information from Stichel (1955-62), 4: 389.

Pyrrhocoris apterus

Firebug   **ENDANGERED**

Order **Hemiptera: Heteroptera**   Family **Pyrrhocoridae**

Pyrrhocoris apterus (L., 1758).

Identification   Southwood & Leston (1959), pp.72-73.

Distribution   Throughout the Holarctic except the extreme north. In Britain the only permanent colony is on the Oarstone Rock off Torbay, south Devon, though two were found at Kimmeridge on the Dorset coast in 1977 (Brown, 1982). It is restricted in area but high in numbers of individuals.

Habitat and ecology   Associated with several plants abroad, particularly limes (*Tilia* species) etc., but in Britain only, or mainly, with tree mallow *Lavatera arborea*. It is mainly phytophagous, but sometimes takes animal food.

Status   A very abundant bug throughout Europe. It may well breed elsewhere apart from the famous Torbay locality (W. R. Dolling, pers. comm.).

Threats   Natural succession?

Conservation   The Oarstone Rock is protected by its inaccessibility.

Author   M. G. Morris, using additional information from Butler (1923), pp.192-195, Stichel (1955-62), 4: 293-295, and Woodroffe (1961).

Macroplax preyssleri

A groundbug

ENDANGERED

Order **Hemiptera: Heteroptera**   Family **Lygaeidae**

Macroplax preyssleri (Fieber, 1837).

Identification   Dolling (1971).

Distribution   Known only from two sites in Somerset: Brean Down, and Dolebury Warren in the Mendips.

Habitat and ecology   Occurs on cliffs and steep hillsides, probably predominantly in hot, dry places. The foodplants are rockroses (*Helianthemum* species). The bug has been taken in association with the very local white rockrose *H. appeninum*, which is locally abundant on Brean Down but occurs at only three other sites in Britain. This plant is a Red Data Book species but is under no threat. *M. preyssleri* occurs in association with the common rockrose *H. nummularium* at its Dolebury Warren site.

Status   A rare native species which has not so far been taken away from the two sites at which it was almost simultaneously taken in 1968 (Dolling, 1971). The record from Dolebury Warren referred to by Dolling consisted of only one specimen.

Threats   No specific threats to *M. preyssleri* are known but the species is assessed as Endangered because of its very restricted area of occurrence and the general vulnerability of the Mendips to quarrying. Brean Down is subject to considerable public pressure, but the habitat of the bug is not thought to be at risk.

Conservation   Brean Down and Dolebury Warren are both National Trust properties and SSSIs. The ecological requirements of *M. preyssleri* are not known but the habitat, with its steep slopes, does not appear to need management.

Author   M. G. Morris.

Henestaris halophilus

A groundbug

VULNERABLE

Order **Hemiptera: Heteroptera**   Family **Lygaeidae**

Henestaris halophilus (Burmeister, 1835).

Identification   Southwood & Leston (1959), p.81.

Distribution   Southern Europe to the southern USSR and Turkestan, and north Africa. In Britain, it is known only from the north Kent Marshes (Higham, Cliffe, etc.), in recent years at Nagden Saltings (P. Hodge, pers. comm.) and on the Swale estuary,

59

Kent. It is apparently long extinct in Devon. It has only been found in small numbers despite much searching (M. Newcombe, pers. comm.).

Habitat and ecology	At the upper edge of saltmarshes, especially where slightly overgrown. Its biology in Britain is not well known.
Status	This species is on the extreme south-western edge of its range, and it survives only in a small area of vulnerable habitat. A. M. Massee took it commonly in the 1950s and 1960s, but its current status needs investigation.
Threats	Very vulnerable to the natural erosion and destruction of saltmarshes, and changes induced by coastal defence, reclamation, etc. Also, increasingly, recreational pressures (W. R. Dolling, pers. comm.).
Authors	M. G. Morris and B. C. Eversham, using additional information from Stichel (1955-62), 4: 114-115.

Ischnodemus quadratus

A chinchbug

ENDANGERED

Order **Hemiptera: Heteroptera**　　　Family **Lygaeidae**

Ischnodemus quadratus Fieber, 1836, formerly regarded as a subspecies of *I. sabuleti* (Fallen).

Identification	Southwood & Leston (1959), pp.82-83 (cf. pl.16:3).
Distribution	A Mediterranean species, in Britain known only from Folkestone Warren, Kent.
Habitat and ecology	Coastal dunes.
Status	Now accepted as a full species, which is morphologically and ecologically distinct from *I. sabuleti*.
Conservation	The extent of the species' distribution should be assessed.
Author	B. C. Eversham, using additional information from W. R. Dolling (pers. comm.).

Peritrechus gracilicornis

A groundbug

ENDANGERED

Order **Hemiptera: Heteroptera**　　　Family **Lygaeidae**

Peritrechus gracilicornis Puton, 1877.

Identification	Southwood & Leston (1959), pp.91 and 93.
Distribution	There are old records, possibly of migrants, in Kent, Sussex, Hampshire and Dorset. It now seems to be established on sand dunes to the east of Studland, Dorset (Allen, 1980).

Habitat and ecology	Coastal dunes and chalk scree; recently, at the edges of dune slacks.
Threats	Possibly the development of dunes for bathing, etc.
Author	B. C. Eversham.

Eremocoris fenestratus

A groundbug   **ENDANGERED**

Order **Hemiptera: Heteroptera**   Family **Lygaeidae**

Eremocoris fenestratus (Herrich-Schaeffer, 1839).

Identification	Woodroffe (1963).
Distribution	There are confirmed records only from Surrey and Buckinghamshire. Old records from Norfolk and Devon may well refer to this species, but it has not been taken there for many years. The most recent report is from Coombe Hill, Buckinghamshire (Woodroffe, 1962). Only six specimens are known from Britain. However, since lygaeids are often elusive, there is no reason to suppose these do not represent established populations.
Habitat and ecology	Among litter beneath juniper bushes *Juniperus communis* on chalk.
Status	Prior to Woodroffe (1963), this species was prone to misidentification. Scottish records, where examined, all refer to *E. abietis* (L.) (W. R. Dolling, pers. comm.). It is possibly extinct in Britain.
Threats	The decline of juniper, and management which does not permit adequate accumulation of litter.
Conservation	A systematic search for the species is needed before positive steps can be taken.
Author	B. C. Eversham.

Lasiacantha capucina

Thyme Lacebug   **VULNERABLE**

Order **Hemiptera: Heteroptera**   Family **Tingidae**

Lasiacantha capucina Germar, 1836.

Identification	Southwood & Leston (1959), pp.138-141 and 147, pl.21:10.
Distribution	Confined to Cornwall within the British Isles, and in recent years seen only at Kynance Cove on the Lizard. Abundant where it occurs.

Habitat and ecology	Among the roots of thyme (*Thymus* species).
Threats	Development.
Conservation	The species' distribution elsewhere in Cornwall should be assessed.
Author	B. C. Eversham.

Physatocheila harwoodi

A lacebug   **ENDANGERED**

Order **Hemiptera: Heteroptera**   Family **Tingidae**

Physatocheila harwoodi China, 1936.

Identification	Southwood & Leston (1959), pp.150-1 and fig.52.
Distribution	Recorded only from a derelict garden at Witchampton, Dorset, in Britain. Also known from Germany.
Habitat and ecology	Associated with lichen-covered field maple *Acer campestre*, and other *Acer* species in Germany. Its biology is unknown.
Status	*Physatocheila* species are small, fairly obscure bugs and *P. harwoodi* may well turn up elsewhere. The association with *Acer* species seems well-established in Germany and England. It was last found in about 1956 (Southwood & Leston, 1959). It was not found by G. E. Woodroffe at the Witchampton site in 1960.
Threats	In 1960 the site had been planted with spruce and the old maple was dying (Bedwell-Woodroffe-Massee Archive, BRC).
Author	M. G. Morris, using additional information from Stichel (1955-62), 3: 335.

Placochilus seladonicus

A capsid bug   **ENDANGERED**

Order **Hemiptera: Heteroptera**   Family **Miridae**

Placochilus seladonicus (Fallen, 1807).

Identification	Nau (1979).
Distribution	Widely distributed in central and northern Europe to southern Russia and Iran. In Britain it is known from a single site, on railway land, near Leighton Buzzard, Bedfordshire. One specimen was taken *c.* 10km to the east but no more could be found.
Habitat and ecology	On field scabious *Knautia arvensis* in long grass. Specimens have been taken in the first half of September.

Status	Discovered in Britain in September 1978. May be found elsewhere in southern or eastern England.
Threats	The site is being encroached by commercial and industrial development. Succession to scrub may also become a danger.
Authors	M. G. Morris and B. C. Eversham, using additional information from B. S. Nau (pers. comm.), Kullenberg (1944), pp.266-267, and Stichel (1955-62), 1: 250.

Pilophorus confusus

A capsid bug   **ENDANGERED**

Order **Hemiptera: Heteroptera**   Family **Miridae**

Pilophorus confusus (Kirschbaum, 1856).

Identification	Woodroffe (1956a); Southwood & Leston (1959), pp.242-243 and pl.42:19.
Distribution	Widely distributed from Europe to Siberia. Known in Britain only from Virginia Water, Surrey, apart from a single record on 4 August 1981 from creeping willow *Salix repens* at Dungeness, Kent (M. Newcombe).
Habitat and ecology	From a damp sandpit (in Britain), on sallows (*Salix* species), etc., among sparse vegetation, and in association with ants. Possibly an ant mimic.
Author	M. G. Morris, using additional information from Stichel (1955-62), 1: 432, and Woodroffe (1956b and 1958).

Halticus macrocephalus

A capsid bug   **ENDANGERED**

Order **Hemiptera: Heteroptera**   Family **Miridae**

Halticus macrocephalus Fieber, 1858.

Identification	Southwood & Leston (1959), pp.244-245.
Distribution	In Britain, known only from Padstow, and Porth Kidney Sands near Lelant, north Cornwall. Apparently not abundant.
Habitat and ecology	On bedstraw (*Galium* species) on sand dunes.
Status	It has only a precarious hold in north Cornwall (W. R. Dolling, pers. comm.).
Threats	Probably the development of bathing-beaches, etc.

Conservation	The extent of the species' distribution along the north Cornwall coast, and how its present sites are being affected by development, need to be assessed.
Author	B. C. Eversham, using additional information from Bannister (1969).

Polymerus vulneratus

A capsid bug   **ENDANGERED**

Order **Hemiptera: Heteroptera**   Family **Miridae**

Polymerus (Poeciloscytus) vulneratus (Wolff, 1801).

Identification	Southwood & Leston (1959), pp.284 and 286.
Distribution	A 'Eurosiberian' species, occurring over most of Europe, eastwards to Siberia. It is restricted to one site in Britain: Great Yarmouth, Norfolk.
Habitat and ecology	Sandhills and dry soil (in England). Associated with lady's bedstraw *Galium verum*.
Status	The species was collected in 1954 (Southwood & Leston, 1959), but it has probably not been looked for since. Reassessment of the population is needed before conservation measures can be proposed.
Threats	Destruction or alteration of the site.
Author	M. G. Morris, using additional information from Stichel (1955-62), 2: 761-762, and Wagner (1973), 1: 443-444.

Tuponia carayoni

A capsid bug   **VULNERABLE**

Order **Hemiptera: Heteroptera**   Family **Miridae**

Tuponia (Tuponia) carayoni Wagner, 1955.

Identification	Nau (1980).
Distribution	A very narrow range: known from only southern France and England. It was found in considerable numbers in a tamarisk hedge at Freshwater, Isle of Wight; and small numbers at Hill Head, Lee-on-Solent, and Christchurch Harbour, Hampshire. (There were many negative records at other tamarisk sites.)
Habitat and ecology	On tamarisk (*Tamarix* species), stenophagous. It is therefore coastal in Britain. Specimens have been taken in late August and early September.

Status	Discovered in Britain in August 1979. Further work is needed to establish its distribution in Britain.
Threats	Sea defences?
Author	M. G. Morris, using additional information from Stichel (1955-62), 1: 383.

Saldula setulosa

A shorebug   **VULNERABLE**

Order **Hemiptera: Heteroptera**   Family **Saldidae**

Saldula (Saldula) setulosa (Puton, 1880).

Identification	Southwood & Leston (1959), pp.327 and 332.
Distribution	Mainly Mediterranean: France and north Africa. In Britain it is known only from Poole Harbour, Dorset.
Habitat and ecology	Sandy silt at the top of the littoral zone (submerged at spring tides). Predacious.
Status	The species is on the edge of its range in Britain.
Threats	Development.
Author	M. G. Morris, using additional information from Stichel (1955-62), 3: 246-247.

Hydrometra gracilenta

Lesser Water-measurer   **ENDANGERED**

Order **Hemiptera: Heteroptera**   Family **Hydrometridae**

Hydrometra gracilenta Horvath, 1899.

Identification	Southwood & Leston (1959), pp.342-343; Macan (1965), p.14.
Distribution	Most of northern and central Europe to Hungary and southern Russia. In Britain it has been recorded from Barton and Sutton Broads, Norfolk, and one locality in the New Forest, Hampshire.
Habitat and ecology	At the margins of shallow lakes with a carr fringe, among large sedges (*Carex* species). Probably predatory and scavenging.
Status	Deterioration of the Norfolk Broads in the last two decades may have affected this species severely. This increases the importance of refinding it in the New Forest site.
Threats	Eutrophication and pollution. Possibly drainage.

Conservation	The sites must be located and the species' presence established. (Apparently, the location of the New Forest site is no longer known.)
Authors	M. G. Morris and B. C. Eversham, using additional information from Stichel (1955-62), 1: 156.

TRICHOPTERA

The Caddis Flies

The small order Trichoptera is allied to the Lepidoptera, with almost 200 species in Britain. It is not a well-studied group, and the drab adults (often crepuscular and nocturnal) are less familiar than the larvae. They also pose a number of problems in identification, which usually requires dissection and microscopic examination.

The Red Data Book includes nine Endangered, four Vulnerable and 18 Rare species. At least two Endangered species are believed to be extinct, and a further two species are listed in the Appendix as having become extinct before 1900. These together amount to 33 species, which represent about 17% of the British caddis fly fauna.

The Trichoptera have aquatic larvae, most of which are phytophagous or omnivorous. Most people are familiar with the characteristic cases which the larvae of many species construct, but a quarter of the British species do not make them. Two-thirds of the Endangered and Vulnerable species occur in rivers and streams, the remainder occurring in still water of one form or another. Improved drainage has resulted in the loss of many ditches. Streams and rivers are frequently straightened and deepened, with associated loss of varied flow regions and marginal vegetation. The extra drainage water often carries an excessive load of silt or nitrogenous fertiliser. Many farm ponds are being lost as they become redundant. Natural vegetational succession in bogs and fens is a threat to species which require open areas in such places, where the water table can be insidiously lowered by the growth of trees.

A useful, though not entirely up-to-date, guide for identification is Macan's *A key to the adults of the British Trichoptera* (1973), while more detail of the anatomy is provided by the *Atlas of European Trichoptera* (Malicky, 1983). For the identification of larvae, Hickin's *Caddis larvae : larvae of the British Trichoptera* (1967) is useful but out of print. In the FBA series, only *A key to the caseless caddis larvae of the British Isles* (Edington & Hildrew, 1981) is so far available, and no key covers all the species. The AES has published a booklet on *The study of stoneflies, mayflies and caddis flies* (Macan, 1982). A new check-list has been published recently (Barnard, 1985), and is followed here.

There is a Trichoptera Recording Scheme organised by the author of these data sheets, and a newsletter is produced. So far only the family Hydroptilidae has been covered by a provisional distribution atlas (Marshall, 1978b).

Hydroptila lotensis

A caddis fly   **VULNERABLE**

Order **Trichoptera**   Family **Hydroptilidae**

Hydroptila lotensis Mosely, 1930.

Identification   Marshall (1978a), pp.13 and 16, figs 11 and 14.

Distribution   Only recorded from a short section of the River Wye near Hereford; all records (1959, 1983 and 1984) are from light traps, so the breeding site can only be inferred.

Habitat and ecology   Rivers; biology unknown.

Conservation   The larva should be discovered and steps taken to ensure adequate habitat representation. An investigation to discover the extent of colonisation of the Wye should be undertaken.

Author   I.D. Wallace, using material sent for identification by B.E. Miles.

Tinodes pallidulus

A caddis fly   **VULNERABLE**

Order **Trichoptera**   Family **Psychomyiidae**

Tinodes pallidulus McLachlan, 1878.

Identification   Macan (1973), p.104, fig.3:13; Fisher (1977); Edington & Hildrew (1981), pp.40 and 53-54, fig. 97.

Distribution   Two sites in Surrey, where it is now extinct, and recently recorded from Leicestershire.

Habitat and ecology   At the margins of small streams, on stones covered by a water film.

Status   The species may be present in other small unpolluted streams in those areas.

Threats   Pollution. One Surrey site visited personally was clogged with sand from motorway development.

Author   I.D. Wallace, using additional information from Hickin (1953, 1967), C. Hobday and M. Greenwood (pers. comms).

Cyrnus insolutus

A caddis fly   **ENDANGERED**

Order **Trichoptera**   Family **Polycentropodidae**

Cyrnus insolutus McLachlan, 1878.

Identification   Macan (1973), p.74, fig.2:3; Edington & Hildrew (1981), pp.26, 49 and 69, fig. 49.

Distribution   Known only from Blelham Tarn (and one Irish site).

Habitat and ecology	Stony lake shores.
Conservation	Blelham Tarn is owned by the National Trust and is much studied by the Freshwater Biological Association. The population should be monitored to check status.
Author	I.D. Wallace, using additional information from Kimmins (1942) and Edington (1964).

Hydropsyche bulgaromanorum Hydropsyche exocellata

Caddis flies   **ENDANGERED +**

Order **Trichoptera**   Family **Hydropsychidae**

Hydropsyche bulgaromanorum Malicky, 1977 (British specimens previously referred to as *H. guttata* Pictet: see Malicky, 1984); *Hydropsyche exocellata* Dufour, 1841.

Identification	Hildrew & Morgan (1974); Malicky (1983), p.123.
Distribution	Southern England, mainly lower reaches of the River Thames. Probably long extinct.
Habitat and ecology	Large rivers.
Status	*H. bulgaromanorum* was last taken in September 1926 at Arundel, West Sussex (Malicky, 1984). *H. exocellata* has not been recorded since 1901.
Threats	Pollution, canalisation, and general river 'improvement'.
Author	I.D. Wallace, using information from Edington & Hildrew (1981).

Hydropsyche saxonica

A caddis fly   **ENDANGERED**

Order **Trichoptera**   Family **Hydropsychidae**

Hydropsyche saxonica McLachlan, 1884.

Identification	Kimmins (1957); Hildrew & Morgan (1974).
Distribution	Bayswater Brook, Headington, Oxfordshire, and somewhere in east Gloucestershire.
Habitat and ecology	Fast-flowing streams.
Status	Not found at Bayswater Brook for about thirty years (probably extinct there). The exact location of the east Gloucestershire site is not known, therefore status cannot be determined.
Threats	Pollution caused by nearby housing development at Headington.

Conservation	Details of some possible sites will be lodged with the NCC by R. M. Badcock.
Author	I.D. Wallace, using information from Badcock (1978) and R.M. Badcock (pers. comm.).

Agrypnia crassicornis

A caddis fly	**ENDANGERED**
Order **Trichoptera**	Family **Phryganeidae**

Agrypnia crassicornis (McLachlan, 1876), previously known as *Agrypnetes crassicornis*.

Identification	Macan (1973), pp.15,16 and 20, figs 1:1 and 1:3; Bray (1967).
Distribution	Only known from Malham Tarn, where there is a large population.
Habitat and ecology	A large calcareous lake.
Status	Not recorded from the Tarn until the 1950s. It may have been introduced from abroad during fish stocking, but it is more likely to be native and overlooked because the adult is flightless.
Conservation	No immediate threats. The significance of the site is appreciated by the nearby Field Studies Council centre. The population should be monitored to check for any decline.
Author	I.D. Wallace, using additional information from Holmes (1963) and Kimmins (1952).

Hagenella clathrata

A caddis fly	**ENDANGERED**
Order **Trichoptera**	Family **Phryganeidae**

Hagenella clathrata (Kolenati, 1848), previously known as *Oligotricha clathrata*.

Identification	Macan (1973), pp.16 and 20, figs 1:1 and 1:3 (as *Oligotrichia clathrata*); Wallace & Wiggins (1978).
Distribution	Only three sites where it has been seen recently (despite searches in several bogs and mosses in north-west England and mid Wales): Whixall Moss, Shropshire; Chartley Moss, Staffordshire; and a small bog at Kinrara, Aviemore.

Habitat and ecology	The marginal areas of raised bogs and mosses. The larvae are found in water between the tussocks of tufted hair-grass *Deschampsia cespitosa* and cotton-grass *Eriophorum vaginatum* where there is probably a slight flow of water over the peat surface. The larvae have not been found in the very wet parts of 'schwingmoors', nor in deep pools on the main part of 'mosses', nor in areas of the mosses that dry up completely in summer.
Status	Decreasing. Was commoner in the past at Whixall and Chartley. Several other old sites have been destroyed.
Threats	Drainage, peat harvesting, and the drying-out and loss of the marginal areas due to invasion by birch and pine. A special threat at Whixall Moss is the expansion of a nearby car dump.
Conservation	Chartley Moss is an NNR. Sites should be managed to maintain suitable habitat. The ecological requirements are not known and a study of the habitats, particularly of their hydrodynamic regime throughout the year, would be of great assistance in conserving this species.
Author	I. D. Wallace, using additional information from E. C. Pelham-Clinton (pers. comm.).

Ironoquia dubia

A caddis fly **VULNERABLE**

Order **Trichoptera** Family **Limnephilidae**

Ironoquia dubia (Stephens, 1837).

Identification	Macan (1973), p.24, fig.1:5; Hiley (1976).
Distribution	A 19th century record for Suffolk, 1930s records for Windsor Forest, and post-1970 records for south-west Berkshire and north-east Hampshire.
Habitat and ecology	Small streams in deciduous woodland which partly dry up in summer.
Status	The adult is very secretive and has not been taken far from suitable breeding sites. The species may be widespread in south-east England, but its habitat is scarce and declining.
Threats	The small woodland streams that the species inhabits could be cleaned out or affected by other drainage schemes designed to improve the woodland. General woodland loss is also a threat.
Conservation	Currently only two definite breeding sites are known. It would be desirable to try to locate other sites so that the best can be protected.
Author	I.D. Wallace, using additional information from Brindle (1964) and P.D. Hiley (pers. comm.).

Grammotaulius nitidus

A caddis fly

ENDANGERED

Order **Trichoptera**

Family **Limnephilidae**

Grammotaulius nitidus (Mueller, 1764).

Identification Malicky (1983), p.182; Hiley (1976).

Distribution Mostly 19th century records from the Fens and from Deal in Kent; also a 1930 record from Essex, 1950s records from the Somerset Levels, and post-1960 records from the Broads of Norfolk and Suffolk.

Habitat and ecology The larval biology is not known in Britain. In Russia the habitat is reported to be shallow, overgrown puddles in marshy areas (Lepneva, 1971).

Threats The cause of decline is not known. It seems likely that the species requires temporary pools, possibly in a disturbed or immature habitat. Its decline may be due to drainage and natural vegetational succession. In the past, extensive use of its localities for grazing and sedge- and reed-cutting would prevent build-up of litter, halt vegetational succession, and produce puddles and ruts.

Conservation It is necessary to locate a breeding site and, when the habitat requirements have been deduced, take appropriate conservation measures and use the information to search for further populations. It seems that long-established reed-cutting localities in the Broads are the most likely places to search for the species.

Author I.D. Wallace.

Limnephilus pati

A caddis fly

ENDANGERED

Order **Trichoptera**

Family **Limnephilidae**

Limnephilus pati O'Connor, 1980.

Identification O'Connor & Barnard (1981).

Distribution Late 19th and early 20th century records from the Fens (and also the Curraghs of the Isle of Man, and Ireland).

Habitat and ecology The larva, and hence the breeding habitat, is unknown to science.

Threats The cause of decline is not known. The comments made for *Grammotaulius nitidus* seem relevant for this species also.

Conservation It is necessary to obtain some modern records, then search for the larval habitat and take necessary conservation steps.

Author I.D. Wallace, using additional information from O'Connor (1980).

Limnephilus tauricus

A caddis fly

VULNERABLE

Order **Trichoptera**

Family **Limnephilidae**

Limnephilus tauricus Schmid, 1964.

Identification O'Connor & Barnard (1981); Hiley (1976) (as *L. hirsutus* (Pictet)).

Distribution 19th century records from the Fens, and a post-1970 record from Woolhampton, Berkshire.

Habitat and ecology Only one larva known to science. Collected from a small dyke in a reed swamp cut in the past for thatch.

Status May be widespread in river valley reed fens in the south of England, but such habitat is now rare.

Threats The cause of decline is not known. The comments made for *Grammotaulius nitidus* seem relevant for this species also.

Conservation It is desirable to obtain further modern records, confirm larval habitat requirements, and take necessary conservation measures at the best sites.

Author I.D. Wallace, using additional information from P.D. Hiley (pers. comm.).

Leptocerus lusitanicus

A caddis fly

ENDANGERED

Order **Trichoptera**

Family **Leptoceridae**

Leptocerus lusitanicus (McLachlan, 1884).

Identification Macan (1973), p.126, fig. 4:10; Wallace (1981).

Distribution The River Thames and tributaries close to the river, on the Oxfordshire/Berkshire border.

Habitat and ecology Large rivers, on submerged tree roots.

Status This species was abundant on the Thames but it now seems to be restricted to quiet areas away from the main navigation routes.

Threats Initial damage to habitat caused by the wash from power-boats necessitates tree removal and bank reinforcement, resulting in complete loss of habitat.

Conservation The exclusion of pleasure boats and the preservation of trees fringing backwaters, e.g. River Thame at Dorchester, and backstream of Dorchester Days Lock on the Thames.

Author I.D. Wallace (see Wallace, 1976).

LEPIDOPTERA: I

The Butterflies

The butterflies represent but two of the 20 superfamilies of Lepidoptera, but are treated here as a distinct group for convenience. There are about 56 resident breeding species in Britain and several migrants. They are undoubtedly the most popular group of insects. The majority are readily identified on the wing and are consequently very well recorded. There has been a distinct trend in recent years away from collecting towards observation and photography.

The Red Data Book includes two Endangered, three Vulnerable and two Rare species. One of the Endangered species, the Large Blue, became extinct in Britain in 1979 and three others are listed in the Appendix (in this case, extinct for 60 years or more). The Chequered Skipper is also extinct in England, but it has recently been discovered in a sufficiently large area of Scotland to place it in the Out of Danger category. At present, however, it remains on Schedule 5 of the Wildlife and Countryside Act 1981, along with the Large Blue, Swallowtail and Heath Fritillary. A second species, the Black Hairstreak, is now also regarded as Out of Danger. A total of 12 species are listed, amounting to over 21% of the British butterfly fauna.

The butterflies discussed here usually produce a single brood in a year (i.e. they are univoltine) and hibernate as larva, pupa or adult according to species. They require not only the right foodplant and habitat for the larvae, but also suitable habitat and nectar-producing flowers for the adults. More exacting requirements increase their vulnerability. For instance the Large Blue spends most of its larval life in the nest of a particular species of ant. Of the seven species discussed here, five occur in woodland or woodland edge, one in marshland and one on grassland. In the case of the woodland species the greatest threat has been the cessation of traditional woodland management : rotational coppicing provides the glades which are so favoured by butterflies. For many other species the ploughing-up of old grassland and the draining of wet meadows has resulted in a considerable fall in numbers. The reason for decline is not always evident, even in the case of the High Brown Fritillary, which has shown the greatest decline of all, and the Chequered Skipper, which has vanished from England.

Books on British butterflies are legion, though the standard work, *South's British butterflies* (Howarth, 1973a), is out of print. However, an abridged version of it, the *Colour identification guide to the butterflies of Britain and Ireland*, was reprinted in 1984. There are numerous field guides, most of them somewhat dominated by European species. Photographic guides are arguably less effective for identification, though those that illustrate all stages of each species – such as *A complete guide to British butterflies* (Brooks & Knight, 1982) – are very useful. The NCC has published booklets on *The conservation of butterflies* (Anon., 1981) and *The management of chalk grassland for butterflies* (Butterflies Under Threat Team, 1986).

There is a Butterfly Recording Scheme, currently operated by the British Butterfly Conservation Society. There is also a Butterfly Monitoring Scheme organised by the Institute of Terrestrial Ecology (Hall, 1981). Up-to-date distribution maps have appeared recently in the *Atlas of butterflies in Britain and Ireland* (Heath, Pollard & Thomas, 1984), which also summarises the ecology of each species using much previously unpublished information.

Carterocephalus palaemon

"Chequered Skipper Butterfly" **OUT OF DANGER**

Order **Lepidoptera**   Family **Hesperiidae**

Carterocephalus palaemon (Pallas, 1771).

Identification Howarth (1973a), pp. 23-25, pls 1 and 2.

Distribution Formerly in scattered woods in England, chiefly in the East Midlands, especially in Cambridgeshire, Northamptonshire and Lincolnshire. Currently widespread in west Scotland, centred on north Argyll. For British map see Heath, Pollard & Thomas (1984), p.15; Collier's (1986) map adds one 10km square in Scotland; for European map see Heath & Leclerq (1981), map 10.

Habitat and ecology England: open woodland, rides, edges and associated grassland. Scotland: damp rank pasture dominated by purple moor-grass *Molinia caerulea*, usually in scrubby areas or on edges of copses. Univoltine. The adults fly in May and June. The larvae feed on grasses, but the full range of species used is uncertain. In England, slender false brome *Brachypodium sylvaticum* and tor grass *B. pinnatum* were used. In Scotland, breeding occurs on partly shaded purple moor-grass, though eggs have been found on slender false brome at Loch Arkaig (Collier, 1986).

Status Believed extinct in England by 1976. Intensively surveyed in 1973-74 and 1980 but no colony was found. Only two colonies were known in Scotland before the early 1970s, but, during surveys, it had been found in 25 different 10km squares by 1984 (Collier, 1986). It is not believed to have spread, merely to have been overlooked. Considered to be "locally common" by Thomson (1980) and probably more colonies await discovery. One Scottish colony occurs continuously along 8km of roadside (Thomson, 1980) and another along 18km of a loch shore (Collier, 1986). European status: Vulnerable (Heath, 1981).

Threats Causes of the English extinctions are uncertain, but Collier (1986) suggests that the major factor was habitat change related to "inadequate ride management, woodland succession after fellings in the 1950s, cessation of coppice systems and the development of coarse grasses in the post-myxomatosis period".

Conservation Now believed to be far more widespread in Scotland than was once thought, with colonies on at least two National Nature Reserves. Studied in England in 1961-69 and in Scotland mainly since 1979 by Collier (Collier, 1986). Subject of surveys in 1973-74 (Farrell, 1975) and 1980 (J. Heath, pers. comm.) in England and since 1975 by the Scottish Wildlife Trust (Sommerville, 1984). Conservation studies are in progress. Listed on Schedule 5 of the Wildlife and Countryside Act 1981.

Author J. A. Thomas.

Papilio machaon

"Swallowtail Butterfly" **VULNERABLE**

Order **Lepidoptera** Family **Papilionidae**

Papilio machaon (L., 1758). The endemic British race is subspecies *britannicus* Seitz, 1907.

Identification
Howarth (1973a), pp.36-38, pls 3 and 6.

Distribution
Only the Norfolk Broads since 1952. Up to the early 19th century it was found in several southern marshlands. From the mid 19th century onwards it had become restricted to the Fens of Lincs, Hunts and Cambs, and the Norfolk Broads. Other records are migrants, escapes and introductions. In 1984 it bred in all suitable habitat in five separate Broads systems, and locally in abundance within each. For map see Heath, Pollard & Thomas (1984), p.31.

Habitat and ecology
Marshland in the Norfolk Broads. Univoltine, with occasionally a partial second brood. The adults fly in May and June. Hibernates as a pupa. The larval foodplant is the local milk parsley or hog's fennel *Peucedanum palustre*; only large exposed plants are used. In the Broads this grows locally in abundance over large areas as large plants, where regular sedge-cutting occurs.

Status
Has declined with the drainage of wetlands and is unlikely to be re established in former areas unless the water table is changed. Locally common in a few areas of the Norfolk Broads, but is also declining there because of drainage, succession, and fragmentation. European status: Indeterminate (Heath, 1981).

Threats
Drainage of wetlands and surrounding land, and the succession of vegetation.

Conservation
Attempts to regenerate new habitat at Wicken Fen were only partially successful and a recent reintroduction failed after a few years. The species' ecology has been studied and the habitat requirements are largely known. Breeds in good numbers on two NNRs and at least three Norfolk Naturalists' Trust reserves, where its habitat is being maintained by sedge-cutting, with excellent results. Some other private breeding sites are being sympathetically managed, following advice from the local Trust and NCC. Listed on Schedule 5 of the Wildlife and Countryside Act 1981.

Author
J. A. Thomas, using information from Dempster & Hall (1980), Dempster, King & Lakhani (1976), and M. S. Warren and M. L. Hall (pers. comm.).

Strymonidia pruni

Black Hairstreak

OUT OF DANGER

Order **Lepidoptera**   Family **Lycaenidae**

Strymonidia pruni (L., 1758).

Identification Howarth (1973a), pp 67-63, pls 11 and 16.

Distribution Relict woods of the east Midlands forest belt: Bernwood, Grendon Underwood, Waddon Chase, Whittlewood, Salcey, Yardley Chase, the Huntingdonshire fen edges, Rockingham and Nassboro Forests. Introduced to Surrey in 1952, where it still survives. For map see Heath, Pollard & Thomas (1984), p.57.

Habitat and ecology Wood edges, glades and adjoining hedgerows and scrub. Univoltine. The adults fly in late June and early July. Overwinters as an egg on the twigs of *Prunus* species. The usual larval foodplant is blackthorn *Prunus spinosa*, but any other *Prunus* is suitable, e.g. wild plum *P. domestica*. It needs continuity of sunny, sheltered banks of *Prunus*. Adults are unable to colonise new habitat unless it is very close to an existing colony.

Status About 30-35 colonies are known. Most are small, but this is typical of the species. No colony is known to have been lost since the 1960s. European status: Vulnerable (Heath, 1981).

Threats Formerly modern silviculture, but most colonies are now conserved.

Conservation Colonies exist on two NNRs and at least ten other (mainly local Trust) reserves. Most other colonies are subject to management agreements. Subject to surveys and conservation research in early 1970s (Thomas, 1975, 1980b).

Author J. A. Thomas.

Maculinea arion

"Large Blue Butterfly"

ENDANGERED +

Order **Lepidoptera**   Family **Lycaenidae**

Maculinea arion (L., 1758). The Cornish population has been named subspecies *eutyphron* Fruhstorfer, 1915.

Identification Howarth (1973a), pp.92-94, pls 17 and 24.

Distribution Formerly occurred along the Atlantic coast of Devon and Cornwall from Tintagel to Clovelly; south Devon, from Bolt Head to Bolt Tail and scattered coastal sites east of Salcombe, and on shales along the south edge of Dartmoor; Polden Hills, Somerset; Cotswolds; near Barnwell Wold, Northants. For map of former distribution see Heath, Pollard & Thomas (1984), p.81. Believed extinct in 1979.

Habitat and ecology	South-facing hillsides of close-cropped, unfertilised pasture on shales or limestone, where the ant *Myrmica sabuleti* occurs abundantly over at least a hectare, and where wild thyme *Thymus praecox* is well distributed. Some shelter by scrub seems to be important on small sites. Univoltine, the adults flying in late June and July. The ova are laid singly on thyme, and the young larvae feed on the flowers until August. Thereafter the larvae occur in nests of *M. sabuleti* where they feed on ant larvae and prepupae. Pupation occurs in May, inside the ants' nest.
Status	Believed extinct in 1979. Has been intensively surveyed in 10 of the last 20 years but no new colony confirmed since 1961. Numerous reputed sightings have, so far, proved groundless, mainly as misidentifications of other blues. It is unlikely that a colony has escaped detection, especially in traditional areas. European status: Endangered (Heath, 1981). World status: Vulnerable (Wells, Pyle & Collins, 1983).
Threats	About half the sites have been destroyed by fundamental changes to the habitat including ploughing, afforestation, urbanisation, and quarrying. The remainder have been undergrazed by both domestic and wild herbivores since the mid 1950s, causing a large reduction of the ant *Myrmica sabuleti*.
Conservation	Many measures taken since the late 1920s; for a fuller account see Spooner (1963), Hunt (1965), Howarth (1973b), Thomas (1980a, 1980b). Efforts were uncoordinated until 1962 when a Joint Committee for the Conservation of the Large Blue Butterfly was formed. Early measures were successful in discovering the last colonies, preventing the fundamental destruction of these sites and deterring collectors, but failed to stem the decline of *M. sabuleti*, which was unnoticed before the mid-1970s. Management agreements were obtained on the last four sites and it has recently proved possible to manage some, at least, so that high densities of *M. sabuleti* are re-established. Unfortunately, this occurred too late to save the Large Blue. Was first protected under the Conservation of Wild Creatures and Wild Plants Act 1975, and is listed on Schedule 5 of the Wildlife and Countryside Act 1981. Surveys of reputed sightings continue each year. Management to improve three former sites is being continued by NCC with promising results. A re-establishment programme commenced at one site in 1983, using stock from Sweden.
Author	J. A. Thomas.

Nymphalis polychloros

	Large Tortoiseshell	**ENDANGERED**
	Order **Lepidoptera**	Family **Nymphalidae**

Nymphalis polychloros (L., 1758).

Identification Howarth (1973a), pp.109-111, pls 23 and 30.

Distribution Very widely distributed in the 19th century through most southern woodlands, but greatly reduced in the 20th century, especially after 1920. There are records from 42 10km squares since 1960, but there are only two reports of its being found in two or more years in the same locality. Almost all records are of single specimens, most probably resulting from migrants and introductions. Also subject to misidentification. Unconfirmed breeding reported recently from North Wales, central Sussex, Wiltshire, and Cornwall. For map see Heath, Pollard & Thomas (1984), p.95. Population size unknown.

Habitat and ecology Wooded areas. Univoltine. The adults fly in July and August, and after hibernation, in spring. The eggs are laid in large batches on twigs. The larvae live gregariously on elms *Ulmus*, willows *Salix*, poplars *Populus*, whitebeams *Sorbus* and other trees, often high up.

Status May only be an occasional migrant nowadays. Continental stock is often reared in captivity and frequently escapes. European status: Indeterminate (Heath, 1981).

Conservation There is a recent record from a property of the National Trust.

Author J. A. Thomas.

Argynnis adippe

	High Brown Fritillary	**VULNERABLE**
	Order **Lepidoptera**	Family **Nymphalidae**

Argynnis adippe (Denis and Schiffermueller, 1775). The British race is subspecies *vulgoadippe* Verity, 1929.

Identification Howarth (1973a), pp.123-125, pls 27 and 36.

Distribution Formerly very widely distributed in most wooded areas south of Cumberland. Now largely confined to the west of Britain (Devon, Cornwall, Wales and the Lake District). For map see Heath, Pollard & Thomas (1984), p.105. Population size unknown.

Habitat and ecology Woods and nearby scrubby land. Univoltine. Adults fly in mid June and July. Overwinters as an egg laid on solid material at the base of bushes, scrub, etc. The larvae feed on violets (*Viola* species).

Status	One of the most rapid declines of all British butterflies. Records from pre-1960 10km squares outnumber post-1960 records by 2:1, and many of the latter are now extinct. The distribution of the decline is wholly from east to west. Still locally common in a few areas of west England, e.g. the Welsh borderland and Lake District.
Threats	The cessation of traditional woodland management and the destruction of woodland edge habitat, and probably other factors.
Conservation	Occurs on at least one NNR, and there are recent records from National Trust properties.
Author	J. A. Thomas.

Mellicta athalia   "Heath Fritillary Butterfly"   **VULNERABLE**

Order **Lepidoptera**   Family **Nymphalidae**

Mellicta athalia (Rottemburg, 1775), formerly known as *Melitaea athalia*.

Identification	Howarth (1973a), pp.132-133, pls 31 and 40.
Distribution	Scattered woods in east Cornwall, Devon, and west Somerset; woods around Canterbury, Kent. Formerly in occasional colonies throughout southern England, but greatly declined in all areas. For map see Heath, Pollard & Thomas (1984), p.115. In 1980 there were three large populations, 23 small-medium, and five very small. Several small-medium and small colonies are probably not viable without immigrants from nearby large colonies. Several large populations were discovered in Somerset in 1984.
Habitat and ecology	Recent coppicing and clearings in woods (in the east), new plantations (in the west), and broad rides. The breeding habitat is always ephemeral. Univoltine, the adults flying in June and early July. The eggs are laid in large batches, and the larvae live communally until the final instar. The main larval foodplants are common cow-wheat *Melampyrum pratense* in eastern localities and ribwort *Plantago lanceolata* and germander speedwell *Veronica chamaedrys* in western localities.
Status	Confined to three woods and one large heathland in the west and three woodland blocks in the east (1984), although some of these contain more than one breeding area. There has been a sharp decline in the number of woods supporting this species in the last decade, especially in the west. A few large populations survive but all are at risk because of the ephemeral nature of the habitat.

Threats   Modern silviculture: the generation of new breeding areas is being outstripped by the loss, through shading and succession, of old ones.

Conservation   Large populations existed in the 1960s on one NNR and one local Trust reserve. Both became overgrown and lost their colonies, but both were recolonised in the 1980s following new management. Three new reserves were established in 1981-83 and are being managed for the butterfly with promising early results. Two re-establishments to former sites were made in 1983-84. Subject of a survey in 1980 by the Joint Committee for the Conservation of British Insects (Warren, Thomas & Thomas, 1980, 1984), and of an NCC/ITE joint conservation research project by M.S. Warren from 1982 to 1985. Listed on Schedule 5 of the Wildlife and Countryside Act 1981.

Author   J. A. Thomas, using additional information from M. S. Warren (pers. comm.).

LEPIDOPTERA: II

The Moths

The moths, which constitute the majority of the Lepidoptera, are one of the larger groups of insects. They are traditionally divided, arbitrarily, into the 'Macrolepidoptera' (about 900 British species) and the 'Microlepidoptera' (about 1500 species). The former are second only to butterflies in popularity, most species being relatively large and readily identified in the hand by the enthusiast. The 'micros', on the other hand, have been somewhat neglected until relatively recently, as they present a number of obstacles to identification. For this reason, only a selection of these has been included in the present edition.

Of the 'macros', the Red Data Book includes 21 Endangered, 12 Vulnerable and 53 Rare species. At least three Endangered species are believed to be extinct, and a further 13 species are listed in the Appendix (in this case, extinct for 50 years or more). As subspecies are more clearly defined and better known than in other orders, a few have been singled out for separate treatment. Five species are on Schedule 5 of the Wildlife and Countryside Act 1981. A total of 99 species is listed, amounting to about 11% of the British macrolepidopteran fauna. The 'micros' are represented by only four Endangered and seven Vulnerable species, a token sample of under 1% of the fauna.

Many moths are reliant on only one or two specific larval foodplants. Of the Endangered and Vulnerable species discussed here, 30% occur in woodland and scrub, 26% in waterside situations (riverbanks, bogs and marsh), 26% on coastal cliffs or dunes, 11% on grassland, etc., and 9% on heathland. The woodland species are most threatened by the cessation of traditional management, in particular the loss of glades formerly resulting from coppicing, and conversion to plantations of uniform species and age structure. The loss of aquatic habitats (discussed above under Trichoptera) has been linked with serious losses in all waterside habitats. The coastal undercliffs and landslips of Dorset and the Isle of Wight are rich in Lepidoptera, but are threatened by development for tourism.

The most recent comprehensive aid to identification of the 'macros' is the *Colour identification guide to moths of the British Isles* (Skinner, 1984), though the earlier *Moths of the British Isles* (South, 1961) is still widely used. *A field guide to the smaller British Lepidoptera* (Emmet, 1979) is useful for identifying the 'micros'. The standard work for both 'macros' and 'micros' is the multi-volume *Moths and butterflies of Great Britain and Ireland* (Heath, 1976; Heath & Emmet, 1979-), of which a fourth volume appeared in 1985. The AES has published both *A lepidopterist's handbook* (Dickson, 1976) and *Practical hints for collecting and studying the Microlepidoptera* (Sokoloff, 1980). The check list by Kloet & Hincks (1972) has been updated by *A recorder's log book or label list of British butterflies and moths* (Bradley & Fletcher, 1979), though it lacks synonymy, and the separate index (Hall-Smith *et al*, 1983) is a necessary supplement.

A national recording scheme for the larger moths operated from 1967 to 1982, but the only schemes running at present are at a regional level. A small number of families of 'micros' are, however, covered by national schemes. Distribution maps are appearing in *Moths and butterflies of Great Britain and Ireland*.

Stigmella torminalis

VULNERABLE

Order **Lepidoptera**   Family **Nepticulidae**

Stigmella torminalis (Wood, 1890), formerly known as *Nepticula torminalis*.

Identification   Meyrick (1928), p.853; A.M. Emmet *in* Heath (1976), p.257, pls 3:1 and 11:31.

Distribution   Known only in Stoke Edith Wood, Hereford & Worcester, where it was reasonably common from 1890 to *c.* 1910, since when it has not been looked for. For map see Heath (1976), p.256.

Habitat and ecology   Woodland where the foodplant, wild service tree *Sorbus torminalis*, occurs.

Status   Owing to difficulties of site access, its present status is unknown.

Author   A.M. Emmet, using information from Wood (1890 and 1908).

Phragmataecia castaneae

Reed Leopard

VULNERABLE

Order **Lepidoptera**   Family **Cossidae**

Phragmataecia castaneae (Huebner, 1790).

Identification   South (1961), 2:324, pl.127; Heath & Emmet (1985); Skinner (1984), p.3, pl.1:7-8.

Distribution   Established in two fens in Cambridgeshire, the Norfolk Broads and one small site in east Dorset.

Habitat and ecology   Univoltine, on the wing in June and July. Nocturnal. In fenland and marshes, where the larvae occur in the stems of reed *Phragmites australis*.

Status   Unchanged; the populations of all sites are fairly stable.

Threats   Not threatened at present, except possibly by pollution in its Norfolk localities.

Conservation   Occurs on five nature reserves.

Author   B. Skinner.

Zygaena purpuralis segontii

Transparent Burnet	**ENDANGERED +**
Order **Lepidoptera**	Family **Zygaenidae**

Zygaena purpuralis (Bruennich, 1763). Subspecies *segontii* Tremewan, 1958 is one of two races in Britain.

Identification
Heath & Emmet (1985); Skinner (1984), p.6, pl. 2:25.

Distribution
Restricted to one site in Gwynedd, North Wales, where it was last noted in 1961.

Habitat and ecology
Univoltine, on the wing from June to early July. Diurnal. On coastal cliffs, where the larvae feed on wild thyme *Thymus praecox*.

Status
Formerly known to occur in several adjacent sites. (In Scotland this species is represented by subspecies *caledonensis* Reiss, which is found on the mainland in Kintyre and western Argyll, and in the Inner Hebrides.)

Author
B. Skinner.

Zygaena viciae argyllensis

"New Forest Burnet Moth"	**ENDANGERED**
Order **Lepidoptera**	Family **Zygaenidae**

Zygaena viciae (Denis & Schiffermueller, 1775). The extinct race is subspecies *ytenensis* Briggs, 1888 (=*anglica* Reiss, 1931). The surviving race is subspecies *argyllensis* Tremewan, 1967.

Identification
Heath & Emmet (1985); Skinner (1984), p.4, pl.2:9.

Distribution
Now confined to one site in western Argyll, where it was discovered in 1963.

Habitat and ecology
Univoltine, on the wing from mid-June to mid-July. Diurnal. Grassy slopes on coastal cliffs. The larvae occur on birdsfoot-trefoil *Lotus corniculatus* and meadow vetchling *Lathyrus pratensis*.

Status
The population is small, but at present stable. It was formerly known to occur in the New Forest, Hampshire, where it was represented by subspecies *ytenensis*. Here it became extinct about 1927 due to afforestation and to over-collecting by commercial entomologists.

Threats
Mildly threatened by cliff erosion and sheep grazing.

Conservation
Listed on Schedule 5 of the Wildlife and Countryside Act 1981.

Author
B. Skinner.

Pachythelia villosella

VULNERABLE

Order **Lepidoptera**   Family **Psychidae**

Pachythelia villosella (Ochsenheimer, 1810).

Identification   Meyrick (1928), p.476; Ford (1946), pp.104-105, pl.11:1, 1a, 1b; Heath & Emmet (1985).

Distribution   Known only in the heathy part of the New Forest on the Dorset/Hampshire border.

Habitat and ecology   Heathland where heathers (*Calluna* and *Erica*) occur.

Status   Included here because it is a species confined to a single locality. There is no evidence of decline or dangerous rarity.

Threats   None, unless land-usage changes.

Author   A.M. Emmet.

Paraleucoptera sinuella

ENDANGERED

Order **Lepidoptera**   Family **Lyonetiidae**

Paraleucoptera sinuella (Reutti, 1853), formerly known as *Leucoptera susinella* (Herrich-Schaeffer).

Identification   Meyrick (1928), pp.808-809; Brown (1954), p.112, pl.9:1; Heath & Emmet (1985).

Distribution   Recorded only from the railway station at Aviemore, and (once) from Grantown-on-Spey, but no longer present at these sites.

Habitat and ecology   Aspen *Populus tremula* spinneys in valleys in the Scottish Highlands.

Threats   The cause of decline is not known. The spinney where it occurred from 1912 until at least 1951 has not been interfered with and there is no evidence of overcollecting. Unfavourable climatic conditions may have been the cause.

Conservation   If, as is quite likely, a new locality is found, the aspens on which it feeds should be conserved.

Author   A.M. Emmet.

Phyllocnistis xenia

Order **Lepidoptera**   Family **Phyllocnistidae**

Phyllocnistis xenia (Hering, 1936).

Identification Pelham-Clinton (1976); Emmet (1976); Heath & Emmet (1985).

Distribution Until recently known in England only from a single clump of the foodplant near St Margaret's Bay, Kent. Two new localities have now been found about fifteen miles north-west of the original colony.

Habitat and ecology On grey poplar *Populus canescens*, in England on chalk, but the latter is probably not a necessary requirement.

Status Fairly common within the known localities. This species has only recently gained a foothold in Britain. If it succeeds in establishing further colonies, it will need no protection.

Threats The lower part of the valley where the moth occurs has executive-type houses with large gardens. If the upper part of the valley were to be utilised for similar development, the species would be destroyed.

Conservation The grey poplars on which the larvae feed require protection.

Author A.M. Emmet, with additional information from Heal (1984) and E.C. Pelham-Clinton (pers. comm.).

Bembecia chrysidiformis

Fiery Clearwing   **ENDANGERED**

Order **Lepidoptera**   Family **Sesiidae**

Bembecia chrysidiformis (Esper, 1782), previously known as *Aegeria chrysidiformis*.

Identification South (1961), 2:347-8, pl.136:9,10; Skinner (1984), p.9, pl.2:49-50; Heath & Emmet (1985).

Distribution Confined to one site in south-east Kent. Occasional specimens have been reported from Sussex, Essex, Hampshire, and elsewhere in Kent.

Habitat and ecology Univoltine, flying in June and July. Diurnal. Rough ground and chalky slopes by the sea. The larvae occur in the roots of docks and sorrels (*Rumex* species).

Status It was formerly more widespread in its one known locality, but the population is at present stable.

Threats Parts of the locality are threatened by cliff erosion.

Author B. Skinner.

Coleophora leucapennella

VULNERABLE

Order **Lepidoptera**   Family **Coleophoridae**

Coleophora leucapennella (Huebner, 1796).

Identification   Meyrick (1928), p.755; Emmet (1979), p.80.

Distribution   Now known only in one wood in west Gloucestershire. One was taken at Denton, Norfolk in 1890. The population is believed to be small.

Habitat and ecology   Amongst ragged robin *Lychnis flos-cuculi* in woodland rides.

Status   The exact location is strictly confidential: it is not known whether it is subject to any threat, and the secrecy surrounding the locality would make conservation measures difficult to implement.

Conservation   Steps should be taken to ensure that the ride where it occurs does not become overgrown.

Author   A.M. Emmet, using information from Barrett (1891) and J.M. Chalmers-Hunt (pers. comm.).

Hypercallia citrinalis

ENDANGERED

Order **Lepidoptera**   Family **Oecophoridae**

Hypercallia citrinalis (Scopoli, 1763), formerly known as *H. christiernana* (L.).

Identification   Meyrick (1928), p.676; Jacobs (1951), pp.192-193, pl.19:16.

Distribution   Very low density on the North Downs, Kent. Formerly recorded in Co. Durham.

Habitat and ecology   Chalk and limestone downland where its foodplant, common milkwort *Polygala vulgaris*, occurs.

Status   Currently known in England only in an area of a few acres near Trottiscliffe, Kent, where it is scarce. It is obviously very precarious if it is really restricted to this one locality. (It is not considered to be endangered in Ireland.)

Threats   It has always been scarce in England. The chief threat is the invasion of its habitat by scrub and the resultant elimination of its foodplant.

Conservation   A party of volunteers cleared scrub in about 1970 and I believe this has been repeated. This work should be continued in order to conserve the foodplant. The Kent Trust for Nature Conservation is already aware of the risk to this species.

Author   A.M. Emmet.

Syncopacma vinella

VULNERABLE

Order **Lepidoptera**   Family **Gelechiidae**

Syncopacma vinella (Bankes, 1898).

Identification   Meyrick (1928), p.640.

Distribution   Discovered in about 1898 near Brighton, East Sussex: the site may have been Ditchling Common where it has persisted, the most recent known record being in 1976. It was also recorded in Ashdown Forest but this site has been destroyed. According to Meyrick, it is only known from Britain. The population is thought to be very small.

Habitat and ecology   Amongst dyer's greenweed *Genista tinctoria* growing in grassy situations.

Threats   None known, other than fire which has occurred in the past.

Conservation   The Common is now administered as a reserve and is wardened. The public, however, has access. The survival of the species depends on the conservation of the foodplant at this site.

Author   A.M. Emmet, using additional information from R. Fairclough (pers. comm.).

Aethes margarotana

VULNERABLE

Order **Lepidoptera**   Family **Cochylidae**

Aethes margarotana (Duponchel, 1836), formerly known as *Phalonia maritimana* Guenee.

Identification   Meyrick (1928), p.487; Bradley, Tremewan & Smith (1973), pp.58-59, pl.24, fig.7.

Distribution   It has been recorded from Deal and Sandwich in Kent, Shoeburyness, St Osyth and Clacton-on-Sea in Essex, and near Thorpeness in Suffolk. It is probably extinct in Kent and Essex, where it was last recorded in 1934, but may persist in Suffolk where it was recorded as recently as 1966.

Habitat and ecology   Amongst sea holly *Eryngium maritimum* on shingle beaches or coastal sand-dunes.

Status   Entomologists do not seem to have looked for it in recent years. One reason is that the adult is rarely seen and almost the only way to find the larva is to dig up the roots of the foodplant where it feeds in October. No conscientious entomologist wishes to do this since the plant itself is under threat. Attempts to establish its present status should therefore be planned in collaboration with botanists.

Threats	The foodplant has been seriously reduced by pressure from holiday-makers on the beaches.
Conservation	Measures taken by local Trusts to conserve the sea holly will benefit the moth, if it still occurs.
Author	A.M. Emmet.

Pristerognatha penthinana

ENDANGERED

Order **Lepidoptera**   Family **Tortricidae**

Pristerognatha penthinana (Guenee, 1845).

Identification	Meyrick (1928), p.573; Bradley, Tremewan & Smith (1979), pp.3536, pl.24, figs 15 and 16.
Distribution	Near Lake Windermere in Cumbria. Meyrick also cites Lancashire, but this is probably an error springing from an ambiguously worded record. Not recorded for seventy years.
Habitat and ecology	Lakesides and boggy situations where touch-me-not *Impatiens noli-tangere* grows.
Status	The species was discovered in 1873 and continued to flourish until the end of the century. Thereafter it declined and was last taken in 1914.
Threats	Overcollecting probably contributed to its decline.
Conservation	If a new colony is discovered it should be carefully conserved.
Author	A.M. Emmet.

Cydia leguminana

ENDANGERED

Order **Lepidoptera**   Family **Tortricidae**

Cydia leguminana (Lienig & Zeller, 1846).

Identification	Meyrick (1928), p.596; Bradley, Tremewan & Smith (1979), pp. 274-275, pl.42, figs 4 and 5.
Distribution	Known from Epping Forest, Essex, until 1890 and from several localities in Cambridgeshire, the most recent being a lane adjoining Wicken Fen where it was relatively common until the trees were felled in 1976. There is now no known colony.
Habitat and ecology	Hedgerows in open country and the margins of woodland where there are aged elms *Ulmus* and probably other trees with excrescences on the bark within which the larvae feed.

Status	There is no outward sign of larval feeding and the adult, which flies in sunshine in late May, is difficult to observe on the wing. It is therefore probable that colonies exist which have been overlooked.
Threats	The cause of its disappearance from Epping Forest is unknown. It flourished at Wicken Fen for over 100 years until its host trees were destroyed. Since the outbreak of Dutch elm disease, mature elms have become a rarity.
Conservation	If a new colony is discovered, it will be dependent on over-mature trees which are liable to be felled. The land-owner should be urged not to do so.
Author	A.M. Emmet.

Stenoptilia graphodactyla

VULNERABLE

Order **Lepidoptera**   Family **Pterophoridae**

Stenoptilia graphodactyla (Treitschke, 1833), formerly known as *S. pneumonanthes* (Buettner).

Identification	Meyrick (1928), p.459; Beirne (1952), pp.173-174, pl.15:5, fig.170.
Distribution	Known only from boggy heaths on the borders of Dorset and Hampshire. Ferndown, St Leonards, Ringwood, Beaulieu Road and Matley Bog have been cited as localities.
Habitat and ecology	Boggy heaths where the very local bog gentian *Gentiana pneumonanthe* grows.
Status	It was discovered in 1906 and was taken sparingly for the next fifty years. There seems to be no confirmed recent record but an entomologist thought he saw evidence of larval feeding at Beaulieu Road in 1969. It probably persists precariously.
Threats	Some of the sites where it was found have been drained and used for building estates.
Conservation	If it is found again the habitat should, if possible, be conserved.
Author	A.M. Emmet, using information from Goater (1974), pp.210-211, and J. Parkinson Curtis, *A list of the Lepidoptera of Dorset* (unpublished).

Eriogaster lanestris

Small Eggar	**VULNERABLE**
Order **Lepidoptera**	Family **Lasiocampidae**

Eriogaster lanestris (L., 1758).

Identification
South (1961), 2:17-18, pls 4-5; Skinner (1984), p.10, pl.4:3-4.

Distribution
Existing very locally in Dorset, Devon, Gloucestershire, Sussex, Essex, Suffolk, Norfolk, Oxfordshire, Somerset, Hereford & Worcester, Hertfordshire, Cambridgeshire, Salop and Yorkshire. For European distribution see Heath & Leclerq (1981), map 12.

Habitat and ecology
Univoltine, flying in February and March. Nocturnal. Hedgerows and bushy places. The larvae occur on blackthorn *Prunus spinosa* and hawthorn (*Crataegus* species).

Status
A much declined species, formerly found not uncommonly over much of England, with its range extending as far north as southern Scotland.

Threats
Threatened by indiscriminate hedge-trimming, destruction of hedgerows, and pollution by agricultural sprays and motor vehicles.

Conservation
Recorded from a National Trust property in Cornwall in 1974, and from a reserve of the Yorkshire Wildlife Trust.

Author
B. Skinner.

Thetidia smaragdaria

"Essex Emerald Moth"	**ENDANGERED**
Order **Lepidoptera**	Family **Geometridae**

Thetidia smaragdaria (F., 1787). The race in Britain is subspecies *maritima* Prout, 1935.

Identification
South (1961), 2:86-87, pls 38 and 48; Skinner (1984), p.17, pl.6:7.

Distribution
Known currently from two, possibly three, sites in south Essex, and one in north Kent.

Habitat and ecology
Univoltine, flying in June and July. Nocturnal. Occurs on the edges of saltmarshes, where the larvae feed on sea wormwood *Artemisia maritima*.

Status
It was formerly found in many suitable localities in Essex along the estuaries of the Thames, Crouch and Blackwater.

Threats
The habitat is threatened by the reconstruction of sea-walls; the foodplant is threatened by the encroachment of surrounding vegetation.

Conservation	Added to the Conservation of Wild Creatures and Wild Plants Act 1975 in 1979, and now listed on Schedule 5 of the Wildlife and Countryside Act 1981.
Author	B. Skinner.

Thalera fimbrialis

Sussex Emerald **ENDANGERED**

Order **Lepidoptera** Family **Geometridae**

Thalera fimbrialis (Scopoli, 1763).

Identification	South (1961), 2:87-88, pl.41; Skinner (1984), pp.17-18, fig.8, pl.6:4.
Distribution	Confined to one site in south-east Kent, where it was first noted in 1950.
Habitat and ecology	Univoltine, on the wing from July to early August. Nocturnal. Occurs on shingle beaches, where the larvae feed on yarrow *Achillea millefolium* and probably other low plants.
Status	Much declined since the early 1970s, though single specimens taken in 1980 and 1984 suggest that the species is still resident at a low density. This transitory resident also occurred in East Sussex from 1953 to 1956.
Threats	Possibly threatened by change of land usage such as gravel extraction or building.
Author	B. Skinner.

Scopula immorata

Lewes Wave **ENDANGERED +**

Order **Lepidoptera** Family **Geometridae**

Scopula immorata (L., 1758).

Identification	South (1961), 2:98, pl.44; Skinner (1984), p.20, pl.6:35.
Distribution	Only known from two small sites in a single wood in East Sussex. The last confirmed record was in 1958, and the last possible sighting was in 1963.
Habitat and ecology	Univoltine, flying in June. Diurnal. Occurs in heathy clearings in mature woodland. The larval foodplant is unknown.
Status	Probably extinct.
Threats	The habitat was destroyed by ploughing and afforestation during the 1950s.

Conservation	The last known site is now a nature reserve, but the present environment would not be suitable for this species should it survive elsewhere.
Author	B. Skinner.

Scopula nigropunctata

	Sub-angled Wave	**VULNERABLE**
	Order **Lepidoptera**	Family **Geometridae**

Scopula nigropunctata (Hufnagel, 1767).

Identification	South (1961), 2:103-104, pl.44; Skinner (1984), p.20, pl.6:32.
Distribution	Now confined to a woodland complex in south-east Kent, where it was first reported in 1951, and a site in East Sussex, located in 1984. The latter appears to be the stronger of the two colonies.
Habitat and ecology	Univoltine, on the wing from June to mid-August. Nocturnal. Occurs in woodland rides and clearings. The larval foodplant is unknown.
Status	A transitory resident, formerly resident in one coastal site in south-east Kent during the last century. Occasional specimens have been recorded elsewhere in Sussex and Kent, probably as the result of migration.
Threats	Threatened by afforestation and the destruction of woodland rides.
Author	B. Skinner.

Eustroma reticulatum

	Netted Carpet	**VULNERABLE**
	Order **Lepidoptera**	Family **Geometridae**

Eustroma reticulatum (Denis & Schiffermueller, 1775).

Identification	South (1961), 2:167-168, pls 66 and 73; Heath (1983); Skinner (1984), p.35, pl.9:14.
Distribution	Occurring locally in several sites in Cumbria, and recently in at least one locality in North Wales.
Habitat and ecology	Univoltine, on the wing from early July to mid-August. Nocturnal. In the wetter parts of open or dense woodland, especially along the sides of streams, where the larvae feed on touch-me-not *Impatiens noli-tangere*.
Status	Satisfactory: the populations are fairly stable.
Threats	Threatened by changes of land usage such as afforestation, building or landscape development (Heath, 1983).

| Conservation | There are colonies at nine sites on National Trust properties in the Lake District. |
| Author | B. Skinner. |

Pareulype berberata

"Barberry Carpet Moth"　　　　　**ENDANGERED**

Order **Lepidoptera**　　　　　Family **Geometridae**

Pareulype berberata (Denis & Schiffermueller, 1775).

Identification	South (1961), 2:141-142, pl.57; Skinner (1984), pp. 36-37, pl.9:40.
Distribution	Currently known from only one site in west Suffolk. The population there is at present stable, despite recent disturbance due to road works.
Habitat and ecology	Bivoltine, on the wing from mid-May to mid-June, and again in August. In hedgerows, where the larvae feed on barberry *Berberis vulgaris*.
Status	Formerly found elsewhere in Suffolk and in one small site in Hampshire, the latter having been destroyed by uncontrolled stubble burning. Occasionally reported from Gloucestershire and West Sussex.
Threats	The foodplant is frequently destroyed by farmers as it is a host plant to the wheat rust fungus *Puccinia graminis*. It is also threatened by spray drift of pesticides and stubble burning.
Conservation	Listed on Schedule 5 of the Wildlife and Countryside Act 1981.
Author	B. Skinner.

Perizoma sagittata

Marsh Carpet　　　　　**VULNERABLE**

Order **Lepidoptera**　　　　　Family **Geometridae**

Perizoma sagittata (F., 1787).

Identification	South (1961), 2:146-147, pl.60, fig.5; Skinner (1984), p.41, pl.10:14.
Distribution	Very local in Cambridgeshire, Nottinghamshire and west Norfolk, where the populations at present are fairly stable.
Habitat and ecology	Univoltine, flying in late June and July. Nocturnal. Fenland, river-banks and marshy places. The larvae feed on common meadow rue *Thalictrum flavum*.

Status	The populations are subject to extreme fluctuation and during the 1940s it was considered to be extinct. The present status is satisfactory.
Threats	Threatened by river-dredging and the reclamation of marshes.
Conservation	Occurs on two nature reserves.
Author	B. Skinner.

Siona lineata

"Black-veined Moth" **ENDANGERED**

Order **Lepidoptera** Family **Geometridae**

Siona lineata (Scopoli, 1763), previously known as *Idaea lineata*.

Identification	South (1961), 2:318-319, pl.121; Skinner (1984), p.66, pl.17:31.
Distribution	Currently at three sites in south-east Kent.
Habitat and ecology	Univoltine, flying in June. Mainly diurnal. On downland and grassy embankments. The larval foodplant is unknown, but probably consists of grasses.
Status	Formerly found elsewhere in Kent and in one small site on the Surrey/Sussex border which was ploughed up. The species declined dramatically during the 1960s, but recovered during the 1970s, and is at present maintaining a satisfactory status.
Threats	The change of land usage. One of its best sites was commissioned for use as a rubbish-tip in the 1970s and was completely destroyed.
Conservation	Present on one nature reserve. Listed on Schedule 5 of the Wildlife and Countryside Act 1981.
Author	B. Skinner.

Clostera anachoreta

Scarce Chocolate-tip **ENDANGERED**

Order **Lepidoptera** Family **Notodontidae**

Clostera anachoreta (Denis & Schiffermueller, 1775).

Identification	South (1961), 1:96-97, pl.27; Heath & Emmet (1979), p.63, pl.4:8; Skinner (1984), p.74, pl.21:9.
Distribution	Currently known from one site in south-east Kent, where it was found to be resident in 1979. For map see Heath & Emmet (1979), p.63. The population is at present stable.

Habitat and ecology	Bivoltine, flying in May and August. Nocturnal. On shingle beaches and other coastal habitats. The larvae occur on sallows and willows (*Salix* species), aspen *Populus tremula*, and poplars (*Populus* species).
Status	A transitory immigrant formerly resident elsewhere in Kent between 1858 and 1912. Occasionally reported from Essex, Suffolk, Sussex and Dorset.
Threats	Possibly threatened by changes of land usage such as gravel extraction or building.
Author	B. Skinner.

Orgyia recens   Scarce Vapourer   **VULNERABLE**

Order **Lepidoptera**   Family **Lymantriidae**

Orgyia recens (Huebner, 1819).

Identification	South (1961), 1:114-116, pls 33 and 49; Heath & Emmet (1979), p.69, pl.4:14-15; Skinner (1984), p.75, pl.21:14-15.
Distribution	Very local in South Yorkshire, south Humberside and north-west Norfolk, with recent records from mid-Lincolnshire. For map see Heath & Emmet (1979), p.69.
Habitat and ecology	Partially bivoltine, on the wing in June and July, and again in late summer and early autumn. Hedgerows, fenland, sandhills, and open woodland. The larvae feed on a variety of deciduous trees and shrubs.
Status	It was formerly found locally over much of southern England and parts of South Wales. It has much declined, but is now regarded as widespread and stable in parts of south Humberside and South Yorkshire, and was recorded from mid-Lincolnshire in 1984 by P. Wilson (R.S. Key, pers. comm.).
Threats	Hedgerow sites arc threatened by the spray drift of insecticides.
Conservation	Recorded from a Norfolk property of the National Trust, and from a reserve of the Lincolnshire and South Humberside Trust for Nature Conservation.
Author	B. Skinner.

Pelosia obtusa

Small Dotted Footman   **ENDANGERED**

Order **Lepidoptera**   Family **Arctiidae**

Pelosia obtusa (Herrich-Schaeffer, 1852).

Identification
Heath & Emmet (1979), p.87, pl.5:11; Skinner (1984), p.78, pl.22:7.

Distribution
At present confined to one site in the Norfolk Broads. For map see Heath & Emmet (1979), p.87.

Habitat and ecology
Univoltine, flying from mid-July to early August. Nocturnal. Occurs in old and undisturbed reed-beds. The larval foodplant is unknown, but is probably algae attached to reed litter.

Status
Its present status appears to be stable. It is a retiring species possibly existing elsewhere in the Norfolk Broads.

Threats
Threatened by drainage and possibly by reed-cutting.

Conservation
The only known site is a nature reserve, but the above threats still apply.

Author
B. Skinner.

Coscinia cribraria

Speckled Footman   **VULNERABLE**

Order **Lepidoptera**   Family **Arctiidae**

Coscinia cribraria (L., 1758). The race which breeds in Britain is subspecies *bivittata* South, 1900.

Identification
South (1961), 2: 68-69, pls 32 and 36; Heath & Emmet (1979), p.96, pl.5:27; Skinner (1984), pp. 80-81, pl.22:25-26.

Distribution
Locally distributed in south-west Hampshire and south-east Dorset. For map see Heath & Emmet (1979), p.97.

Habitat and ecology
Univoltine, flying in July and August. Mature heathland. The larval foodplant is unknown.

Status
It underwent a temporary decline during the late 1950s and early 1960s, but has now recovered and is maintaining a satisfactory status.

Threats
Threatened by afforestation and heathland fires.

Author
B. Skinner.

Eugraphe subrosea

Rosy Marsh Moth

ENDANGERED

Order **Lepidoptera**

Family **Noctuidae**

Eugraphe subrosea (Stephens, 1829), formerly known as *Coenophila subrosea*.

Identification
South (1961), 1:142, pl.50; Heath & Emmet (1979), p.166, pl.9:8-9; Skinner (1984), p.90, pl.26:19-20.

Distribution
Currently known from only two sites in Ceredigion, Dyfed. For map see Heath & Emmet (1979), p.167.

Habitat and ecology
Univoltine, flying in July and August. Nocturnal. Acid bog and fenland, where the larvae feed on bog myrtle *Myrica gale*.

Status
The populations of both sites are stable. Formerly found in the fenlands of Cambridgeshire during the last century, but not recorded after 1850, by which time its habitats had been drained and destroyed.

Threats
Possibly threatened by fire.

Conservation
Both sites are nature reserves.

Author
B. Skinner.

Pachetra sagittigera

Feathered Ear

ENDANGERED +

Order **Lepidoptera**

Family **Noctuidae**

Pachetra sagittigera (Hufnagel, 1766). The British race is subspecies *britannica* Turner, 1933.

Identification
South (1961), 1:172-173, pl.63; Heath & Emmet (1979), p.210, pl.11:2829; Skinner (1984), p.96, pl.29:5.

Distribution
A very local species occurring on the North Downs of Surrey and Kent, but with the exception of the unconfirmed report of a specimen in Surrey in 1983, it has not been seen since 1963. For map see Heath & Emmet (1979), p.211.

Habitat and ecology
Univoltine, flying in May and June. Nocturnal. On chalk downland, where the larvae feed on a variety of grasses.

Status
Possibly extinct. Formerly a local species, but not uncommon where found. Apart from the North Downs it has in the past been noted in Wiltshire, Buckinghamshire and Hampshire. The cause of its decline is not known.

Conservation
One of its original sites is a nature reserve.

Author
B. Skinner.

101

Hadena irregularis	Viper's Bugloss	ENDANGERED
	Order **Lepidoptera**	Family **Noctuidae**

Hadena irregularis (Hufnagel, 1766), formerly known as *Anepia irregularis*.

Identification South (1961), 1:186-187, pl.68; Heath & Emmet (1979), p.231, pl.12:16; Skinner (1984), pp. 99-100, pl.29:38.

Distribution Currently known from single sites in south-west Norfolk and west Suffolk. For map see Heath and Emmet (1979), p.230.

Habitat and ecology Univoltine, flying in June and July. Nocturnal. In the Breckland, where the larvae feed on Spanish catchfly *Silene otites*.

Status Formerly found in numerous sites in the Breckland of Norfolk, Suffolk and Cambridgeshire.

Threats Threatened by changes in land usage such as building and farming. The foodplant is itself a Rare species (Perring & Farrell, 1983) requiring soil disturbance to allow it to flourish.

Author B. Skinner.

Cucullia gnaphalii	Cudweed Shark or The Cudweed	ENDANGERED
	Order **Lepidoptera**	Family **Noctuidae**

Cucullia gnaphalii (Huebner, 1813). The race in Britain is subspecies *occidentalis* Boursin, 1945.

Identification South (1961), 1:214-215, pl.76; Heath & Emmet (1983), p.46, pl.1:9; Skinner (1984), p.108: pl.32:8.

Distribution Not recorded recently outside a few woodland sites in south-east Kent and East Sussex. For map see Heath & Emmet (1983), p.47.

Habitat and ecology Univoltine, flying in June and July. Nocturnal. In woodland rides and clearings, when the larvae feed on golden-rod *Solidago virgaurea*.

Status Formerly found locally in Surrey, Hampshire, and elsewhere in Kent and Sussex. The cause of decline is not known.

Author B. Skinner.

Acronicta strigosa

Marsh Dagger   **ENDANGERED** +

Order **Lepidoptera**   Family **Noctuidae**

Acronicta strigosa (Denis & Schiffermueller, 1775), formerly known as *Apatele strigosa*.

Identification
South (1961), 1:266-267, pl.89; Heath & Emmet (1983), p.136, pl.5:10; Skinner (1984), p.120, pl.35:34.

Distribution
A local species occurring in Cambridgeshire, but not recorded since 1933. For map see Heath & Emmet (1983), p.137.

Habitat and ecology
Univoltine, flying in late June and July. Nocturnal. In mature hedgerows, the edges of fenland, and marshy commonland. The larvae feed mainly on hawthorn (*Crataegus* species).

Status
Possibly extinct. Formerly an uncommon species and easily overlooked; also recorded casually from Gloucestershire, Hereford & Worcester, and Norfolk. The cause of decline is not known.

Author
B. Skinner.

Photedes morrisii morrisii

Morris's Wainscot   **VULNERABLE**

Order **Lepidoptera**   Family **Noctuidae**

Photedes morrisii (Dale, 1837), formerly known as *Arenostola morrisii*. The nominate subspecies is one of two races in Britain (see below).

Identification
South (1961), 1:335, pl.118; Heath & Emmet (1983), p.217, pl.7:46; Skinner (1984), p.131, pl.38:29.

Distribution
Very local in Dorset and east Devon. The populations are small, but at present stable. For map see Heath & Emmet (1983), p.217.

Habitat and ecology
Univoltine, on the wing from late June to mid-July. Nocturnal. On coastal undercliffs, where the larvae feed on tall fescue *Festuca arundinacea*.

Status
The present status is satisfactory.

Threats
Threatened by cliff erosion and tourism.

Author
B. Skinner.

Photedes morrisii bondii

Bond's Wainscot   **ENDANGERED**

Order **Lepidoptera**   Family **Noctuidae**

Photedes morrisii (Dale, 1837). Subspecies (or aberration) *bondii* Knaggs, 1861 is one of two races in Britain (see above).

Identification	South (1961), 1:335; Heath & Emmet (1983), p.217, pl.7:47; Skinner (1984), p.131, pl.38:30.
Distribution	Confined to one small site in south-east Kent.
Habitat and ecology	Univoltine, flying in July. Nocturnal. On the grassy slopes of coastal cliffs, where the larvae feed on tall fescue *Festuca arundinacea*.
Status	It has always been confined to the one site, where it appears to be seriously declining.
Threats	Threatened by urban development.
Author	B. Skinner.

Luperina nickerlii gueneei

Sandhill Rustic   **VULNERABLE**

Order **Lepidoptera**   Family **Noctuidae**

Luperina nickerlii (Freyer, 1845). Subspecies *gueneei* Doubleday, 1864 is one of four races in Britain (see below).

Identification	South (1961), 1:292-293, pl.98; Heath & Emmet (1983), p.228, pl.8:12; Skinner (1984), p.133, pl.38:43.
Distribution	Occurs in several localities in North Wales, and one in Lancashire. For map see Heath & Emmet (1983), p.230.
Habitat and ecology	Univoltine, flying in August. Nocturnal. On coastal sandhills, where the larvae occur in the roots of sand couch-grass *Elymus farctus*.
Status	The present status is satisfactory.
Threats	Possibly threatened by tourism.
Conservation	Occurs in one nature reserve.
Author	B. Skinner.

Luperina nickerlii leechi	Sandhill Rustic	**ENDANGERED**
	Order **Lepidoptera**	Family **Noctuidae**

Luperina nickerlii (Freyer, 1845). Subspecies *leechi* Goater, 1976 is one of four races in Britain (see above).

Identification Heath & Emmet (1983), p.228, pl.8:3-4; Skinner (1984), p.133, pl.38:44.

Distribution Confined to a small site in south-west Cornwall, where it was first noted in 1974.

Habitat and ecology Univoltine, flying in August. Nocturnal. On sand-shingle beaches where the larvae occur in the roots of sand couch-grass *Elymus farctus*.

Status The population is at present stable, although part of the habitat was ravaged by sea gales in the winter of 1979/80.

Threats Threatened by sea gales.

Author B. Skinner.

Gortyna borelii	Fisher's Estuarine Moth	**VULNERABLE**
	Order **Lepidoptera**	Family **Noctuidae**

Gortyna borelii Pierret, 1837. The race in Britain is subspecies *lunata* Freyer, 1839.

Identification Heath & Emmet (1983), p.247, pl.8:33; Skinner (1984), p.135, pl.39:3.

Distribution Confined to one area in north-east Essex. For map see Heath & Emmet (1983), p. 246.

Habitat and ecology Univoltine, on the wing in September and October. Nocturnal. In marshy fields and waste ground. The larvae occur in the roots of sulphur-weed *Peucedanum officinale*.

Status First noted in Britain in 1968; its present status is satisfactory.

Threats Threatened by changes in land usage, such as farming. The foodplant is itself a Rare species (Perring & Farrell, 1983).

Conservation Present on one nature reserve.

Author B. Skinner.

Sedina buettneri

Blair's Wainscot   **ENDANGERED +**

Order **Lepidoptera**   Family **Noctuidae**

Sedina buettneri (Hering, 1858).

Identification	South (1961), 1:331-333, pl.121; Heath & Emmet (1983), p.262, pl.9:21; Skinner (1984), p.138, pl.39:27.
Distribution	Resident in one site on the Isle of Wight from 1945 to 1952. A single specimen was recorded from East Sussex in 1966.
Habitat and ecology	Univoltine, on the wing in October. Nocturnal. On coastal marshland, where the larvae occur in the stems of lesser pond-sedge *Carex acutiformis*.
Status	Probably extinct.
Threats	The only site was destroyed by draining and burning.
Author	B. Skinner.

Acosmetia caliginosa

"Reddish Buff Moth"   **ENDANGERED**

Order **Lepidoptera**   Family **Noctuidae**

Acosmetia caliginosa (Huebner, 1813).

Identification	South (1961), 1:298-299, pl.100; Heath & Emmet (1983), p.286, pl.9:49-50; Skinner (1984), p.141, pl.40:17-18.
Distribution	Occurring in a few sites in the northern half of the Isle of Wight. For map see Heath & Emmet (1983), p.287.
Habitat and ecology	Univoltine, on the wing from late May to early July. Nocturnal. In woodland rides and clearings. The larvae feed on saw-wort *Serratula tinctoria*.
Status	Its present status is probably fairly stable. Formerly found in the New Forest, Hampshire, during the last century, and from one site in south-east Hampshire where it was last recorded in 1961.
Threats	Threatened by afforestation.
Conservation	Listed on Schedule 5 of the Wildlife and Countryside Act 1981.
Author	B. Skinner.

Deltote bankiana	Silver Barred	**VULNERABLE**
	Order **Lepidoptera**	Family **Noctuidae**

Deltote bankiana (F., 1775), formerly known as *Eustrotia bankiana.*

Identification
South (1961), 1:350-351, pl.129; Heath & Emmet (1983), p.309, pl.10:15; Skinner (1984), p.145, pl.40:41.

Distribution
Resident in two sites in Cambridgeshire, and one in south-east Kent. For map see Heath & Emmet (1983), p.310.

Habitat and ecology
Univoltine, on the wing in June and July. Nocturnal. In marshes and fenland, where the larvae feed on fenland grasses.

Status
Long established in Cambridgeshire, where its status is satisfactory. Recently found in Kent where it was probably established by an immigrant parent. Other suspected immigrants are reported occasionally elsewhere in southern England.

Threats
The Kent site is threatened by marshland reclamation.

Conservation
Both Cambridgeshire sites are nature reserves.

Author
B. Skinner.

Emmelia trabealis	Spotted Sulphur	**ENDANGERED** +
	Order **Lepidoptera**	Family **Noctuidae**

Emmelia trabealis (Scopoli, 1763).

Identification
South (1961), 1:345-346, pl.126; Heath & Emmet (1983), p.311, pl.10:16; Skinner (1984), p.145, pl. 40:42.

Distribution
Its last known locality, an old asparagus field in west Suffolk, was ploughed up in 1960 and the species has not been noted here or elsewhere since. For map see Heath & Emmet (1983), p.310.

Habitat and ecology
Univoltine, on the wing from mid-June to early July. Diurnal. On waste ground, fallow fields and roadside verges. The larvae feed on bindweed *Convolvulus arvensis.*

Status
Possibly extinct. Formerly widespread, but local, in the Breckland district of East Anglia, but by the early 1950s it had declined to a few sites, and by the mid 1950s to one.

Threats
The cutting and spraying of roadside verges, and changes of land usage such as farming and afforestation.

Author
B. Skinner.

Tyta luctuosa   The Four-spotted   **VULNERABLE**

Order **Lepidoptera**   Family **Noctuidae**

Tyta luctuosa (Denis & Schiffermueller, 1775), formerly known as *Acontia luctuosa*.

Identification
South (1961), 1:380-381, pls 111 and 142; Heath & Emmet (1983), p.368, pl.12:16-18; Skinner (1984), p.154, pl.41:34.

Distribution
Locally resident in Dorset, Suffolk, Hertfordshire, Kent, Essex and Nottinghamshire; and casually reported from Hampshire, Buckinghamshire, Surrey, and Hereford & Worcester. For map see Heath & Emmet (1983), p.369.

Habitat and ecology
Mainly univoltine, flying in June and July. Diurnal and nocturnal. On chalk downland, flowery embankments, breckland, etc. The larvae feed on bindweed *Convolvulus arvensis*.

Status
A much decreased species, formerly widespread and locally common over the southern half of England.

Threats
Threatened by reclamation of waste ground, etc.

Conservation
There are 1950s records from two National Trust properties in Surrey.

Author
B. Skinner.

Colobochyla salicalis   Lesser Belle   **ENDANGERED**

Order **Lepidoptera**   Family **Noctuidae**

Colobochyla salicalis (Denis & Schiffermueller, 1775).

Identification
South (1961), 1:383-384, pls 42 and 148; Heath & Emmet (1983), p.377, pl.12:19; Skinner (1984), p.155, pl.41:36.

Distribution
Confined to a single woodland complex in south-east Kent. For map see Heath & Emmet (1983), p.376.

Habitat and ecology
Univoltine, flying in June and July. Nocturnal. In woodland, where the larvae feed on aspen *Populus tremula*.

Status
Evidently declining. Its present site, discovered in 1932, constitutes the only known locality this century, although evidence suggests that this species may have been at one time resident in north Kent and Surrey.

Threats
Threatened by re-afforestation and destruction of the foodplant, although it temporarily thrives in areas of felled woodland containing young aspen growth.

Author
B. Skinner.

COLEOPTERA

The Beetles

The Coleoptera are one of the largest orders, numbering some 3900 species in Britain, divided among 97 families. They are also one of the better-studied groups, following only the Lepidoptera in popularity. The group is very diverse, with a number of well-defined taxonomic subdivisions and habitat groupings encouraging the enthusiast to specialise. The majority of species require the assistance of at least a hand lens for identification, and in many cases it is necessary to examine specimens more closely under a microscope. Some groups require expert assistance.

Although most beetle groups are relatively well-recorded they are not adequately covered in the more popular literature, and it was thought worth considering them in some detail in the present work. Consequently, half the species accounts included here concern the Coleoptera: the Red Data Book lists 142 Endangered, 84 Vulnerable and 266 Rare species. At least ten of the Endangered species are believed to be extinct, and a further 54 species are listed in the Appendix as having become extinct before 1900. Four of the six Category 5 (Endemic) species are also listed in one of the threatened categories. One species, the "Rainbow Leaf Beetle" *Chrysolina cerealis*, is on Schedule 5 of the Wildlife and Countryside Act 1981. 21 of the Rare species are designated as Category 3* (recently discovered or recognised), including ten aquatic species. Altogether 546 species are listed, amounting to 14% of the British beetle fauna.

Beetles occur in all habitats, but of the Endangered and Vulnerable species the most important ones are woodlands (40%), coastal situations (21%), wetlands (19%) and grasslands (11%). Ancient woodlands are perhaps the most important and most vulnerable single habitat for RDB species in Britain. About 90 Endangered and Vulnerable beetles are confined to this habitat, representing a fifth of species of all orders described in these accounts. Semi-natural woodlands are continually being clear-felled and lost to farmland or coniferous plantation. Even when maintained as broadleaved woodland they are frequently replaced by large stands of uniform age and species structure. Dead wood is a very valuable commodity for many beetles and is much threatened by the 'tidying-up' of forests and the removal of over-mature trees and dead and fallen timber. Many species are extremely localised: a glance through these pages will reveal a number known only from such famous sites as the New Forest and Windsor Forest and Great Park, where ancient oaks with dead limbs and rotten centres provide a classic habitat. Species dependent on old pines are now confined to a few remnants of the ancient Caledonian pine forest in the Scottish Highlands. The mountain tops of that region provide another very special habitat, with three beetle species occurring only on very few peaks. The other habitats have been discussed under the preceding orders.

Though somewhat out of date, the only identification guide this century to attempt to cover all British species is Joy's two-volume *A practical handbook of British beetles* (1932, reprinted 1976). A number of families are covered by *Handbooks* in the RESL's series, though half of these are out of print. *Beetles of the British Isles*

(Linssen, 1961) provides a useful introduction, now also out of print. *A key to the families of British Coleoptera (and Strepsiptera)* was published recently in the Field Studies Council's AIDGAP series (Unwin, 1984). The very cheap but well-illustrated *A field guide in colour to beetles* (Harde, 1984, edited by Hammond) is a worthwhile purchase and covers many RDB species. The AES has published *A coleopterist's handbook* (Walsh & Dibb, 1974).

Fourteen BRC recording schemes cover several of the major beetle groups, some of them issuing regular newsletters. Revised distribution maps have appeared for the Elmidae (Holland, 1980). Preliminary atlases have been produced for the Carabidae (Luff, 1982) and are appearing for the aquatic species (Foster, 1981, 1983, 1984, 1985). Coleopterists can subscribe to *The Coleopterist's Newsletter*, and aquatic specialists can join the Balfour-Browne Club.

Omophron limbatum

A ground beetle   **ENDANGERED**

Order **Coleoptera**   Family **Carabidae**

Omophron limbatum (F., 1777).

Identification   Farrow & Lewis (1971); Lindroth (1974), p.18, figs 9 and 10; Harde (1984), fig. 89:9.

Distribution   Only known from flooded gravel pits at Rye Harbour, East Sussex, and between Dungeness and Lydd, Kent. The population has been locally substantial in the past, but now appears to be much reduced. It could not be found at either site in 1982, though a small colony was located at Rye Harbour in 1983.

Habitat and ecology   Adults on and in sand bordering flooded gravel pits.

Status   Possibly indigenous in Britain in the 19th century, apparently now re-established from Europe.

Threats   Infilling of gravel pits or construction of yacht moorings at the edge of lakes. Also the development of caravan sites around the gravel pits. The Lydd site has now been landscaped, and *O. limbatum* is no longer present.

Author   M.L. Luff, using additional information from Allen (1971a), E. Philp (1973 and pers. comm.), and P. Hodge (pers. comm.).

Carabus intricatus

Blue Ground Beetle   **ENDANGERED**

Order **Coleoptera**   Family **Carabidae**

Carabus intricatus L., 1761.

Identification   Lindroth (1974), p.22; Harde (1984), fig.83:6.

Distribution   Only recently recorded from Haldon Moor, Teignmouth, south Devon (1959), and Boconnoc Park, Lostwithiel, Cornwall (1972). Population presumably very small as the adult is the largest and one of the most conspicuous of British *Carabus* species.

Habitat and ecology   In stumps and under the bark of old hardwood timber where a thick humus layer is present.

Status   A relict population in extreme south-west Britain.

Threats   The removal of old and dead hardwood timber.

Author   M.L. Luff.

Dyschirius obscurus

A ground beetle   **ENDANGERED**

Order **Coleoptera**   Family **Carabidae**

Dyschirius obscurus (Gyllenhal, 1827).

Identification	Lindroth (1974), p.36; Shephard (1970).
Distribution	Doubtful old records from Norfolk and Lancashire. Recently found at Rye Harbour, East Sussex (1969), Aylesford (1963), between Dungeness and Lydd, Kent (1970 to date), and Sheringham, Norfolk (1981). Population apparently substantial where it occurs. In 1982 it was present only in small numbers at the Lydd locality, and in good numbers at Aylesford.
Habitat and ecology	In bare sand bordering standing water. Often found in company with *Omophron limbatum* (q.v.).
Status	Possibly a recent introduction or reintroduction from Europe into south-east England.
Threats	As for *Omophron limbatum*.
Author	M.L. Luff, using additional information from E.G. Philp (1973 and pers. comm.) and G. Wildridge (pers. comm.).

Trechus rivularis

A ground beetle   **ENDANGERED**

Order **Coleoptera**   Family **Carabidae**

Trechus (*Trechus*) *rivularis* (Gyllenhal, 1810).

Identification	Lindroth (1974), p.45, fig.29e.
Distribution	Originally restricted to Wicken Fen and Whittlesey Mere, Cambridgeshire. Recently also recorded from Lopham Fen, east Norfolk, and Askham Bog, North Yorkshire (1970s).
Habitat and ecology	In litter in fens.
Status	A fenland relict population.
Threats	Fen drainage.
Conservation	Wicken Fen is owned by the National Trust, Askham Bog is a reserve of the Yorkshire Wildlife Trust, and the Lopham Fen site is a reserve managed by the Suffolk Trust for Nature Conservation.
Author	M.L. Luff, using additional information from Omer-Cooper *et al* (1928) and R.C. Welch (pers. comm.).

Trechus subnotatus

A ground beetle **ENDANGERED**

Order **Coleoptera** Family **Carabidae**

Trechus (*Trechus*) *subnotatus* Dejean, 1831.

Identification Lindroth (1974), p.45.

Distribution South Devon and the Huddersfield area, West Yorkshire. Populations small in all localities.

Habitat and ecology In vegetable matter, soil and rubble. Mainly coastal.

Status Introduced, probably on more than one occasion; apparently established but not spreading.

Threats The Devon site is threatened by the dumping of refuse.

Author M.L. Luff, using additional information from P. Hodge and M. Denton (pers. comms).

Bembidion humerale

A ground beetle **ENDANGERED**

Order **Coleoptera** Family **Carabidae**

Bembidion (*Bembidion*) *humerale* Sturm, 1825.

Identification Crossley & Norris (1976).

Distribution Only known from Thorne and Crowle Moors, South Yorkshire/Humberside. The population is possibly substantial as the species is widespread and locally abundant at the site.

Habitat and ecology Adults are found on peat in fens. It is most abundant where the peat is moist and largely bare of vegetation, such as damp hollows left after cutting operations.

Status Probably a relict population which has increased in numbers. There is a 1983 record by P.S. Kendall from Hatfield Moor, about 10km south of Thorne Moor (R.S. Key, pers. comm.).

Threats Drainage of the site. Also the destruction of habitat by the commercial extraction of peat.

Conservation Part of 'Thorne and Crowle Waste' is now an NNR, and the remainder of it is an SSSI. The reserve area, however, is mostly densely vegetated and is not the most suitable habitat for the species.

Author M.L. Luff, using additional information from R. Crossley (pers. comm.).

Bembidion virens

A ground beetle

ENDANGERED

Order **Coleoptera**

Family **Carabidae**

Bembidion (Plataphus) virens Gyllenhal, 1827.

Identification	Lindroth (1974), p.61, fig.35e.
Distribution	Almost restricted to the shore of Loch Maree, Ross & Cromarty (Highland), where it was found as recently as 1976. There is an old record (Doncaster Museum) from Mallaig, Lochaber. Recently also found at Strath Oykel in Sutherland (Owen, 1984).
Habitat and ecology	In shingle by lakes and estuaries.
Status	A relict population.
Threats	Possible disturbance such as the extraction of shingle for building material.
Author	M.L. Luff.

Pterostichus aterrimus

A ground beetle

ENDANGERED

Order **Coleoptera**

Family **Carabidae**

Pterostichus (Omaseus) aterrimus (Herbst, 1784).

Identification	Lindroth (1974), p.71, fig.46b.
Distribution	Originally restricted to the fens of East Anglia but not recorded there since 1910. Found from 1969 to 1973 in a formerly marshy area south of Denny Wood in the New Forest, Hampshire. Population probably small; the species has not been found since 1973.
Habitat and ecology	In wet bogs and fens at the edge of water on muddy or peaty soils.
Status	A relict fen population, recently spread or introduced to the New Forest.
Threats	Drainage of fens.
Conservation	The 1969 site has been drained, but adjacent areas are protected at the moment.
Author	M.L. Luff, using additional information from D. Appleton (1970 and pers. comm.).

Agonum sahlbergi

A ground beetle **ENDANGERED +**

Order **Coleoptera** Family **Carabidae**

Agonum sahlbergi (Chaudoir, 1850).

Identification Lindroth (1974), p.83. Dark specimens of *A. muelleri* Herbst may be misidentified as *A. sahlbergi*.

Distribution Only known from "R. Clyde below Glasgow". No British records since 1914; presumed now extinct.

Status A former glacial relict, or introduction.

Author M.L. Luff, using additional information from Lindroth (1960).

Amara fusca

A ground beetle **VULNERABLE**

Order **Coleoptera** Family **Carabidae**

Amara fusca Dejean, 1828.

Identification Lindroth (1974), p.93.

Distribution Restricted to a few localities, mainly in the extreme south-east of England. The most recent record is from Swanley, Kent (1942). Population small, at most.

Habitat and ecology On dry sand or gravel with sparse vegetation.

Status At the north-western limit of its range; possibly extinct in Britain.

Threats Urbanisation and habitat disturbance by man.

Author M.L. Luff.

Harpalus cupreus

A ground beetle **ENDANGERED**

Order **Coleoptera** Family **Carabidae**

Harpalus (Harpalus) cupreus Dejean, 1829.

Identification Lindroth (1974), p.104.

Distribution Known in Britain only from a field at Sandown, Isle of Wight. The latest recorded capture was in 1914. The population is probably small as it is a conspicuous species.

Habitat and ecology Found in agricultural situations on dry soils.

Status	Probably introduced in the late 19th century. Possibly now extinct.
Author	M.L. Luff.

Harpalus honestus

A ground beetle	ENDANGERED +
Order **Coleoptera**	Family **Carabidae**

Harpalus (Harpalus) honestus (Duftschmid, 1812).

Identification	Allen (1964c); Lindroth (1974), p.104, fig.73d.
Distribution	On chalk hills at Streatley, Berkshire (1905); not recorded since. Also old records (ca.1795) from Charlton, north Kent. Possibly now extinct, as it is a conspicuous species.
Habitat and ecology	Found in chalk pits.
Status	Presumed extinct.
Author	M.L. Luff.

Scybalicus oblongiusculus

A ground beetle	ENDANGERED +
Order **Coleoptera**	Family **Carabidae**

Scybalicus oblongiusculus (Dejean, 1829).

Identification	Lindroth (1974), p.109, fig.77d.
Distribution	Southern England, mainly Dorset: only Weymouth and Ringstead since 1900, but not found since 1926.
Habitat and ecology	In chalk grassland, usually under stones.
Status	A former introduction, now presumed extinct.
Author	M.L. Luff.

Acupalpus elegans

A ground beetle	ENDANGERED
Order **Coleoptera**	Family **Carabidae**

Acupalpus elegans (Dejean, 1829).

Identification	Lindroth (1974), p.116, figs 82c and 84a.
Distribution	Kent, Essex, Hampshire and Yorkshire. The only recent records are from Stoke Junction, north Kent, and Barton Cliffs, south Hampshire. Population presumed small.

Habitat and ecology	In coastal saltmarshes and wet flushes.
Status	Isolated relict populations.
Threats	The destruction of habitat.
Author	M.L. Luff, using additional information from L.S. Whicher and A.B. Drane (pers. comms).

Panagaeus cruxmajor

A ground beetle **VULNERABLE**

Order **Coleoptera** Family **Carabidae**

Panagaeus cruxmajor (L., 1758).

Identification	Lindroth (1974), p.120, figs. 88a and 88b; Harde (1984), fig.107:5.
Distribution	Formerly as far north as Yorkshire in suitable habitats. Now restricted to Wicken Fen, although it has not been found there for some years.
Habitat and ecology	At the edge of standing water, with a soft soil and rich vegetation.
Status	Relict.
Threats	Fen drainage.
Conservation	Wicken Fen is a property of the National Trust.
Author	M.L. Luff.

Chlaenius nitidulus

A ground beetle **ENDANGERED**

Order **Coleoptera** Family **Carabidae**

Chlaenius nitidulus (Schrank, 1781).

Identification	Lindroth (1974), p.122, fig.89d; Harde (1984), fig.105:9.
Distribution	Restricted to a few sites on the coast in Dorset (Charmouth), the Isle of Wight and Sussex. Not recorded since 1930. The population is very small, if indeed it is not extinct.
Habitat and ecology	In vegetation in damp places on the coast.
Status	At the northern limit of its distribution, possibly now extinct in Britain.
Author	M.L. Luff.

Chlaenius tristis

A ground beetle   **ENDANGERED**

Order **Coleoptera**   Family **Carabidae**

Chlaenius tristis (Schaller, 1783).

Identification   Lindroth (1974), p.121, fig.89b.

Distribution   There are old records from the Fens, but it was believed extinct in Britain until a single specimen was recorded from Cors Geirch, Lleyn Peninsula, Gwynedd (1970s). The population is probably small, as only one specimen was found in an extensive survey.

Habitat and ecology   In bogs and fens.

Status   An isolated relict population.

Threats   The drainage of wetland.

Conservation   Cors Geirch is an NNR.

Author   M.L. Luff, using additional information from A. Warne (pers. comm.).

Callistus lunatus

A ground beetle   **ENDANGERED**

Order **Coleoptera**   Family **Carabidae**

Callistus lunatus (F., 1775).

Identification   Lindroth (1974), p.122; Harde (1984), fig.107:1.

Distribution   Found locally on chalk downland in Kent (Wye, Shoreham, Otford Downs), Surrey (Mickleham, Coulsdon, Chipstead, Reigate) and Berkshire (Streatley). It has declined since the 1930s and the most recent record is Shoreham, west Kent (1953), despite extensive subsequent searching for the species. A 'probable' individual was seen at Juniper Bottom, Box Hill, in 1983. For map see Luff (1982), map 91. Population small, at most.

Habitat and ecology   On chalk grassland and in chalk pits.

Status   At the northern limit of its range, possibly now extinct in Britain.

Threats   Reduction in open chalk grassland; possibly human interference.

Conservation   Juniper Bottom is a property of the National Trust.

Author   M.L. Luff, using additional information from A.A. Allen and K.N.A. Alexander (pers. comms).

Lebia cruxminor

A ground beetle   **ENDANGERED**

Order **Coleoptera**   Family **Carabidae**

Lebia cruxminor (L., 1758).

Identification	Lindroth (1974), p.126.
Distribution	Formerly very rare but widespread; the only post-1970 records are from Bodmin Moor, Cornwall, and Ditchling Common, East Sussex (1984). Usually only single specimens.
Habitat and ecology	In damp meadows and woodland: the larva is ectoparasitic, probably on the leaf beetle *Galeruca tanaceti* L.
Status	Relict, once more widespread.
Threats	A reduction in the range or abundance of the leaf beetle host, though this feeds on a wide variety of plants.
Author	M.L. Luff.

Dromius longiceps

A ground beetle   **VULNERABLE**

Order **Coleoptera**   Family **Carabidae**

Dromius longiceps Dejean, 1826.

Identification	Lindroth (1974), p.128, fig.94a.
Distribution	Restricted to fens and coastal localities in eastern England: Shirebrook, Sheffield, South Yorkshire; Blacktoft Sands, North Ferriby, Swinefleet and Brough, Humberside; Swaby, Lincolnshire; Tuddenham, Suffolk; Wicken Fen, Cambridgeshire; and Wheatfen and Hickling Broads, Norfolk. Isolated small populations.
Habitat and ecology	In fens with reed *Phragmites*. The larvae have been found in reed stems.
Status	A relict fenland species.
Threats	Drainage of fens. The Shirebrook site is threatened with damage from road construction.
Conservation	Hickling Broad is an NNR; Wicken Fen is owned by the National Trust; Blacktoft Sands is a reserve of the RSPB.
Author	M.L. Luff, with additional information from Sheffield City Museum.

Dromius sigma	A ground beetle	**VULNERABLE**
	Order **Coleoptera**	Family **Carabidae**

Dromius sigma (Rossi, 1790).

Identification	Lindroth (1972); Lindroth (1974), p.130, fig.95a.
Distribution	Recently only in Yorkshire: Askham Bog, Inkle Moor and Elland gravel pits. Formerly also from the Norfolk Broads and Thames Marshes.
Habitat and ecology	In shaded situations in fens and marshes.
Status	Probably a relict.
Threats	Drainage of sites. Inkle Moor is threatened by colliery tipping.
Conservation	Askham Bog is a reserve of the Yorkshire Wildlife Trust.
Author	M.L. Luff, using additional information from P. Hodge, R.S. Key and M. Denton (pers. comms).

Polystichus connexus	A ground beetle	**VULNERABLE**
	Order **Coleoptera**	Family **Carabidae**

Polystichus connexus (Fourcroy, 1785).

Identification	Lindroth (1974), p.133, fig.96c.
Distribution	Mostly coastal in extreme south and south-east England. All post-1970 records are from the coasts of Kent, Essex and Sussex. Populations are probably very localised and small.
Habitat and ecology	On the coast and on river banks, in cracks in bare soil and at the base of cliffs.
Status	At the northern limit of its range and apparently declining in abundance.
Threats	Human disturbance to coastal sites.
Author	M.L. Luff.

Drypta dentata

A ground beetle

ENDANGERED

Order **Coleoptera**

Family **Carabidae**

Drypta dentata (Rossi, 1790).

Identification

Lindroth (1974), p.133.

Distribution

Restricted to the extreme south coast of England from Dorset to Kent. The only recent locality is Brownsea Island, Poole Harbour, 1977. Population small.

Habitat and ecology

On shady coastal silt or sand.

Status

Relict, and may be extinct.

Threats

Coastal development and public usage.

Conservation

Brownsea Island is a property of the National Trust.

Author

M.L. Luff, using additional information from M. Speight (pers. comm.).

Haliplus furcatus

A water beetle

ENDANGERED

Order **Coleoptera**

Family **Haliplidae**

Haliplus furcatus Seidlitz, 1887.

Identification

Balfour-Browne (1940), pp.144-146; Balfour-Browne (1953), p.8, figs 11h and 14b.

Distribution

Exclusively from Somerset in brick pits and drains near Burnham-on-Sea and Bridgwater. It has been "common" in the Bridgwater locality. For map see Foster (1981), p.5.

Habitat and ecology

Stagnant open fresh water on low ground. Holmen (1981) indicates an association with small, temporary pools in Denmark.

Status

The first record was in 1916 and the last in 1939. Publicity in *Balfour-Browne Club Newsletter* No.9 (1978) failed to elicit further records. Extensive collecting at Bridgwater in 1978 and 1979 by P.J. Hodge, J.A. Owen and G.N. Foster was unsuccessful; various surveys of the Levels in 1979-81 were also unsuccessful.

Threats

There are no records for the Somerset Levels proper so it would appear that the most likely explanation for its loss lies in encroachment of vegetation, mainly reed *Phragmites australis*, over the man-made, open habitats once available.

Author

G.N. Foster.

Laccophilus obsoletus

A water beetle   **VULNERABLE**

Order **Coleoptera**   Family **Dytiscidae**

Laccophilus obsoletus Westhoff, 1881, formerly known as *L. variegatus* (Germar, 1817).

Identification
Balfour-Browne (1940), pp.181-182; Balfour-Browne (1953), p.19.

Distribution
In south-east England and the Humber valley, with modern records only for the Lewes Levels, East Sussex. Small isolated populations. For map see Foster (1981), p.11.

Habitat and ecology
Freshwater and weakly saline drains in lowland fens, not exclusive to grazing fen.

Status
There are old records for south-east Yorkshire, east Kent, East and West Sussex and south Hampshire. There are few substantiated modern records. The beetle was rediscovered on Thorne Waste (South Yorkshire) in the 1950s. There is a single record from Canterbury (Kent) in 1958, and a single record for the Pevensey Levels (East Sussex) in 1972. The only site with a number of modern records is the northern end of the Lewes Levels.

Threats
Change from mixed farming to arable farming. Construction of the Lewes bypass appeared to improve the status of this species in cleared dykes for a while, and indicates the importance of dyke management in sustaining this beetle.

Conservation
One of the older sites, Thorne Waste, is an NNR, and another old site, Pevensey Levels, is partly an SSSI. The northern end of the Lewes Levels is not at present notified as an SSSI.

Author
G.N. Foster, using additional information from Bunting (1955), Hodge (1978), and J.H. Flint and J.A. Owen (pers. comms).

Bidessus unistriatus

A water beetle   **ENDANGERED**

Order **Coleoptera**   Family **Dytiscidae**

Bidessus unistriatus (Schrank, 1781).

Identification
Balfour-Browne (1940), pp.189-191; Balfour-Browne (1953), p.13, fig. 20c; Harde (1984), fig. 111:5.

Distribution
Dorset, south Hampshire, Greater London, Cambridgeshire, Norfolk, east Suffolk and East Sussex. For map see Foster (1981), p.15. Rarely classed as "common".

Habitat and ecology
Fen conditions, including slightly brackish water, in drains, man-made ponds, duneslack ponds, etc.

Status	Apart from Catfield Fen, east Norfolk, where specimens were found in 1977 and 1978, the last known site was at Camber in 1947, other records being for the 19th century and the early 20th century.
Threats	The decline in the major centre in the Norfolk Broads is probably due to a change in the method of managing dykes and in a loss of grazing fen with the expansion of arable farming. Losses from other sites may be due to disturbance and pollution, e.g. the development of Camber as a holiday centre (Foster, 1972).
Conservation	Catfield Fen is part of an NCR Grade 1* SSSI (Ratcliffe, 1977), and the owner has been told of the presence of rare water beetles on the site.
Author	G.N. Foster, using additional information from Foster (1982) and F. Balfour-Browne's card index in the Royal Scottish Museum.

Hydroporus rufifrons

A water beetle   **VULNERABLE**

Order **Coleoptera**   Family **Dytiscidae**

Hydroporus rufifrons (Mueller, 1776).

Identification	Balfour-Browne (1940), pp.315-319; Balfour-Browne (1953), p.18, figs 25b and 28b.
Distribution	Old records cover much of the eastern coastal counties from Essex to the Forth, with a new record from Epworth Turbary, Humberside. Western records run from Carmarthen to Argyll, with recent records only for the Lake District, Dumfries & Galloway, and Strath Orchy (Argyll). Early published records are unreliable owing to confusion in use of the name *H. piceus* Stephens. It is often extremely difficult to locate but can be abundant in the autumn. For map see Foster (1984), p.20.
Habitat and ecology	Mainly found in temporary marshes in old oxbow systems, and, in the Lake District, in peat pools.
Status	This species appeared to have died out in the eastern part of its range and some well-known western sites, e.g. Thurstonfield Lough, Cumbria, have also been thoroughly surveyed without finding it.
Threats	Improvement, especially drainage, of riverside pasture and canalization of waterways.
Conservation	Kenmure Holms is an SSSI. Other sites are not at present notified, and should be considered.
Author	G.N. Foster, using additional information from Angus (1964), Maitland (1963), D. Bilton (pers. comm.), and the F. Balfour-Browne card index in the Royal Scottish Museum.

Hydroporus scalesianus

A water beetle   **VULNERABLE**

Order **Coleoptera**   Family **Dytiscidae**

Hydroporus scalesianus Stephens, 1828.

Identification
Balfour-Browne (1940), pp.281-285; Balfour-Browne (1953), p.17.

Distribution
England north to Co. Durham and Cumbria, with most records for Norfolk. It is often common but all populations are isolated. For map see Foster (1984), p.20.

Habitat and ecology
Relict habitats in fen and fen carr, and sometimes in peat bogs or in sedge beds at the edge of open water.

Status
There are old records for Yorkshire, Hertfordshire, south Hampshire and Norfolk, from which it was originally described. Modern records are for Hart Bog in Co. Durham, Biglands Bog in Cumbria, Catfield Fen, Myhills Marsh, East Walton Common, Thompson Common and ponds in the Stanford Training Area, all in Norfolk. The absence of this boreal flightless species from northern Britain can best be explained by it having been stranded in periglacial hollows on the edge of the last glacial advance.

Threats
Any form of drainage eliminates this species. According to the subfossil record in Flandrian deposits in Somerset, this species can, however, survive through the hydroseral succession in a range of habitats. This diversity of habitats is seen in modern populations in Norfolk. Disturbance is the key factor.

Conservation
Most sites are scheduled or are known for their entomological interest. Myhills Marsh is part of Hickling Broad NNR, and Thompson Common is now a Norfolk Naturalists' Trust reserve. Biglands Bog is a reserve of the Cumbria Trust for Nature Conservation but is subject to pollution from farm effluent. The presence of rare aquatic insects should be taken into account when notifying the remaining sites, and management agreements should be considered for the Stanford Training Area site and for Hart Bog SSSI.

Author
G.N. Foster, using additional information from Foster (1982), Horsfield & Foster (1982), Bilton (1984), and the 1982 Norfolk Survey.

Graptodytes flavipes

A water beetle

VULNERABLE

Order **Coleoptera**

Family **Dytiscidae**

Graptodytes flavipes (Olivier, 1795), formerly known as *Hydroporus flavipes* and wrongly known as *G. concinnus* (Stephens) in Continental Europe.

Identification
Balfour-Browne (1940), pp.261-264; Balfour-Browne (1953), p.15.

Distribution
Breeding centres in west Cornwall, Dorset and the New Forest, with singletons occasionally reported from Surrey and East Sussex. For map see Foster (1983), p.11. It can be abundant in temporary ponds.

Habitat and ecology
Pools and slow-running water on heathland. Capable of flight.

Status
Earlier in this century *G. flavipes* was known from Dyfed, most southern coastal counties and a few East Anglian fens. There are now ten post-1950 10km square records (compared with a total of 32 pre-1950 squares) for the Goonhilly Downs (Cornwall), the Purbeck area (Dorset), the New Forest (Hampshire), Bookham Common (Surrey) and Southease on the Lewes Levels (East Sussex).

Threats
Loss of heathland habitats by the disturbance of tourism, urbanisation, nuclear power stations, etc., and intensification of agriculture.

Conservation
Present on the Lizard NNR, Cornwall.

Author
G.N. Foster, using additional information from Hodge (1979) and the records of L.E. Barnes, J. Blackburn, D.A. Cooling, D.E. Coombe, J. Cooter, A.P. Foster and G.N. Foster.

Agabus brunneus

A water beetle

VULNERABLE

Order **Coleoptera**

Family **Dytiscidae**

Agabus brunneus (F., 1798).

Identification
Balfour-Browne (1950), pp.65-68; Balfour-Browne (1953), p.21.

Distribution
Very localised within the New Forest area and west Cornwall. For map see Foster (1983), p.18.

Habitat and ecology
In intermittent streams in base-poor areas. 'Semisubterranean'.

Status	There are records for west Cornwall, south Devon, south Wiltshire and south Hampshire. The only recent records are for Gwithian in 1981 and Porthtowan in the 1960s (but not in the 1981 survey) in Cornwall, and, in the New Forest area, Hamptworth (Wiltshire) in 1976 and Widden Bottom (Hampshire) in 1978. This is, however, a species for which collectors are reluctant to reveal their source, and there are probably other undisclosed records for the New Forest.
Threats	Unknown – probably disturbance.
Author	G.N. Foster, using additional information from Nash (1979), and the records of A. Eve, A. P. Foster, P. J. Hodge and D.R. Nash.

Agabus striolatus

A water beetle **VULNERABLE**

Order **Coleoptera** Family **Dytiscidae**

Agabus striolatus (Gyllenhal, 1808).

Identification	Balfour-Browne (1950), pp.135-137; Balfour-Browne (1953), p.22; Foster (1982).
Distribution	Exclusively from the Broadland of east Norfolk. The adults occur in extremely small numbers in spring and autumn.
Habitat and ecology	Pits (tree-holes, etc.) in relict fen carr and wet woodland, drying out in summer.
Status	Reported between 1839 and 1855 in the Horning area and rediscovered there and on the Ant and Bure Marshes and Hickling Broad in 1978-81. No other British records have been substantiated. This is a rare beetle throughout its range.
Threats	The encroachment of carr onto old mowing fen around the Broads may explain the recent rediscovery of this species. Nevertheless the habitat is fragile, being subject to total drying-out on the one hand or loss in swamp woodland on the other, and also being easily disturbed or polluted.
Conservation	The Woodbastwick Marshes sites are part of the Bure Marshes NNR, Myhills Marsh is part of Hickling Broad NNR, and the Barton Broad sites are in or near to the Norfolk Naturalists' Trust reserve. The Catfield Fen site is, with the Barton Broad area, part of an NCR Grade 1* SSSI (Ratcliffe, 1977). The owners and occupiers of most known sites have been notified of the presence of rare beetles and of the habitats that they prefer. Recognition of the national (and possibly international) importance of the beetle and its habitat should be included in reserve management plans.
Author	G.N. Foster, using information from Foster (1982).

Agabus undulatus

A water beetle

VULNERABLE

Order **Coleoptera**

Family **Dytiscidae**

Agabus undulatus (Schrank, 1776).

Identification
Balfour-Browne (1950), pp.103-107; Balfour-Browne (1953), p.21.

Distribution
Gloucestershire, the Vale of York, the Cambridgeshire Fens, and the Breckland. For map see Foster (1983), p.21.

Habitat and ecology
Eutrophic fens in drains and sedge beds, and neighbouring clay ponds with rich vegetation. Flightless.

Status
This used to be an uncommon species found in much of England, and is too distinct and easily caught to have escaped attention recently. It is now confined to the northern part of its earlier range at Sandhurst (Gloucestershire), to Askham Bog (North Yorkshire) and neighbouring ponds at Aldersyde, Fulford and Melbourne, to Woodwalton and Wicken Fens (Cambridgeshire) and nearby ponds, and to ponds in west Norfolk.

Threats
This is a relict species, but, unlike several fen rarities, it is able to survive in man-made habitats occupying the primary site. The destruction of fen habitats must nevertheless explain the contraction of its range.

Conservation
Wicken Fen is National Trust property and is managed as a nature reserve, Woodwalton Fen is an NNR, Askham Bog is a Yorkshire Wildlife Trust reserve and Sandhurst is a reserve of the Gloucestershire Trust for Nature Conservation. Many of the best sites lie just outside existing reserves (so far as their boundaries are known), and extension of the existing reserves is therefore desirable.

Author
G. N. Foster, using additional information from Palmer (1981) and Atty (1983) and the records of D. Barnes, G.N. Foster and N. G. Webb.

Rhantus aberratus

A water beetle   **ENDANGERED +**

Order **Coleoptera**   Family **Dytiscidae**

Rhantus aberratus Gemminger & von Harold, 1868. Formerly known as *Rantus adspersus* (F.), and referred to on the Continent as *Rhantus bistriatus* (Bergstraesser).

Identification
Balfour-Browne (1953), p.26, figs. 40f and 41b. Balfour-Browne (1950, pp.239-243) misleadingly indicated that this species could only be confused with *R. exsoletus* (Forster); in the field it resembles *R. bistriatus* (= *R. suturellus* (Harris)).

Distribution
Exclusively from East Anglia (Cambridgeshire, south Essex and east Norfolk). Only one caught this century.

Habitat and ecology
The previous distribution in Britain suggests an association with meres, Continental records being for fens and drains in peat bogs.

Status
The last specimen was found in September 1904 at Potter Heigham, Norfolk. Extensive surveys of grazing fen drains in the area in the 1980s (e.g. by R.J. Driscoll) were unsuccessful. Possibly extinct.

Threats
Possibly reduced near to extinction by drainage of the East Anglian meres, mainly in the 1830s.

Author
G.N. Foster, using additional information from Driscoll (1978).

Graphoderus bilineatus

A water beetle   **ENDANGERED +**

Order **Coleoptera**   Family **Dytiscidae**

Graphoderus bilineatus (Degeer, 1774).

Identification
Angus (1976). No formal publication in English exists.

Distribution
Exclusively from Catfield Fen, east Norfolk, where it used to occur in small numbers.

Habitat and ecology
Fen drains, possibly in deep water. The larvae are pelagic. Studies in Switzerland (Brancucci, 1980) suggest that populations are extremely localised and sedentary.

Status
Detected by Angus (1976) in a series of *G. cinereus* (L.) which was collected by F. Balfour-Browne and T.H. Beare at Catfield Fen between 1904 and 1906. It is actually an easily recognised species which should have been detected in recent surveys of grazing fen areas of the east Norfolk Broadland, where it seems to have been replaced by *Hydaticus* species. Possibly extinct. A rare species throughout its range.

Threats
Possibly reduced to extinction by drainage of the East Anglian meres (although there are no authenticated 19th century records).

Author
G.N. Foster.

Graphoderus zonatus

A water beetle **ENDANGERED**

Order **Coleoptera** Family **Dytiscidae**

Graphoderus zonatus (Hoppe, 1795). Formerly misidentified as *Graphoderus cinereus* (L.), which is included here as a Rare species.

Identification Angus (1976). No formal publication in English exists.

Distribution Exclusively from Woolmer Bog, north Hampshire, where it is sometimes common.

Habitat and ecology Open water in peat bogs. The larvae are pelagic.

Status First reported from the site (as *G. cinereus*) by Allen (1953). Gilbert White (1789) described the site as a sandy-bottomed lake, and Balfour-Browne (1940) reported that in 1938 the site was covered with a thin layer of peat and that the water level could no longer be maintained during summer. *G. zonatus* may have colonised the site when it became suitable in the 20th century; on the other hand, Ratcliffe (1977) indicated a possible origin as a peat-cutting and *G. zonatus* may be relict. The species was last reported in 1984.

Threats Ratcliffe (1977, 2:168) reported possible loss of this species (owing to the use of insecticides to control mosquitoes). Other military operations seem to have had no effect either, but the general drop in water level and loss of open water habitat are more important.

Conservation The presence of the species is known to the wildlife management group reporting to the Ministry of Defence. Pond construction at the site may have been beneficial to this species. The site is an NCR Grade 1 SSSI (Ratcliffe, 1977). Open water habitat must be maintained.

Author G.N. Foster, using additional information from R.B. Angus, B. Barns and F.D. Goodliffe.

Spercheus emarginatus

A water beetle **ENDANGERED**

Order **Coleoptera** Family **Hydrophilidae**

Spercheus emarginatus (Schaller, 1783).

Identification Balfour-Browne (1958), pp.80-87.

Distribution In the 19th century it occurred in the eastern fens north to Askham Bog, North Yorkshire. Exclusively from east Suffolk this century. Often abundant when it occurs.

Habitat and ecology	Eutrophic fens among emergent vegetation. Females carry egg cocoons in late spring, and the buoyant, black larvae complete their development in a fortnight, pupation taking 5-6 days.
Status	The only reported find this century was at an unnamed site near Beccles in 1956 (Forster, 1956). Fens neighbouring Beccles have been drained (M. George, pers. comm.).
Threats	Drainage and pollution of fens. Presumably the conversion of grazing fens to arable land would be detrimental but it seems that the construction of fen drains themselves last century was damaging.
Author	G.N. Foster.

Helophorus laticollis

A water beetle · **VULNERABLE**

Order **Coleoptera** · Family **Hydrophilidae**

Helophorus laticollis Thomson, 1853.

Identification	Angus (1971); Angus (1978).
Distribution	Possibly confined to the New Forest now.
Habitat and ecology	In temporary grassy pools in the spring.
Status	It has been possible to show that records outside Dorset, south Hampshire and the Surrey heaths should refer to *H. strigifrons* Thomson. Angus (1971) suggested that it was a glacial relict in England and (1978) indicated that he knew of no records since the late 1960s for its last known stronghold in the New Forest.
Threats	Loss of temporary wet heathland habitats.
Conservation	Sites are within the New Forest conservation area.
Author	G.N. Foster.

Paracymus aeneus

A water beetle · **ENDANGERED**

Order **Coleoptera** · Family **Hydrophilidae**

Paracymus aeneus (Germar, 1824).

Identification	Joy (1932); Balfour-Browne (1958), pp.45-46.
Distribution	Exclusively from Essex and the Isle of Wight. Usually common when it occurs.
Habitat and ecology	Saltmarshes.

Status	A survey of Essex sites by A.C. Warne failed to reveal this distinctive species, the only known site now being the mud flats at Bembridge (Isle of Wight) neighbouring a rubbish tip. The Bembridge site was discovered by J.L. Henderson in 1928 (not 1923 as stated by Balfour-Browne, 1958), rediscovered by D. Appleton in 1973 (Appleton, 1975), and reported still there by P.J. Hodge in 1983.
Threats	Loss of saltmarsh habitat through rubbish disposal is the main threat to its last known site.
Conservation	The Bembridge site is not an SSSI at present.
Author	G.N. Foster.

Hydrochara caraboides

Lesser Silver Water Beetle   **ENDANGERED**

Order **Coleoptera**   Family **Hydrophilidae**

Hydrochara caraboides (L., 1758), formerly known as *Hydrous caraboides*.

Identification	Balfour-Browne (1958), pp.10-14; Harde (1984), fig. 119:7.
Distribution	Scattered records north to Askham Bog (North Yorkshire), with authenticated records in sufficient numbers to indicate breeding in the London Marshes, Somerset Levels and Cambridgeshire Fens. Unlike *Hydrophilus piceus* (L.), which fluctuates in adult numbers from site to site and year to year on the Somerset Levels, *H. caraboides* appears in small numbers as adults in undisturbed dykes each year.
Habitat and ecology	Lowland fens in dykes with diverse emergent vegetation. The biology in Somerset has been studied by Mrs L. Brown and by A. Eve (unpublished). In France Maillard (1970) has published concerning egg cocoon construction. Dr Eve's difficulty in rearing larvae beyond the first instar suggests that snails are required for the diet as in *H. piceus* larvae.
Status	The last report of numbers sufficient to indicate breeding outside Somerset was in 1938 at Woodwalton Fen (Cambridgeshire), the major centre having been the London Marshes in the 19th century. Reports for coastal sites in Lancashire and Wales have not been authenticated; it is possible that the species occurs undetected in such areas although this is becoming increasingly remote. The species is concentrated in the peat areas of the Somerset Levels around Westhay and Shapwick (see A.P. Foster, 1984).

Threats	The disappearance of this species from all but one area of fenland is best explained by the intensification of drain management and the resulting disturbance. Drastic drain clearances using mechanical means or herbicides remove both *H. piceus* and *H. caraboides* but only the former species appears capable of recolonising cleared drains. Drains with reed *Phragmites australis* and ivy duckweed *Lemna trisulca*, such as now dominate Woodwalton Fen, are unsuitable for *H. caraboides*.
Conservation	The only breeding area lies in and around Shapwick Heath NNR. Adults from Somerset could be introduced into sites in East Anglian fens, where there is suitable undisturbed vegetation and the opportunity to observe progress.
Author	G.N. Foster, using additional information from A. Eve (pers. comm.).

Teretrius fabricii

ENDANGERED +

Order **Coleoptera**   Family **Histeridae**

Teretrius fabricii Mazur, 1972, formerly known as *Teretrius picipes* (F.).

Identification	Halstead (1963), p.9, figs 3 and 17.
Distribution	In the late 19th century it was known from the London area, with isolated records from Bungay (Norfolk), Swansea (West Glamorgan) and Bristol (Avon).
Habitat and ecology	Preys on the immature stages of *Lyctus brunneus* Stephens, *L. linearis* (Goeze) and other bostrichoid beetles.
Status	Allen (1963) describes the *locus classicus* at Upper Norwood (West Sussex) where it was "taken freely from oak palings" in 1876-79 with another predator, the clerid beetle *Tilloidea unifasciatus* (F.). Allen was of the opinion that the last specimens were taken at Ashtead and Oxshott, Surrey, in 1907. It is most probably extinct in Britain.
Threats	Although there has been a decline in *Lyctus* infestations since 1945 N.E. Hickin still regarded them as a substantial pest in 1963. The absence of this predator is, therefore, difficult to explain.
Author	R.C. Welch.

Hypocaccus metallicus

Order **Coleoptera**   Family **Histeridae**

Hypocaccus metallicus (Herbst, 1792).

Identification Halstead (1963), p.13, fig.31.

Distribution One pre-1925 record by A. Ford from Dorset. Most specimens are from Kent and East Sussex. Mablethorpe, Lincolnshire, is the most northerly locality.

Habitat and ecology In dung, carrion, etc., on coastal sandhills.

Status This species has apparently declined since the early part of this century. The British Museum (Natural History) collections contain specimens taken at Sandwich, Kent, in 1938 and Hunstanton, Norfolk, in 1946. It is usually common on the Camber Sandhills, Kent, and also occurs at Rye harbour, East Sussex (P.J. Hodge, pers. comm.).

Threats Public pressure, and changes in the land use of coastal sand dune systems.

Conservation The species could well be present on the LNR at Sandwich.

Author R.C. Welch.

Hypocaccus rugiceps

VULNERABLE

Order **Coleoptera**   Family **Histeridae**

Hypocaccus rugiceps (Duftschmid, 1805).

Identification Halstead (1963), p.13; Harde (1984), fig. 121:8.

Distribution Apart from one pre-1925 record from Dorset by A. Ford and an old record by Fowler for Paisley (Strathclyde), all the rest are for the coastline from Wales to Cumbria.

Habitat and ecology In dung, carrion, etc., on coastal sandhills.

Status Although widely distributed in the past, the only recent records are from Cumbria in the 1960s. Angus (1964) between 1960 and 1963 found one at Drigg Sands and two at the north end of Walney Island. There is a specimen in the British Museum (Natural History) collected in 1968 from Sandscale Haws, just across a narrow channel from the Walney site. The species has been taken at Pembrey near Llanelli, Dyfed, in 1974 and 1982 (J.A. Owen, pers. comm.). Large numbers were found in a dead gull at Rhosneigr, Anglesey, in 1979 (R.S. Key, pers. comm.).

Threats Public pressure, urbanisation, and changes in the land use of coastal sand dunes.

Conservation	The species may still be present in protected coastal reserves, e.g. Ainsdale Sand Dunes NNR. The Walney-Sandscale dunes are an NCR Grade 1 site (Ratcliffe, 1977).
Author	R.C. Welch.

Paromalus parallele-pipedus

ENDANGERED

Order **Coleoptera**   Family **Histeridae**

Paromalus parallelepipedus (Herbst, 1792). Formerly known as *Microlomalus parallelepipedus*.

Identification	Halstead (1973), p.11, fig.22.
Distribution	Only known in Britain from the New Forest, Hampshire, and from east Kent.
Habitat and ecology	Under bark.
Status	Fowler (1887-91, 3) mentions three or four specimens from the New Forest. Later (Fowler & Donisthorpe, 1913) he lists one more from Brockenhurst. Joy (1932) did not include this species and Halstead describes it as "very rare indeed". The only modern record is of one specimen taken from under bark in Pennipot Wood, Canterbury, Kent, by J.A. Parry in 1952 (Allen, 1971c).
Threats	Not known, but the destruction of ancient trees and removal of dead wood may be contributory factors.
Conservation	Nothing specific can be recommended, apart from measures to ensure a continuing succession of old trees and dead wood in the New Forest and in the Kent locality.
Author	R.C. Welch.

Hister quadrimaculatus

VULNERABLE

Order **Coleoptera**   Family **Histeridae**

Hister quadrimaculatus L., 1758.

Identification	Halstead (1963), p.9; Harde (1984), fig. 123:7.
Distribution	Southern England, mainly coastal localities from Weymouth (Dorset) to Clacton (Essex), with most specimens from Kent.
Habitat and ecology	In dung, carrion, etc. Mainly from coastal sites, but not sand dunes.

Status

This species is now very rare. The only recent record appears to be of a single specimen found under a stone in a field at Stoke, north Kent, by L.S. Whicher on 1 June 1952 (Whicher, 1952).

Author

R.C. Welch.

Paralister obscurus

VULNERABLE

Order **Coleoptera**   Family **Histeridae**

Paralister obscurus (Kugelann, 1792). Formerly known as *Margarinotus stercorarius* (Hoffmann).

Identification

Halstead (1963), p.10, fig.12.

Distribution

Scattered coastal localities in south-western counties, Wales and the Lancashire dune systems. There are old records for Netley (Hampshire) and Norfolk, and a very old, probably erroneous, London record.

Habitat and ecology

In dung, chiefly among sandhills.

Status

This species does not appear to have been recorded since the early part of this century.

Threats

Public pressure and land use changes in coastal dune systems.

Conservation

Former localities such as Braunton Burrows, Devon, and the Ainsdale area are now managed as NNRs.

Author

R.C. Welch.

Ochthebius aeneus

A water beetle   **ENDANGERED +**

Order **Coleoptera**   Family **Hydraenidae**

Ochthebius aeneus Stephens, 1835.

Identification

Balfour-Browne (1958), pp.160-163. His idea that this is a habitat form of *O. minimus* (F.) is wrong (see d'Orchymont, 1952).

Distribution

Oxfordshire, north Essex, Greater London, Surrey, south Hampshire, the Isle of Wight and possibly East Sussex, a Glamorgan record being incorrect. At one time abundant on heaths around London.

Habitat and ecology

The precise habitat is not really known. *O. aeneus* was mainly found on lowland heath, sometimes in brackish water.

Status	Possibly extinct. The last British record that can be authenticated is for a specimen from "The Salts, St. Leonards" in 1913; this was assigned to East Sussex by G.N. Foster (1972), but may well be referable to south Hampshire.
Threats	Loss of wetland heath habitats in southern England.
Author	G.N. Foster.

Ochthebius lenensis

A water beetle **VULNERABLE**

Order **Coleoptera** Family **Hydraenidae**

Ochthebius lenensis Poppius, 1907.

Identification	Balfour-Browne (1958), p.164.
Distribution	The Dornoch and Moray Firths, where it is often in large numbers and to the exclusion of other beetles.
Habitat and ecology	Grassy pools in merse.
Status	First discovered at Tain, Ross & Cromarty, in 1939, with records in 1950s for Tain and Redcastle (Ross & Cromarty), Kirkhill (Inverness), and Findhorn Bay and Lossiemouth (Moray). The most recent record is for Ardersier (Inverness) in 1979.
Threats	Oil-related developments, major oil spillages and oil spillage treatments. Also a possible barrage/reclamation scheme in the Moray Firth.
Author	G.N. Foster, using additional information from J.A. Owen and J. Parry (pers. comms).

Hydraena palustris

A water beetle **VULNERABLE**

Order **Coleoptera** Family **Hydraenidae**

Hydraena palustris Erichson, 1837.

Identification	Balfour-Browne (1958), pp.183-186.
Distribution	Norfolk only. Isolated populations at low densities.
Habitat and ecology	Mossy swamps in eutrophic/mesotrophic fens.
Status	*H. palustris* appears to have died out at Wicken Fen, Sutton Broad Fen and Askham Bog. The beetle is a relict species surviving in three 'pingo'-like systems of periglacial hollows in west Norfolk, in a peat cutting/marl pond in the Stanford Training Area, and at Catfield Fen in east Norfolk.

Threats	Disturbance of relict sites. The encroachment of carr into open mossy areas such as mowing fen.
Conservation	Catfield Fen is part of an NCR Grade 1* SSSI (Ratcliffe, 1977), and Thompson Common is a Norfolk Naturalists' Trust nature reserve. The occupiers of two other sites have been notified of the sites' entomological interest. Management agreements should include the control of carr.
Author	G.N. Foster; see also Palmer (1981).

Ptilium affine

ENDANGERED

Order **Coleoptera**   Family **Ptiliidae**

Ptilium (Ptilium) affine Erichson, 1845.

Identification	Joy (1932), pp. 571-574.
Distribution	Only known this century from Wicken Fen (Cambridgeshire), where it is present in very low numbers.
Habitat and ecology	Fowler (1887-91, 3:132) states that "it appears to be found under dung", although this is unlikely. It has more recently been found in sedge litter.
Status	Fowler describes how three examples had been swept at Wicken Fen. He also "received two specimens from the south of England" (locality unknown). Omer-Cooper & Tottenham (1932) only give Fowler's record. C. Johnson (pers. comm.) has retaken it at Wicken Fen in the 1970s by sieving sedge refuse.
Threats	Lowering of water table in fenland.
Conservation	The site is managed by the National Trust to maintain fenland conditions.
Author	R. C. Welch.

Micridium halidaii

ENDANGERED

Order **Coleoptera**   Family **Ptiliidae**

Micridium halidaii (Matthews, 1869), formerly known as *Ptilium halidayi*.

Identification	Joy (1932), pp. 571-574.
Distribution	Only found as single specimens from three localities, Sherwood Forest (Nottinghamshire), Richmond Park (London) and Windsor Forest (Berkshire).

Habitat and ecology	Under bark or in heart rot of ancient oaks *Quercus*, probably associated with the mycelia of the bracket fungus *Polyporus sulphureus*.
Status	Originally recorded in June 1867 when A. Matthews (1868) found a single specimen under the bark of a dead oak in Sherwood Forest. C. Johnson has retaken the species in the Forest at Birklands in 1977. In May 1980 J. A. Owen (1981) found a specimen in the rotten wood from inside a hollow but living ancient oak tree in Windsor Forest, and has also recorded it recently (1984, pers. comm.) from Richmond Park.
Threats	Loss of ancient oaks and lack of suitably-aged replacement trees.
Conservation	Forest authorities have been made aware of the value of retaining dead and dying oaks in ancient forest.
Author	R. C. Welch, using additional information from Carr (1916), p.324.

Microptilium palustre

ENDANGERED

Order **Coleoptera**   Family **Ptiliidae**

Microptilium palustre Kuntzen, 1914.

Identification	C. Besuchet & E. Sundt *in* Freude, Harde & Lohse (1964-83), 3:328.
Distribution	Only known from Wicken Sedge Fen, Cambridgeshire. A rare species on the Continent recorded from Denmark to Spain.
Habitat and ecology	Found in sedge refuse at Wicken. A marshland species on the Continent. Biology unknown.
Status	Found "in good numbers" by C. Johnson in 1977.
Conservation	The only known British locality is owned and managed by the National Trust.
Author	R. C. Welch.

Microptilium pulchellum

ENDANGERED

Order **Coleoptera**   Family **Ptiliidae**

Microptilium pulchellum (Allibert, 1844).

Identification	Joy (1932), pp.568-569.
Distribution	Only known from Bradfield (Berkshire) and Earith (Cambridgeshire).

Habitat and ecology	Possibly a marshland species in Britain as it is on the Continent.
Status	Fowler (1887-91, 3:128) states that two specimens were taken by G. B. Waterhouse but he did not know in what locality. N. H. Joy (Fowler & Donisthorpe, 1913) recorded *M. pulchellum* in grass tufts from the edge of a pond at Bradfield, Berkshire. This locality was searched by C. Johnson and the species was thought by him to be extinct by the 1970s. On 18 May 1980 J. A. Owen (pers. comm.) found a few specimens by sieving litter at the edge of an old gravel pit near Earith, Cambridgeshire, and C. Johnson collected more specimens there in 1981.
Author	R. C. Welch.

Ptinella limbata   ENDANGERED

Order **Coleoptera**   Family **Ptiliidae**

Ptinella limbata (Heer, 1841).

Identification	Freude, Harde & Lohse (1964-83), 3:329-330; Joy (1932), pp.568-569.
Distribution	19th century records for major ancient forest areas: Sherwood (Nottinghamshire), Forest of Dean (Gloucestershire), Cannock Chase (Staffordshire), and the New Forest (Hampshire); there are more recent records from Oxfordshire, Berkshire, Cambridgeshire and Inverness District (Highland).
Habitat and ecology	Under the bark of both deciduous and coniferous trees.
Status	There is some uncertainty over published records of *Ptinella* species. C. Johnson (1975) described two species new to the British list: *P. errabunda* Johnson (the earliest specimen dating from 1925 although the species is now widespread and very common) and *P. cavelli* (Broun) (dating from 1936), both believed to be recent introductions, possibly from New Zealand. It may be that older records of *P. limbata* are correct. Fowler (1887-91, 3:110-111) reports how A. Matthews found it in abundance under the bark of a dead beech in Sherwood Forest; Mr Blatch also took it there and in the Forest of Dean and in Cannock Chase. Joy (1932) lists it as very rare in Oxfordshire, Berkshire and Cambridgeshire. There is an old Sharp specimen from the New Forest but this species was not recorded by A. Williams and E. A. Gardner during their late-1960s survey of the Forest. C. Johnson (pers. comm.) believes that it may be extinct in England but found it recently under the bark of dead trees at Guisachan, Inverness.
Author	R. C. Welch.

Aglyptinus agathidioides

Order **Coleoptera**   Family **Leiodidae**

Aglyptinus agathidioides Blair, 1930. Also listed in Category 5 (Endemic).

Identification   Blair (1930).

Distribution   An endemic species only known from one male and one female collected at Potters Bar, Hertfordshire, by E. C. Bedwell on 14 April 1912.

Habitat and ecology   The only specimens were obtained from the nest of a moorhen *Gallinula chloropus*.

Status   Unknown. No specific search of the type locality has been undertaken. A number of coleopterists have searched moorhen nests but all of these, and recent examination of the nests of moorhens and mute swans in Cambridgeshire and Northamptonshire, have proved unsuccessful. Probably not a nidicolous species, more likely to be associated with reed litter.

Author   R. C. Welch, using additional information from Donisthorpe (1931) and Donisthorpe & Walker (1931, p.40).

Silpha carinata

A carrion beetle   **ENDANGERED**

Order **Coleoptera**   Family **Silphidae**

Silpha carinata Herbst, 1783, formerly known as *Silpha griesbachiana* Stephens.

Identification   Nash (1975, 1977).

Distribution   Recent records are from three adjacent 1km grid squares near Salisbury, Wiltshire. There is an old record from Winchester, Hampshire (Stephens, 1827-35, 3:26; 1839, p.115). The population is small and extremely localised.

Habitat and ecology   The first British records of *S. carinata* were from carcasses, but recent specimens have been found in a heap of damp straw, in moss and under a stone, all at the margin of deciduous woodland. Adults were attracted to dead fish in baited pitfall traps and in experiments were fed on a variety of plant and dead animal material. Teneral adults and larval exuviae found in August 1976 and other adults found in April suggest that *S. carinata* overwinters as an adult (Nash, 1977).

Status	In five visits over a three-year period from April 1974 to April 1977 D. R. Nash found fifteen specimens of *S. carinata* in one very local area (four of these were caught in pitfall traps baited with dead fish). The only previous record of *S. carinata* in Britain is "Carcases, Winchester: 6" (Stephens, 1839). Elsewhere he states "Winchester Mr A. Griesbach. The only specimen I have yet seen: it is in the collection of the British Museum" (Stephens, 1827-35). Neither this nor any of the other Winchester specimens appear to be extant in British collections.
Author	R. C. Welch.

Eutheia formicetorum

VULNERABLE

Order **Coleoptera**   Family **Scydmaenidae**

Eutheia formicetorum Reitter, 1881.

Identification	Easily confused with other *Eutheia* species: specialist identification is necessary. C. Besuchet *in* Freude, Harde & Lohse (1964-83), 3:273-274; Allen (1969c), pp.239-240.
Distribution	Known from Windsor Forest (Berkshire), the New Forest (Hampshire), and Prattle Wood (Oxfordshire). The population is probably small and localised.
Habitat and ecology	The decaying wood of old trees, including oak *Quercus* and beech *Fagus*. Probably a predator of mites. Adults have been collected in Britain in April and June-August.
Status	Probably near the northern limit of its overall range in southern England. Apparently restricted to ancient forest areas in the south, for which there is a total of about 13 records. Small (1.2 mm) and easily overlooked. There are records from the New Forest (1912), Prattle Wood (1915) and Windsor Forest (1942). J. A. Owen (pers. comm.) took a specimen at the last locality in June 1982.
Threats	Any threat to areas of ancient forest. The removal of dead timber.
Conservation	Measures to conserve ancient forest and its dead wood fauna.
Author	P. M. Hammond.

Eutheia linearis

Order **Coleoptera**   Family **Scydmaenidae**

Eutheia linearis Mulsant, 1861.

Identification   Easily confused with other *Eutheia* species: specialist identification is necessary. C. Besuchet *in* Freude, Harde & Lohse (1964-83), 3:273-274; Allen (1969c), pp.239-240.

Distribution   Known from Sherwood Forest (Nottinghamshire), Windsor Forest (Berkshire), the New Forest (Hampshire) and "Frome Wood". Also recorded (Brown & Crowson, 1980) from Rowardennan, Stirling (Central), but the author of this entry has had no opportunity to confirm this record. The population is probably small and localised.

Habitat and ecology   Under the bark of dead and dying wood, especially of mature oaks *Quercus*. Probably a predator of mites. Adults have been collected in Britain in April, May, July and October. Larvae, possibly of this species, have been collected in June.

Status   Apparently more or less restricted to old oak forests. Small (1.25 mm) and easily overlooked. Probably still present in some of the ancient forests of England, for which there are about 12 records in all, but there are no recent records. The most recent are Frome Wood (1906), Windsor Forest (1934), and Sherwood Forest (1913). The unconfirmed record for Rowardennan relates to specimens collected in 1969 and 1978.

Threats   Any threat to areas of ancient forest. The removal of dead timber.

Conservation   Measures to conserve ancient forest and its dead wood fauna.

Author   P. M. Hammond.

Neuraphes carinatus

Order **Coleoptera**   Family **Scydmaenidae**

Neuraphes carinatus (Mulsant, 1861).

Identification   Much confused with other species of *Neuraphes*: specialist identification is necessary. H. Franz *in* Freude, Harde & Lohse (1964-83), 3:279-284; Allen (1969c), pp.240-241.

Distribution   South-east England. Known from some seven localities in Kent (Brasted and Lenham), East Sussex (Ditchling) and Surrey (Box Hill, Caterham, Chipstead and Weybridge). The records are all for single specimens. The populations are probably small.

Habitat and ecology Moss, litter, etc. on sheltered chalky hillsides. One was taken from a nest of the ant *Formica fusca* L. Probably a predator of mites. Adults have been collected in Britain in March-May, July and August.

Status Small (1.3 mm) and easily overlooked. The most recent record is for 1941, but probably still to be found in some of the localities listed above, and perhaps others.

Threats Any threat to the maintenance of sheltered chalky hillsides in south-east England, i.e. ploughing or other drastic disturbances.

Conservation Any measures to conserve sheltered chalky hillsides in south-east England.

Author P. M. Hammond.

Microscydmus minimus

VULNERABLE

Order **Coleoptera**　　　　　　　　Family **Scydmaenidae**

Microscydmus minimus (Chaudoir, 1845).

Identification Easily confused with *M. nanus* (Schaum): specialist identification is necessary. H. Franz *in* Freude, Harde & Lohze (1964-83), 3:293-294.

Distribution Sherwood Forest (Nottinghamshire), Bagots Park (Staffordshire), Windsor Forest (Berkshire) and the New Forest (Hampshire). The populations are mainly small and highly localised, though it is apparently widespread at Windsor (J. A. Owen, pers. comm.).

Habitat and ecology Cavities in old hollow oaks *Quercus*. Probably a predator of mites. Adults have been collected in Britain in April, May and July.

Status Probably confined to old oak forests. There are post-1970 records for each of the four known localities, including three sites at Windsor in 1980-84.

Threats Any threat to the ancient forest areas in question. The removal of dead timber, especially old fallen oaks.

Conservation Measures to conserve ancient forest and its dead wood fauna.

Author P. M. Hammond.

Euconnus pragensis

Order **Coleoptera**   Family **Scydmaenidae**

Euconnus pragensis (Machulka, 1823), formerly misidentified in Britain as *Euconnus claviger.*

Identification
Joy (1932), p.482; Donisthorpe & Walker (1931), p.41, pl. D:3; H. Franz *in* Freude, Harde & Lohse (1964-83), 3: 294-299.

Distribution
Only known from Windsor Forest. The population is probably very small and localised.

Habitat and ecology
In the decaying wood of old trees, in company with the ant *Lasius brunneus* (Latreille); apparently truly myrmecophilous. Probably a predator of mites. Adults have been collected in Britain in August and October.

Status
Like several other beetle species associated with *Lasius brunneus*, Windsor Forest is the only recorded site for *E. pragensis* in Britain. Small (1.6 mm) and with a highly localised habitat, so easily overlooked. There are three British records, of which the most recent is for 1940.

Threats
Any threat to areas of ancient forest. The removal of dead timber, especially that occupied by *Lasius brunneus.*

Conservation
Measures to conserve ancient forest and its dead wood fauna.

Author
P. M. Hammond.

Scaphium immaculatum

Order **Coleoptera**   Family **Scaphidiidae**

Scaphium immaculatum (Olivier, 1790).

Identification
Joy (1932), pp.475-476; Donisthorpe & Walker (1931), pp.60-61, pl.F:1; Harde (1984), fig. 135:7.

Distribution
Only known from St Margaret's Bay, Kent.

Habitat and ecology
Apparently a thermophilous species on the Continent, found in dunes in Holland and in moss, floating wood and litter and rotting fungi in Germany.

Status
Possibly a chance immigrant, known from 19 specimens found by P. Harwood between 1918 and 1936 on the Kent coast near St Margaret's Bay, north of Dover. The first were taken in April/May 1918 (Harwood, 1918), and the remainder (mainly in September) in 1921-36 (E.C. Bedwell Collection, Norwich Museum: A.B. Drane, pers. comm.).

Author
R. C. Welch.

Olophrum assimile

A rove beetle

ENDANGERED

Order **Coleoptera**

Family **Staphylinidae**

Olophrum assimile (Paykull, 1800).

Identification Tottenham (1954), p.30.

Distribution The Nethy Bridge district, Highland, and Dun Fell, Cumbria. It is highly localised, but populations may be of moderate size. On Dun Fell ten pitfall traps at 820m caught 57 individuals during three years of trapping (1976-78), while ten traps at 850m caught 977 individuals during one season (1978) of trapping. Similar numbers of traps at six other (lower) altitudes on Dun Fell caught no *O. assimile*, suggesting that its population there is restricted to the summit area.

Habitat and ecology In wet moss and litter, on mountains only (in Britain). A predator. Wing polymorphic. The peak adult activity is May-June and October-November.

Status Probably confined to a few mountain-tops and possibly to the two from which it has been recorded. The species is distinctive and has been searched for on a number of other 'suitable' mountains. The relict populations of this boreo-alpine species found in Britain are of interest in that they exhibit morphological differences among themselves and from Continental populations.

Conservation The summit area of Dun Fell, where relict populations of several other beetle species also occur, should be protected from any major changes.

Author P. M. Hammond.

Orochares angustatus

A rove beetle

ENDANGERED

Order **Coleoptera**

Family **Staphylinidae**

Orochares angustatus (Erichson, 1840).

Identification Tottenham (1954), p.28 and fig.52.

Distribution There are two confirmed British records (both for single individuals): Boxmoor, Hertfordshire, and Bradfield, Berkshire. There are also two published records (probably false) for Tweeddale (Borders). *If* it is still present in Britain the breeding populations are undoubtedly small and localised.

Habitat and ecology	Decaying vegetable matter, such as compost, decaying cabbage stems, old root vegetables, etc., and dung. The adults are winter-active (October to April).
Status	The two confirmed records are for 1888 and 1903. Its breeding range may not reach the British Isles and it is probably not an established species in Britain.
Author	P. M. Hammond.

Phyllodrepa nigra

A rove beetle   **VULNERABLE**

Order **Coleoptera**   Family **Staphylinidae**

Phyllodrepa nigra (Gravenhorst, 1806), formerly known as *Hapalaraea nigra*.

Identification	Tottenham (1954), p.21. Easily confused with the common *P. floralis* (Paykull), but the absence of patches of wing-folding spicules from the fifth abdominal tergite in *P. nigra* should enable recognition of the species.
Distribution	Windsor Forest, Berkshire. There are also possibly reliable but unconfirmed records for Oxfordshire (Fowler), the New Forest, Hampshire (Donisthorpe; Walker), Swanage, Dorset (Pearce), and Colyton, south Devon (Ashe). The population is probably small and localised.
Habitat and ecology	Largely a woodland species and, in Britain, probably restricted to areas of established woodland. Adults have been collected from a variety of situations, including decaying tree fungi, sap flows on old trees, pigeon dung, a hornet's nest (*Vespa crabro* L.), etc., but they are most commonly found on blossom (in spring) and in the decaying wood or mould of old, generally hollow trees. Larvae have been discovered (in Germany) in a hollow oak occupied by jackdaws and, as with other *Phyllodrepa* species, larval development probably usually takes place in nests, in the case of *P. nigra* those of birds (starlings, jackdaws, pigeons, owls, etc.) in hollow trees. The adults and larvae are probably predaceous and/or scavengers. Adults have been collected (in Britain and northern Europe) in January-June and September-November. The adults are probably quiescent during mid-summer and breed in the autumn, with the larvae overwintering.
Status	Known with certainty only from Windsor Forest, where the species has been collected in a number of years between 1925 and 1984. Not all of the records for other localities are likely to be reliable, but *P. nigra* may well occur in other ancient forest areas such as the New Forest. The species' overall distribution is of a 'Continental' type and in southern England it is at the extreme western limit of its range.

Threats	Any threat to areas of ancient forest.
Conservation	Measures to conserve areas of ancient forest, and the protection of old hollow oaks and other trees in these areas.
Author	P. M. Hammond.

Xylodromus testaceus

A rove beetle   **ENDANGERED**

Order **Coleoptera**   Family **Staphylinidae**

Xylodromus testaceus (Erichson, 1840).

Identification	Tottenham (1954), p.27.
Distribution	"London area"; Gumley, Leicestershire; and Blean Woods, east Kent. The populations are probably small and highly localised.
Habitat and ecology	Under bark and in rotten wood.
Status	The species' range appears only just to include southern England. The only 20th century records are for Blean Woods (1913 and 1950). *X. testaceus* may still occur there and/or in other southern English woodlands.
Conservation	Protection of Blean Woods and the conservation of the dead wood fauna to be found there.
Author	P. M. Hammond.

Eudectus whitei

A rove beetle   **ENDANGERED**

Order **Coleoptera**   Family **Staphylinidae**

Eudectus whitei Sharp, 1871.

Identification	Tottenham (1954), p.36 and fig.69. A small but highly distinctive species.
Distribution	Ben-a-Bhuird (Deeside, 1871); Cross Craig (Rannoch district, 1921); Meall Garbh (Rannoch district, 1980 and 1981); Ben Macdui (1968); Cairngorms NNR (1968 and 1969); Cairn Gorm (1982); Sgurr Mhor (Ross & Cromarty, 1982); Ingleborough (North Yorkshire, 1913); and Pen-y-ghent (North Yorkshire, 1952, 1953 and 1967). The populations are highly localised and, because suitable mountain-top areas are of limited size, probably not very large, but the population in the Cairngorms NNR, at least, appears to be healthy.

Habitat and ecology	A mountain-top species favouring exposed situations at or near mountain summits. Found at the roots of short vegetation and in moss such as *Racomitrium* at altitudes between 610m and 1180m. In 1968 and 1969 R. C. Welch collected 55 specimens in pitfall traps placed between 1130m and 1180m in the Cairngorms; *E. whitei* appeared to be most numerous in very barren areas with many loose granite chips. The adults are active in June and early July but, in at least some cases, this may be followed by a period of quiescence. Active adults were collected in August by W. O. Steel. In the Cairngorms in 1968 and 1969 pitfalls trapped adults from the first sampling date (3 July) until 12 September (R. C. Welch, in litt.). A full-grown larva was found by Steel in May and pupae in June, indicating that the species overwinters as a larva.
Status	Apparently still well-established on mountain summits in the Cairngorms and Rannoch areas. The species is found at sites difficult of access and is not easy to collect, as it is small and slow-moving and hides itself away under stones, moss, etc. *E. whitei* is probably to be found, as yet undiscovered, on mountain tops additional to those listed above. The species has a special interest because of the relict status of its British populations. I have seen no non-British specimens which are likely to be conspecific with those from Britain, although the species is reported from Novaya Zemlya, USSR. There are no records for other countries. It is possible that some records for the closely related (but clearly distinct) *E. giraudi* Redtenbacher from Scandinavia should be referred to *E. whitei*.
Conservation	Several of the sites are in the Cairngorms NNR.
Author	P. M. Hammond.

Manda mandibularis

A rove beetle	**VULNERABLE**
Order **Coleoptera**	Family **Staphylinidae**

Manda mandibularis (Gyllenhal, 1827), formerly known as *Acrognathus mandibularis*.

Identification	Tottenham (1954), p.39 and fig.72; Harde (1984), fig.140:3.
Distribution	The New Forest, Hampshire; Epping Forest, Essex; Windsor Forest, Berkshire; Darenth Wood, Ashford and Tonbridge, Kent; Bookham, Claygate and Woking, Surrey. The populations are probably very localised.

Habitat and ecology	Found on the banks of still water, in mud, wet moss and debris. Apparently more or less confined to wooded areas. The species has been collected in numbers on the wing during its evening flight period. Adults have been collected in Britain during the months April-June. Probably saprophagous and/or feeds on algae.
Status	Most records are for the 19th century or very early 20th century. There are post-1930 records for only two localities: Ashford and Bookham. The species was regularly collected at Bookham until 1943 (and perhaps later) but I am aware of no records after that date. However, as individuals of *Manda* are not easy to find, it is quite likely that the species persists in one or more British localities. It appears to be at the north-western limit of its range in southern England.
Threats	Any threat to areas of established woodland in southern England, and more particularly to ponds in these woodlands.
Conservation	Protection of New Forest and other forest ponds from pollution and damage.
Author	P.M. Hammond.

Planeustomus flavicollis

A rove beetle   **VULNERABLE**

Order **Coleoptera**   Family **Staphylinidae**

Planeustomus flavicollis Fauvel, 1871.

Identification	Tottenham (1954), p.40.
Distribution	Only recorded from the New Forest, Hampshire, and Caterham, Surrey. The populations are probably small and very localised.
Habitat and ecology	Virtually nothing is known of the habits and preferred habitats of this species in Britain but, like other species of *Planeustomus*, it may be assumed that *P. flavicollis* adults burrow in wet sand, mud or fine gravel in waterside situations. Adults have been collected in Britain in June and July. Probably saprophagous and/or feeds on algae.
Status	Doubt has been expressed (Tottenham, 1954) concerning the taxonomic status of this species or, at least, the status of British specimens so identified. I have compared British specimens with Fauvel's two original specimens from near Verviers, Belgium, and consider them likely to belong to the same species. There appear to be no further records for *P. flavicollis*, but I have seen a further specimen, from the Caucasus (Fauvel collection), which I regard as belonging to this species. As noted by Allen (1970b), *P. flavicollis* appears to be a perfectly distinct, although apparently

rarely collected, species. Only two British specimens of *P. flavicollis* are known, collected at Caterham, Surrey, by G. C. Champion in 1875 and in the New Forest by D. Sharp in 1912. In view of the paucity of records for the species in other parts of its range and the lack of any information concerning its biology, its status as a British species must remain uncertain. Individuals of all species of *Planeustomus* appear to be rarely found except when they emerge from their burrows for flight in the evening. The short elytra and reduced eyes of *P. flavicollis* indicate that flight may be rare or lacking in this species.

Author   P. M. Hammond.

Bledius crassicollis

A rove beetle   **VULNERABLE**

Order **Coleoptera**   Family **Staphylinidae**

Bledius crassicollis Boisduval & Lacordaire, 1835.

Identification   Allen (1974b); G. A. Lohse, *in* Freude, Harde & Lohse (1964-83), 4:97. Specialist identification is necessary; it is often confused with *B. occidentalis* Bondroit.

Distribution   Only known from Herne Bay (east Kent) and Totland Bay (Isle of Wight). The populations are probably small and very localised.

Habitat and ecology   The adults and larvae are subcolonial and burrow in moist sand or clay, mostly in the vicinity of fresh water. Like other *Bledius* species it is probably herbivorous, feeding on algae in burrows. In Britain it has so far been found only on the coast. The population discovered at Totland Bay was found in a patch of moist clay in which the beetles made shallow, largely horizontal burrows. Adults have been collected in Britain in April and May.

Status   *B. crassicollis* was collected at Herne Bay in 1914 by Sharp, and at Totland Bay in 1973, where a "thriving colony" was discovered by D. Appleton. Most old records for this species are to be referred to its relative *B. occidentalis*. The recent record (Allen, 1974b) for Dungeness is also to be referred to the latter species.

Conservation   Protection of the coastal sites where the species has been found. *Bledius* colonies tend to shift rapidly from one area to another.

Author   P. M. Hammond.

Bledius dissimilis	A rove beetle	VULNERABLE
	Order **Coleoptera**	Family **Staphylinidae**

Bledius dissimilis Erichson, 1840.

Identification Tottenham (1954), p.52.

Distribution Bridlington and North Ferriby (Humberside), and Sheffield Bottom (Theale, Berkshire). It is probably very localised but populations at two of the three known localities appear to be of reasonable size. Several hundred adults were observed in an area of a few square metres at Sheffield Bottom.

Habitat and ecology The adults and larvae are subcolonial and burrow in wet sand or clay, mostly in the vicinity of fresh water. Like other *Bledius* species it is probably herbivorous, feeding on algae in its burrows. At two of the known British localities the species has been found in vertical bare sandy or clayey cliff, whereas in Berkshire a colony was found in bare horizontal patches of fine muddy clay at the edge of a flooded gravel-pit. Adults have been collected in Britain from June to October.

Status *B. dissimilis* was first discovered at Bridlington in 1878 and was found there not uncommonly until at least 1952. The species has been looked for at and near Bridlington during the past few years without success; the site has changed considerably and has been buried by blown sand. Extensive colonies were discovered at North Ferriby on earth cliffs by the Humber in 1977 and in gravel workings at Sheffield Bottom in 1978. These recent finds suggest that the species may well be more widespread.

Threats The site at North Ferriby is close to several factory developments (P. J. Hodge, pers. comm.).

Conservation *Bledius* colonies tend to shift from site to site and may be difficult to conserve.

Author P. M. Hammond.

Bledius filipes	A rove beetle	ENDANGERED
	Order **Coleoptera**	Family **Staphylinidae**

Bledius filipes Sharp, 1911.

Identification Tottenham (1954), p.54; G. A. Lohse *in* Freude, Harde & Lohse (1964-83), 4:92-93.

Distribution In and at the foot of clay cliffs on the Norfolk coast (Mundesley, Overstrand, Cromer, Sheringham and West

Runton). The populations are probably small and, at any one time, very localised.

Habitat and ecology The adults and larvae are subcolonial and burrow in moist sand or clay. Like other *Bledius* species it is probably herbivorous, feeding on algae in its burrows. *B. filipes* apparently prefers to burrow in vertical banks. Although all British records are for coastal localities the species is found in the vicinity of fresh water, mostly on the banks of large rivers, as well as on coastal cliffs. Adults have been collected in Britain from June to August.

Status This species was first described in 1911 on the basis of specimens collected at Overstrand (in 1897) and Mundesley. *B. filipes* continued to be found on the stretch of coast between Sheringham and Mundesley until at least 1918, but further records are lacking until the species was discovered at West Runton in 1980 by I. Carter. The West Runton colony was still flourishing in 1982 (J. A. Owen, pers. comm.). In the intervening years the species had been searched for, particularly between Cromer and Overstrand, without success. *B. filipes* may be expected to persist at several sites along this part of the Norfolk coast, with the precise location of colonies shifting from time to time. The species is widespread in central Europe and appears to be common in the Rhine estuary. Like *Nebria livida* (L.) and other beetle species, *B. filipes* is likely to be a 'Rhine relict' in Britain; i.e. it has persisted on the east coast of England since the time (prior to the formation of the English Channel) that this area formed part of the Rhine estuary.

Threats Changes of land use on the north Norfolk coast and the building of sea defences at the base of crumbling cliffs.

Conservation Protection of the coastal sites where the species has been found. *Bledius* colonies tend to shift from one site to another as local conditions change, and may be difficult to conserve.

Author P. M. Hammond.

Bledius furcatus

A rove beetle   **ENDANGERED**

Order **Coleoptera**   Family **Staphylinidae**

Bledius furcatus (Olivier, 1811).

Identification Tottenham (1954), p.50, fig. 90.

Distribution Wells-next-the-Sea and Holkham (Norfolk), Enfield (Greater London), Ringmer (East Sussex), Ipswich (Suffolk) and "North Wales". Populations are probably very localised.

Habitat and ecology	The adults and larvae are subcolonial and burrow in the mud of estuaries, salt-marshes and coastal mud-flats. Like other *Bledius* species it is probably herbivorous, feeding on algae in its burrows. Adults have been collected in Britain from July to September.
Status	The records for Enfield, Ipswich and "North Wales" are all for individual captures and are for the pre-1910 period. *B. furcatus* has been known to occur on the Norfolk coast in the vicinity of Wells since the mid-19th century. There are many records for this locality, the most recent of which known to me is for 1909. The species has been searched for at Wells in recent years without success, and was widely considered to be extinct in Britain. However, a single individual of *B. furcatus* was collected at Ringmer in 1976 by P. Hodge at a mercury vapour light. This may have flown from the north coast of France where the species is locally common. However, it is equally possible that *B. furcatus* persists as a British insect with colonies at one or more sites on the south coast. The species is at the north-western limit of its range in southern England and, although common in southern Europe, appears to be rarer today in many parts of northern Europe where it was once more common.
Conservation	*Bledius* colonies tend to shift from site to site and may be difficult to conserve.
Author	P. M. Hammond.

Carpelimus schneideri

A rove beetle · **ENDANGERED**

Order **Coleoptera** · Family **Staphylinidae**

Carpelimus schneideri (Ganglbauer, 1895), formerly known as *Trogophloeus schneideri* or *T. hemerinus* Joy.

Identification	Tottenham (1954), p.44.
Distribution	Anthorn (Wampool Estuary, Cumbria), and Hunstanton (Norfolk). Populations are probably very localised.
Habitat and ecology	Burrows in the mud of estuaries and salt-marshes; confined to the vicinity of salt water. Quite often found in the burrows of *Bledius* species (e.g. *B. atricapillus* (Germar) and *B. tricornis* (Herbst)). Probably grazes algae after the manner of *Bledius* species.

Status	First recorded as British in 1913. There appear to be no later British records after Cameron (1917) pointed out the species' true identity and noted its occurrence at Anthorn and Hunstanton. Possibly often overlooked owing to its small size and occurrence in a little-sampled habitat (coastal mud-flats). The species is at the north-western limit of its range in England.
Author	P. M. Hammond.

Thinobius newberyi

A rove beetle   VULNERABLE

Order **Coleoptera**   Family **Staphylinidae**

Thinobius newberyi Scheepeltz, 1925. Also listed in Category 5 (Endemic).

Identification	Tottenham (1954), p.56, fig.89.
Distribution	Near Aviemore (Strathspey, Inverness) and Great Salkeld (Cumbria). Populations are probably very localised. Appears to be endemic to Great Britain.
Habitat and ecology	Under stones and in gravel beside clean mountain streams and rivers. Probably feeds on fragments of plant material. Adults have been collected in Britain in the months May and July-September.
Status	First discovered at Great Salkeld, under stones on a gravel bed at the side of a stream in 1907, and found at the same site sparingly until at least 1909. It was later found near Aviemore in 1938, under stones on sandy ground near the River Druie. The species may be expected to occur at other suitable localities in the north of Britain, but there appear to be no recent captures and the species has not been recorded from Continental Europe. The pale colour and small eyes characteristic of this species suggest that it normally occurs deep in stream-side gravel and is unlikely to be detected easily.
Author	P. M. Hammond.

Stenus fossulatus

A rove beetle   ENDANGERED

Order **Coleoptera**   Family **Staphylinidae**

Stenus fossulatus Erichson, 1840.

Identification	Tottenham (1954), p.62, fig.133.
Distribution	Castle Eden Dene, Co. Durham. Probably very localised, but the population at Castle Eden is apparently of a good size.

Habitat and ecology	On wet mud, clay or sand, not necessarily beside water. The species appears to favour chalky soil. Found in Britain on earthslips of calcareous clay, most commonly in open areas with a sparse growth of herbs, with *Bembidion stephensi* Crotch and *B. nitidulum* (Marsham). A predator, probably of Collembola.
Status	First discovered at Castle Eden by C. E. Tottenham, who collected 22 specimens in 1936. Rediscovered in the same area by Reid (1982) in July 1981, when it was found to be abundant on five earthslips between grid references NZ 440400 and NZ 432397. The population at Castle Eden Dene is presumably a long-established relict one.
Threats	No obvious threat at Castle Eden as long as landslips continue.
Conservation	The colony is within Castle Eden Dene NNR.
Author	P. M. Hammond.

Stenus glacialis

A rove beetle — **ENDANGERED**

Order **Coleoptera** Family **Staphylinidae**

Stenus glacialis Heer, 1839.

Identification	Tottenham (1954), p.70, fig.172; Johnson (1967); G.A. Lohse *in* Freude, Harde & Lohse (1964-83), 4:126.
Distribution	The Cheviots, the "Dee district" of Scotland and the Ochil Hills. Populations are probably small and very localised.
Habitat and ecology	A mountain species. In wet moss at high altitude. Predatory.
Status	The "Dee district" (Sharp) and Cheviots (Hislop) records are for the 19th century. I have examined the Cheviot specimens. The species has recently been rediscovered by R. Lyszkowski in Scotland (Ochil Hills). *S. glacialis* is widespread in the mountains of Central Europe but absent from Scandinavia, so that the Scottish localities are by far the northernmost known in a highly disjunct range. Further investigations are needed to establish the extent of the species' British range, but it is unlikely to occur in *many* northern British mountain areas, as a number of these have been well investigated for Staphylinidae.
Author	P. M. Hammond.

Lathrobium rufipenne

A rove beetle   **VULNERABLE**

Order **Coleoptera**   Family **Staphylinidae**

Lathrobium rufipenne Gyllenhal, 1813.

Identification
Joy (1932), p.133-134; G.A. Lohse *in* Freude, Harde & Lohse (1964-83), 4:150. Much confused with other species of *Lathrobium*, especially *L. ripicola* Czwalina. The male genitalia are highly distinctive.

Distribution
A number of old records for this species have been shown to be false. Old records which require confirmation, but may be correct, are for the Manchester district (Barton Moss, Stretford and Staly Brushes) and Brigg, Humberside. Confirmed records are for Delamere Forest (Cheshire) and Horning Fen and Upton Broad (Norfolk). Populations are probably very localised.

Habitat and ecology
A fen and bog species. Confirmed British records are for wet reed litter and *Sphagnum* beds. Adults have been collected in Britain in the months April, May, August, September and December. A predator.

Status
The present status of this species in Britain is difficult to gauge because of past confusion with related species. The only British records which I have been able to confirm are for Delamere Forest, where the species was found regularly between 1905 and 1912, and again in April 1980 (P. Hodge); Horning Fen (19th century records only); Upton Broad, found in May 1980 (Hammond). *L. rufipenne* may persist in other suitable fen or bog localities.

Threats
Any threat to areas of ancient fen or to the Broads area.

Conservation
Measures to conserve areas of fen and broad. Upton Broad is a nature reserve of the Norfolk Naturalists' Trust.

Author
P. M. Hammond.

Scopaeus laevigatus

A rove beetle   **ENDANGERED**

Order **Coleoptera**   Family **Staphylinidae**

Scopaeus laevigatus (Gyllenhal, 1827).

Identification
Allen (1969a), p.200.

Distribution
Seaton (south Devon), and possibly also Axbridge (Somerset) (see Allen, 1969a, p.202). Populations are probably small and very localised.

Habitat and ecology	On damp sand beside fresh water. In Britain found beside springs and pools in coastal 'chines' and the broken faces of sandy cliffs. Predatory. Adults have been collected in Britain in April, June and September.
Status	Known with certainty to occur only at Seaton, where specimens were collected in 1949, 1950 and 1951. I know of no subsequent records, but the species may well persist at Seaton and, perhaps, elsewhere on the south coast of England. Devon represents the north-westernmost extension of the species' range.
Threats	Any change of land use at Seaton or similar coastal localities in south Devon.
Conservation	Protection of landslip areas at Seaton and elsewhere on the south Devon coast.
Author	P. M. Hammond.

Scopaeus minimus

A rove beetle	**VULNERABLE**
Order **Coleoptera**	Family **Staphylinidae**

Scopaeus minimus (Erichson, 1839).

Identification	Allen (1969a), p.200.
Distribution	Slapton Ley (south Devon) and Helston (west Cornwall). Populations are probably small and very localised.
Habitat and ecology	In fine shingle or gravel near water. In Britain known only from coastal localities. A predator. Adults have been collected in Britain from April to August.
Status	Known with certainty only from Slapton Ley (records from 1869 to 1943) and Helston (1947). I know of no very recent records, but the species probably still occurs at these two localities and, perhaps, in other suitable places on the south coast of Devon and Cornwall. Also recorded from Ramnor (New Forest), but the record requires confirmation. *S. minimus* is at the north-westernmost limit of its range in south-west England.
Conservation	Protection of shingle areas on the foreshore at Slapton Ley.
Author	P. M. Hammond.

Scopaeus minutus

A rove beetle   **VULNERABLE**

Order **Coleoptera**   Family **Staphylinidae**

Scopaeus minutus Erichson, 1840.

Identification   Allen (1969a), p.200.

Distribution   Charmouth and Bridport (Dorset). The populations are probably small and very localised.

Habitat and ecology   On damp sand beside fresh water. In Britain found beside springs and pools in coastal 'chines' and the broken faces of sandy cliffs. A predator. Adults have been collected in Britain in June and September.

Status   Known with certainty to occur only at Charmouth and Bridport. A recent record for Slapton Ley (Allen, 1970a) appears to be in error. Records for the Dorset coast extend from 1924 to 1934; the species is likely to persist in the Charmouth area and perhaps elsewhere on the coast of Dorset and south-east Devon. The south coast of England represents the north-westernmost extension of the species' range.

Threats   Any change of land use in the coastal localities where the species occurs.

Conservation   Protection of cliff areas at Charmouth and Bridport

Author   P. M. Hammond.

Astenus subditus

A rove beetle   **ENDANGERED**

Order **Coleoptera**   Family **Staphylinidae**

Astenus subditus (Mulsant & Rey, 1878).

Identification   Coiffait (1960), p.63; G.A. Lohse *in* Freude, Harde & Lohse (1964-83), 4:136.

Distribution   Whitsand Bay, east Cornwall. The population is probably small and localised.

Habitat and ecology   At the roots of grass and in moss, etc., in sandy or chalky situations. Predatory. Adults have been collected in Britain in April.

Status   Long confused with *A. procerus* (Gravenhorst) (= *filiformis* (Latreille)), a species more or less confined to the south coast in Britain, and also rare today. However, examination of all available British material of *Astenus* has revealed specimens of *A. subditus* from only one locality: Whitsand Bay, on the south coast of east Cornwall. The species was collected there by Donisthorpe in April 1907 and, at about the same period, by J. J. Walker. I know of no recent collections from Whitsand Bay or of any attempts to see if the species is still to be found there. The locality may well have changed considerably since 1907.

Threats   Any change of land use at Whitsand Bay.

Conservation   Further investigation of the only known British locality is needed.

Author   P. M. Hammond.

Philonthus dimidiatipennis

A rove beetle   **VULNERABLE**

Order **Coleoptera**   Family **Staphylinidae**

Philonthus dimidiatipennis Erichson, 1840.

Identification   Daltry (1958); G. A. Lohse *in* Freude, Harde & Lohse (1964-83), 4:185.

Distribution   Walberswick, Suffolk. The population is probably very localised.

Habitat and ecology   Found in saltmarshes and on the banks of brackish water. A predator.

Status   *P. dimidiatipennis* is widely distributed around the Mediterranean and also occurs in the vicinity of salt water east at least to the Caspian Sea. On the Atlantic coast of Europe it is also widespread, but was not reported north of Brittany before about 1950. In recent years the species has been found to occur on the Dutch coast, as well as in England. At Walberswick *P. dimidiatipennis* was discovered in June 1956 and collected there again in 1957. I know of no later records for this locality but the species may well still occur on the Suffolk coast.

Conservation   Protection of brackish marsh areas south of Walberswick.

Author   P. M. Hammond.

Cafius cicatricosus

A rove beetle   **ENDANGERED**

Order **Coleoptera**   Family **Staphylinidae**

Cafius cicatricosus (Erichson, 1840).

Identification   Joy (1932), p.115.

Distribution   Portsmouth, Milton Creek and Southsea (Hampshire); Ryde (Isle of Wight); Worthing and Shoreham-by-Sea (West Sussex). The populations are probably very localised.

Habitat and ecology	Restricted to the sea-shore, where it is found most commonly in and under drifted seaweed. A predator, mostly of dipterous larvae. Adults have been collected in Britain in the months May-October.
Status	Records for the south coast localities listed above extend from 1871 to 1908, when the species was found at Southsea and Milton Creek. I know of no subsequent records. The south coast of Britain represents the northernmost extension of the species' range.
Threats	Pollution of south coast beaches.
Conservation	Further investigaton is needed to establish whether the species still occurs in Britain.
Author	P. M. Hammond.

Emus hirtus

A rove beetle
ENDANGERED

Order **Coleoptera**
Family **Staphylinidae**

Emus hirtus (L., 1758).

Identification	Joy (1932), p.113; Harde (1984), fig. 147:4. A large and highly distinctive species. Long golden pubescence covering the head and pronotum, coupled with its size (c.20 to 25mm in length), make this beetle unmistakable.
Distribution	There are early 19th century records for the New Forest (Hampshire), Parley Heath (Dorset), Beachamwell (Norfolk), Guildford and Coombe Wood (Surrey), and Devon. Records for the second half of the 19th century cover Redruth (Cornwall), the New Forest, Southend (Essex), and Darland Hill, Sheerness and Sittingbourne (Kent). 20th century records are mostly for a small area straddling the Thames estuary: Sheerness district, Harty Marshes, Isle of Sheppey, Gillingham, Port Victoria, Cliffe, Isle of Grain, Faversham Creek and Canterbury (Kent); Benfleet, Canvey Island and near Southend (Essex). Other records are from Pevensey Bay, East Sussex (Ford), Merrow near Guildford, Surrey (Lloyd), and Midger Wood, Avon (Lear). The populations are undoubtedly small and localised, if indeed it is still in existence.
Habitat and ecology	On and in *fresh* cow and horse dung. Also sometimes found on carrion, on decaying fungi, and at sap exuding from tree stumps. Adults are active from April to November but the great majority of British records are for May-June. Larvae and adults prey on other insects, especially dipterous larvae.

| Status | Kentish records cover the years 1909 to 1950, the most recent being for Home Farm, Isle of Grain, June 1939 (Massee), and Old Park, Canterbury, May 1950 (Parry). In Essex the species was collected near Southend, June 1947 (Down), on Canvey Island, August 1949 (Weal) and at Benfleet in the 1950s (Watts). *E. hirtus* is at the north-western limit of its range in England and is generally rare today in the more northerly parts of Continental Europe. The species has suffered a decline during the present century in much of Central Europe. This seems likely to have involved climatic factors, and *E. hirtus* may no longer be a resident of the British Isles, the 1984 Avon record possibly being an accidental introduction. |

| Author | P. M. Hammond, using information from Allen (1962, 1964b), Huggins (1962), Brown (1963), Parry (1979) and Lear (1986). |

Velleius dilatatus

A rove beetle   **ENDANGERED**

Order **Coleoptera**   Family **Staphylinidae**

Velleius dilatatus (F., 1787).

| Identification | Joy (1932), p.107; Harde (1984), fig. 147:9. A large and highly distinctive species. |

| Distribution | The New Forest (Hampshire), Windsor Forest (Berkshire), Cokethorpe Park (Oxfordshire), Moccas Park (Hereford & Worcester), Wanstead (Greater London), Bury St Edmunds district (Suffolk), and Castle Drogo (Devon). |

| Habitat and ecology | Inhabits hornets' nests (*Vespa crabro* L.) in old trees. Adults and larvae of *V. dilatatus* prey on the dipterous larvae which occur in hornets' nest debris. There is no evidence that they are kleptoparasitic. Adults are sometimes collected at the exuding sap of *Cossus* (goat moth) trees. Adults have been collected in Britain in the months June-August and October. The populations are probably very small and localised. |

| Status | The single records for three of the known localities are old. Those for Windsor Forest (1952), Moccas Park (1964) and Castle Drogo (?) are more recent. Only the New Forest area has a number of records, extending from 1864 to 1971. The species is likely to persist in the New Forest area and, perhaps, in other areas of ancient forest or park woodland. Its continued presence in the British Isles depends very much on the fortunes of its host, the hornet. |

| Threats | Any threats to the ancient forest areas where it occurs and, more particularly, to hornets and their nesting sites. |

Conservation	Hornets' nests in the New Forest and Windsor Forest require protection. Castle Drogo Estate is a property of the National Trust.
Author	P. M. Hammond.

Quedius balticus

A rove beetle **ENDANGERED**

Order **Coleoptera** Family **Staphylinidae**

Quedius balticus Korge, 1960.

Identification	Last (1963), pp.43-45.
Distribution	Wicken Fen, Cambridgeshire, and Upton Broad, Norfolk. The populations are probably very localised.
Habitat and ecology	Damp litter, mostly in fens and marshes, and possibly confined to fen districts. Adults have been collected in Britain in February and May-August. Predatory.
Status	First described in 1960, up to which time it had been confused with *Q. molochinus* (Gravenhorst) (more or less generally distributed in the British Isles). The overall range of *Q. balticus* remains unclear, and its distribution in Britian uncertain. Records for Wicken Fen include captures in many years (from 1923), and the species is probably well-established there. One individual was collected at Upton Broad in 1980. *Q. balticus* may be expected to occur elsewhere in the Fen and Broad districts, although searching in some of the more likely areas has so far met with no success.
Threats	Any threat to areas of ancient fen.
Conservation	Wicken Fen is owned by the National Trust, and Upton Broad is a reserve of the Norfolk Naturalists' Trust. Measures to protect areas of fen and broad are needed.
Author	P. M. Hammond.

Acylophorus glaberrimus

A rove beetle **ENDANGERED**

Order **Coleoptera** Family **Staphylinidae**

Acylophorus glaberrimus (Herbst, 1784).

Identification	Joy (1932), p.106. A highly distinctive species.
Distribution	Barnes, Merton and Richmond, Greater London, and also near Brockenhurst (Balmer Lawn), New Forest. The populations are probably fairly small and highly localised.

Habitat and ecology	Among semi-aquatic vegetation, mostly in *Sphagnum* moss, often at the edge of ponds. Adults have been collected in Britain from May to September. Predatory; usual prey unknown, but probably a very restricted range.
Status	Records for ponds in London (Barnes, Merton, Richmond) date from 1859 and extend to at least 1876. The species would seem unlikely to persist in this area, which has undergone considerable development in the past hundred years. There were no other British records until 1970 when *A. glaberrimus* was discovered in the New Forest. It has since been collected in some numbers at this one locality (Marl Pits at Balmer Lawn) and probably still occurs there.
Threats	Any threat to the aquatic habitats at the New Forest locality where it occurs.
Conservation	Protection of the "Marl Pits" area at Balmer Lawn.
Author	P. M. Hammond.

Tachinus bipustulatus

A rove beetle

VULNERABLE

Order **Coleoptera**   Family **Staphylinidae**

Tachinus bipustulatus (F., 1792).

Identification	Joy (1932), p.92.
Distribution	There are old records for a number of localities in the London area (Bedford Park, Catford, Charlton, Ealing, Enfield, Regent's Park, Richmond Park, and Putney). There are also 19th century records for Addington and Chatham (Kent) and Wicken (Cambridgeshire), and 20th century records for Woking (Surrey), the New Forest (Hampshire), Windsor Forest (Berkshire), and Ryde (Isle of Wight). The populations are probably small and localised.
Habitat and ecology	Associated with sap-flows from deciduous trees, especially those resulting from attack by goat moth *Cossus* larvae. Adults have been collected in Britain from June to August. Predatory.
Status	The most recent records for this species are those for Windsor Forest (1930s). It is possibly now extinct in Britain, but if still present it is most likely to persist in forest areas such as the New Forest. Apparently at the north-western limit of its range in southern England, and the species' recent decline in Britain may involve climatic factors.
Conservation	Conservation of ancient forest areas in southern England.
Author	P. M. Hammond.

Euryusa optabilis

A rove beetle

VULNERABLE

Order **Coleoptera**　　　　　　　　Family **Staphylinidae**

Euryusa optabilis Heer, 1839.

Identification	Joy (1932), p.79.
Distribution	Southern England: 19th century records for Addington, Kent; Hainault Forest & Epping Forest (Loughton), Essex; Highgate, Greater London; Ilfracombe, north Devon; Shirley, Surrey; and Tilgate Forest, West Sussex. There are 20th century records for Windsor Forest and Silwood Park, Berkshire, and the New Forest, Hampshire (Denny Wood). The populations are probably small and localised.
Habitat and ecology	In the decaying wood of old trees, in company with the ant *Lasius brunneus* (Latreille) (and sometimes other species, e.g. *L. fuliginosus* (Latreille) and *L.* niger (L.)), but not an obligatory myrmecophile. Sometimes found in litter at the base of old beeches *Fagus* or oaks *Quercus*, especially those attacked by goat moth *Cossus* larvae. Adults have been collected in Britain in most months. Probably predatory.
Status	Taken on many occasions in Windsor Forest between about 1910 and 1938, and again in June 1983 (J. A. Owen). The Silwood Park record is for 1964 and the New Forest record also for the same period. The species may persist in other ancient forest areas in southern Britain.
Threats	Any threat to the ancient forest areas in question. The removal of dead timber, especially that occupied by *Lasius brunneus*.
Conservation	Measures to conserve areas of ancient forest and its dead wood fauna.
Author	P. M. Hammond.

Euryusa sinuata

A rove beetle

ENDANGERED

Order **Coleoptera**　　　　　　　　Family **Staphylinidae**

Euryusa sinuata Erichson, 1837.

Identification	Joy (1932), p.79.
Distribution	Windsor Forest and Silwood Park, Berkshire, and Langley Park, Buckinghamshire. The populations are probably small and very localised.

Habitat and ecology	In the decaying wood of old trees, in company with the ant *Lasius brunneus* (Latreille); apparently not an obligatory myrmecophile, as Continental records refer to individuals found in decaying wood without ants. Adults have been collected in Britain in most months. Probably predatory.
Status	With such a highly localised habitat it is easily overlooked, but is possibly restricted to Windsor Forest and nearby old park woodland. Windsor Forest records cover twelve different years from 1923 to 1983. The Silwood Park record is for 1964 and that for Langley Park for 1979. The species' Continental range suggests that it is unlikely to occur in England much further north.
Threats	Any threat to the ancient forest areas in question. The removal of dead timber, especially that occupied by *Lasius brunneus*.
Conservation	Measures to conserve areas of ancient forest and its dead wood fauna.
Author	P. M. Hammond.

Tachyusida gracilis

A rove beetle   **ENDANGERED**

Order **Coleoptera**   Family **Staphylinidae**

Tachyusida gracilis (Erichson, 1837).

Identification	Joy (1932), pp.74-75, 80.
Distribution	Only known from Windsor Forest, Berkshire. The population is probably small and very localised.
Habitat and ecology	In the wood mould of old trees, especially oaks *Quercus*. Most British captures have been from nests of the ant *Lasius brunneus* (Latreille), but the species is apparently not an obligatory myrmecophile. Probably predatory. Adults have been collected in Britain in the months May, August and October.
Status	A distinctive species with apparently very specialised habitat requirements. Possibly restricted to Windsor Forest, where specimens were collected in October 1926, May 1945, 1972, and August 1982. Scarce throughout its Continental range (mainly Central Europe) and regarded in mainland Europe as a relict 'Urwald' species.
Threats	Any threat to the ancient forest area in question. The removal of dead trees and timber.
Conservation	Measures to conserve ancient forest and its dead wood fauna.
Author	P. M. Hammond.

Amarochara bonnairei

A rove beetle　　　　　　　　　　　　**ENDANGERED**

Order **Coleoptera**　　　　　　　　　Family **Staphylinidae**

Amarochara bonnairei (Fauvel, 1865).

Identification　Joy (1932), p.36.

Distribution　Mickleham (Surrey), Tring (Hertfordshire) and the New Forest (Hampshire). The populations are probably small and undoubtedly very localised.

Habitat and ecology　Apparently a more or less strictly woodland species, found mostly in damp places. Reputedly myrmecophilous and often found in company with either of the ants *Lasius brunneus* (Latreille) or *L. fuliginosus* (Latreille), in old tree stumps, moss and leaf litter. All but two of the known British specimens were collected from the runs of *L. fuliginosus* at the root of an old beech tree *Fagus*, but were not found in the nest of these ants. Probably predatory. Adults have been collected in Britain in the months May-July (April-August in Germany).

Status　Records for the three known British localities extend from 1862 to 1915, in which year a single individual was collected by Sharp in the New Forest. *A. bonnairei* is apparently at the northern limit of its range in southern England (it is absent from Scandinavia), but may still occur in the New Forest or other wooded areas in the south of England.

Conservation　Measures to conserve areas of ancient forest in southern England.

Author　P. M. Hammond.

Stichoglossa semirufa

A rove beetle　　　　　　　　　　　　**VULNERABLE**

Order **Coleoptera**　　　　　　　　　Family **Staphylinidae**

Stichoglossa semirufa (Erichson, 1839).

Identification　Joy (1932), pp.16-21 and 34. Figured by G.A. Lohse *in* Freude, Harde & Lohse (1964-83), 5:285.

Distribution　The Colchester district (Essex), the Lyndhurst district (New Forest), and Elsworth Wood (Cambridgeshire). The populations are probably small and very localised.

Habitat and ecology　In the decaying wood and wood mould of old deciduous trees, and at the foot of these trees. Adults have been collected in Britain in May and June. Probably a predator.

Status	Likely to be at the edge of its overall range in southern England. There are only three British records: one individual beaten from an oak *Quercus* near Colchester, May 1898, one found under loose bark of a standing beech *Fagus* near Lyndhurst, May 1969, and three taken from field maple *Acer campestre* by fogging with insecticide, June 1983. The circumstances suggest that the species is established in Britain, but probably confined to areas of ancient forest in the south.
Threats	Any threat to ancient forest areas where the species occurs. The removal of dead timber.
Conservation	Measures to conserve ancient forest and its dead wood fauna.
Author	P. M. Hammond, using additional information from Welch (1984).

Haploglossa picipennis

A rove beetle **VULNERABLE**

Order **Coleoptera** Family **Staphylinidae**

Haploglossa picipennis (Gyllenhal, 1827), formerly known as *Microglossa picipennis*.

Identification	Joy (1932), p.29.
Distribution	Known only from Wales, two south Devon localities and two neighbouring localities on Speyside (Highland). It is possible that moderate numbers of *H. picipennis* can build up locally in the nests of raptors, particularly those using an established nest site. Otherwise it is extremely localised in its distribution.
Habitat and ecology	In Britain known only from the nests of raptorial birds including buzzard *Buteo buteo*, sparrowhawk *Accipiter nisus* and osprey *Pandion haliaetus*. The larvae are unknown, but the larvae and adults are almost certainly predators upon the larvae of flies (Diptera) and fleas (Siphonaptera) and other small nidicolous invertebrates.
Status	The first British records are from buzzards' nests collected in mid-Wales and near Exeter in July 1929. Joy (1930) also reports one specimen being swept by Dr. Nicholson in Devon in the same year. Later a single specimen was also recorded from a buzzard's nest at Bellever, Dartmoor (south Devon), on 19 August 1957 (Allen, 1977). The only other known localities are both on Speyside. On 6 September 1966 several were extracted from a sparrowhawk's nest at Polchar, Aviemore (Welch, 1979a), five specimens were obtained from an osprey's nest at Loch Garten in November 1979 (Carter *et al*, 1980), and others from osprey nests at

four other sites in 1983 (J. A. Owen, pers. comm.). The limited availability of raptor nests for study impedes the aquisition of further records of this species. However, a number of sparrowhawks' nests have been examined from Dumfries & Galloway, Anglesey and Windsor Forest (Berkshire) without finding further specimens.

Conservation

The Loch Garten osprey's nest site has 24-hour wardening during the breeding season and other raptors have legal protection for themselves and their nesting sites.

Author

R. C. Welch.

Aleochara inconspicua

A rove beetle

VULNERABLE

Order **Coleoptera**

Family **Staphylinidae**

Aleochara inconspicua Aube, 1850.

Identification

Welch (1965).

Distribution

The first confirmed record, by Blair (1933), is of one female collected in a hollow in a cliff face at Dunwich, west Suffolk. The next published record was by Dobson (1964) of its parasitising wheat bulb fly puparia in moderate numbers near Whittlesey and Peterborough, Cambridgeshire, although in May 1953 J. Bond had found a few parasitising puparia at Crowland, south Lincolnshire, and in June 1953 C. E. Tottenham found seven in small clumps of couch-grass *Elymus repens* on an allotment in Cambridge. Between July 1974 and January 1975 three males were collected in pitfall traps on a reseeded area of Royston Heath, Hertfordshire, bordered on one side by various cereal crops. A single female was recently identified in some pitfall trap material collected by M. L. Luff from a walled garden at Heddon-on-the-Wall, south Northumberland (Welch, 1983b). Very localised and usually occurring singly or in small numbers.

Habitat and ecology

The larvae are parasitic in the puparia of the wheat bulb fly *Delia coarctata* (Fallen) (Diptera, Anthomyiidae) (Dobson, 1964; Welch, 1965). The adults are predaceous on fly larvae and other small invertebrates. This species has never been recognised parasitising other species of Anthomyiidae which have been studied more extensively.

Status

Possibly restricted to the one host, *Delia coarctata*.

Threats

Possibly at risk from insecticidal sprays, etc, used against its host.

Author

R. C. Welch.

Aleochara maculata

A rove beetle   **VULNERABLE**

Order **Coleoptera**   Family **Staphylinidae**

Aleochara maculata Brisout, 1863.

Identification   Joy (1932), pp.26-28; Welch (1965).

Distribution   Originally recorded from shingle banks of the River Lyn, north Devon, by Gorham (1870) from a specimen collected some years earlier. Only known from thirteen localities in nine vice-counties in southern England (mainly in the Home Counties). The most northerly record is from Church Stretton, Shropshire, by W. G. Blatch in 1891. The most recent specimens were swept in Windsor Forest, Berkshire, by A. A. Allen on 30 August 1941 (Allen, 1942) and 22 May 1946.

Habitat and ecology   Presumed to be parasitic in the larval stages within dipterous puparia, with the adult being predacious. Mainly found singly by sweeping. The habitat is unknown but a number of specimens have been collected in woodland.

Status   Not recorded in Britain since 1946. This species has always been rare throughout its known European range. Its apparent loss from Britain may be due to a contraction of its overall range in Western Europe.

Author   R. C. Welch.

Aleochara moesta

A rove beetle   **VULNERABLE**

Order **Coleoptera**   Family **Staphylinidae**

Aleochara moesta Gravenhorst, 1802, formerly known as *A. crassiuscula* Sahlberg.

Identification   Joy (1932), pp.26-28; Welch (1965).

Distribution   Known from twelve sites in eight vice-counties in southern England, the most northerly being from Cheshire. Originally found in some numbers by Champion (1908) under dung at Great Yarmouth, east Norfolk. It was taken regularly by J. J. Walker in the Oxford area in the same period but the last known record is that of C. E. Tottenham at Cambridge in April 1945. The name *A. moesta* was also in common use by British coleopterists for either *A. sparsa* Heer or *A. diversa* Sahlberg (including the more recently recognised *A. albovillosa* Bernhauer). Early records indicate that it could be locally common.

Habitat and ecology	The larvae are presumed to be parasitic within dipterous puparia, and the adults predacious upon dipterous larvae and other small invertebrates. Apparently associated with dung and manure heaps.
Status	Not recorded in Britain for 37 years, despite a considerable amount of Coleoptera-collecting from dung.
Author	R. C. Welch.

Aleochara villosa

A rove beetle   **VULNERABLE**

Order **Coleoptera**   Family **Staphylinidae**

Aleochara villosa Mannerheim, 1830.

Identification	Joy (1932), pp.26-28; Welch (1965).
Distribution	Prior to 1930 this species was known from twenty scattered localities in fourteen vice-counties including Braemar, Deeside. Most specimens in British collections originate from pigeon cotes in Scarborough, North Yorkshire, from 1880. It was last taken in that area in 1930, and the same year B. S. Williams reported collecting single specimens at Harpenden, Hertfordshire, during 1926 and 1927. It was not until fifty years later that it was found in numbers in the base of a dovecote at Wytham, Oxford, in August 1980 (Welch, 1982), and again the following year. It may be common within its very localised specific habitat.
Habitat and ecology	The larvae are parasitic within dipterous puparia (Muscidae). The adults are predacious on dipterous larvae and small invertebrates. Typically found in very dry straw and droppings in dovecotes, stables, etc.
Status	Very localised. It was found to be well-established at only one site after not having been recorded for fifty years.
Threats	This species may only have survived in the very few dovecotes which have remained in continuous use up to the present day.
Author	R. C. Welch.

Bibloplectus tenebrosus

VULNERABLE

Order **Coleoptera**   Family **Pselaphidae**

Bibloplectus tenebrosus (Reitter, 1880).

| Identification | Pearce (1957), pp.19-20, figs 12 and 18. |
| Distribution | Older records from the New Forest area, Brockenhurst and Hurn, in south Hampshire. Early records from Glamorgan |

170

were later deleted by Pearce (1971). There are recent records from Askham Bog, North Yorkshire (1970); Hickling Broad, east Norfolk (1979); and Woodwalton Fen (1977) and Holme Fen (1980), Cambridgeshire. The populations are presumably small and localised.

Habitat and ecology

In thick deep moss in bogs and swamps, or in grass tussocks. The larva is unknown.

Status

Not recorded during a survey of the New Forest in late 1960s/early 1970s. Pearce (1971) writing in May 1970 states: "In recent years it has occurred on Askham Bog to C. Johnson, E. W. Aubrook and myself." A single male was sieved from sedge refuse in Woodwalton Fen on 24 May 1977 by C. Johnson. 27 were collected in ten pitfall traps placed in an area of *Sphagnum squarrosum/S. fimbriatum* at Holme Fen, 2-16 May 1980. A single male and female were collected at Hickling Broad on 24 May 1979 by C. Johnson. A species easily overlooked which may survive in small local populations in other East Anglian fens.

Threats

Drainage of bogs and fens, or drying out due to scrub invasion.

Conservation

Hickling Broad, Woodwalton Fen and Holme Fen are NNRs. The Holme Fen site needs to be maintained by controlling scrub invasion. Askham Bog is a reserve of the Yorkshire Wildlife Trust.

Author

R. C. Welch, using additional information from Welch (1979b, 1983a).

Plectophloeus nitidus

ENDANGERED

Order **Coleoptera**   Family **Pselaphidae**

Plectophloeus nitidus (Fairmaire, 1857).

Identification

Pearce (1957); see also C. Besuchet *in* Freude, Harde & Lohse (1964-83), 5:324-326. Specialist identification is necessary. Two species of *Plectophloeus* are now known to occur in Britain, and further species of the genus may await discovery.

Distribution

Windsor Forest (Berkshire), Sherwood Forest (Nottinghamshire), Moccas Park (Hereford & Worcester), and Blenheim Park (Oxfordshire). The populations are probably very small and very localised.

Habitat and ecology

In rotten wood. Most British records are for old red-rotten oaks *Quercus* and all are for areas of long-established deciduous forest and park woodland. A predator, probably of mites. Adults have been collected in Britain in the months May-October.

Status	This small species (1.0-1.5 mm in length) is no doubt easily overlooked and may well persist in all of the British localities from which it is known, although there are post-1950 records for only three of them. *P. nitidus* was collected at Blenheim Park in 1954, at Moccas Park in 1950 and again in 1975, and in Windsor Forest on various occasions in 1980-82 (J. A. Owen, pers. comm.).
Threats	Any threat to areas of ancient forest. The removal of dead timber.
Conservation	Measures to conserve ancient forest and its dead wood fauna.
Author	P. M. Hammond.

Batrisodes buqueti

ENDANGERED

Order **Coleoptera** Family **Pselaphidae**

Batrisodes buqueti (Aube, 1833), formerly misidentified in Britain as *B. adnexus* (Hampe).

Identification	Pearce (1957), p.24 (but note that *B. buqueti* has relatively slender antennae; the words "robust" and "slender" in Pearce's couplet 1 should be transposed).
Distribution	Only known from Windsor Forest, Berkshire. The population is probably small and very localised.
Habitat and ecology	Found in the decaying wood of old deciduous trees, usually in association with ants of the genus *Lasius*. British records are all for specimens taken in association with *Lasius brunneus* (Latreille). A predator, probably of mites. Adults have been collected in Britain in June and August.
Status	Recorded only from Windsor Forest, where single individuals have been found on four occasions (in 1924, 1926 and 1939). Donisthorpe (1939) reports that he had examined "hundreds" of *Lasius brunneus* nests at Windsor but had found this species only twice. *B. buqueti* is either a rare species at Windsor or is very difficult to find.
Threats	Any threat to areas of ancient forest. The removal of dead timber, especially that occupied by *Lasius brunneus*.
Conservation	Measures to conserve ancient forest and its dead wood fauna.
Author	P. M. Hammond.

Batrisodes delaporti

ENDANGERED

Order **Coleoptera**   Family **Pselaphidae**

Batrisodes delaporti (Aube, 1833).

Identification   Pearce (1957), p.24 (but note that *B. delaporti* has relatively stout antennae; the words "robust" and "slender" in Pearce's couplet 1 should be transposed).

Distribution   Only known from the Windsor Forest area, Berkshire. The population is probably very small and localised, though it is apparently commoner than *B. buqueti.*

Habitat and ecology   Associated with the ant *Lasius brunneus* (Latreille) and usually found only in the ants' nests, in the decaying wood of old deciduous trees. A predator, probably of mites. Adults have been collected in Britain in most months.

Status   Like several other beetle species associated with *Lasius brunneus*, the only recorded site for *B. delaporti* in Britain is Windsor Forest. More than 200 individuals were collected by Donisthorpe between 1924 (when the species was first discovered in Britain) and 1939, from various *L. brunneus* nests. Specimens were taken on five occasions in May-June 1983 and April 1984 (J. A. Owen, pers. comm.). Five specimens were found in a *L. brunneus* nest in a large oak at Silwood Park, Ascot, Berkshire, in June 1964 (R. C. Welch, pers. comm.).

Threats   Any threat to areas of ancient forest. The removal of dead timber, especially that occupied by *Lasius brunneus.*

Conservation   Measures to conserve ancient forest and its dead wood fauna.

Author   P. M. Hammond.

Claviger longicornis

ENDANGERED

Order **Coleoptera**   Family **Pselaphidae**

Claviger longicornis Mueller, 1818.

Identification   Pearce (1957), p.11.

Distribution   Kirtlington (Oxfordshire), Sully (South Glamorgan), Box Hill (Surrey), and Wootton (Isle of Wight). The populations are probably small and very localised.

Habitat and ecology	Found in the nests of the ants *Lasius umbratus* (Nylander) and *L. mixtus* (Nylander), which usually occur under deeply-embedded stones in limestone districts. Occasionally found in the nests of other *Lasius* species. Adults have been collected in Britain in the months May-June and August-October. Notes concerning the behaviour and general biology of *C. longicornis* are provided by Donisthorpe & Chapman (1913).
Status	First discovered in Britain by J. J. Walker, who collected five individuals at Kirtlington in 1906. The species was found again at Kirtlington in 1913 and, in the same year, was collected in reasonable numbers at Box Hill. Further records are for Sully (1916) and Wootton (1928). No recent records for the species have been traced, but it is likely to persist in southern England, at suitable sites on limestone where the host ants are to be found.
Author	P. M. Hammond.

Trox perlatus ENDANGERED

Order **Coleoptera** Family **Trogidae**

Trox perlatus Goeze, 1777, formerly misidentified in Britain as *T. hispidus* (Pontoppidan).

Identification	Britton (1956), p.6 and fig.13.
Distribution	Only known from Devon and Dorset.
Habitat and ecology	In animal debris near the coast. Continental specimens have been found under the nests of birds-of-prey on the Atlantic cliffs.
Status	Introduced as British in 1860 by Waterhouse, on the authority of specimens for which he did not know the locality. An old specimen collected by Rev. H. Matthews also existed without data (Fowler, 1887-91, 4:46). Pearce (1926) reported a single specimen collected by R. B. Benson at Tyneham, Dorset, on 8 August 1922, the identity of which was eventually settled by Allen (1967). P. Harwood (1929) collected small numbers of *T. perlatus* in the skins of two very young dead lambs on the cliffs above Worbarrow Bay near Lulworth Cove in March 1929 and April 1930 (A.B. Drane, pers. comm.), thus confirming this species as British. *T. perlatus* does not appear to have been recorded since and was not found during an intensive survey of the Lulworth Ranges by ITE in 1975.
Author	R. C. Welch.

Aegialia rufa

ENDANGERED

Order **Coleoptera**   Family **Scarabaeidae**

Aegialia rufa (F., 1792), formerly known as *Rhysothorax rufus*.

Identification Britton (1956), p.9.

Distribution Known from sandy coasts of the Liverpool district between the Rivers Ribble and Dee – Birkdale, Southport, Formby, Wallasey and New Brighton (Merseyside); and Barmouth (Meirionnydd). Adults occur during May and June with extreme irregularity, being abundant some years with only two or three (or none) recorded in other years.

Habitat and ecology Occurs on coastal sand dunes. Biology unknown.

Status First taken at New Brighton, Wallasey, in June 1862, and spasmodically taken in abundance (e.g. 1885, 1886 and 1905). Johnson (1962b) comments that *A. rufa* was apparently locally common on the Lancashire and Cheshire sandhills up to around 1906, but does not appear to have been recorded since then. He thought it possible that it could still occur around Birkdale but must be quite rare. Williams (1969) found a single specimen on the dunes at Formby on 12 July 1963 together with *A. arenaria* (F.), but no more were found during subsequent visits to the area. Jackson (1907) recorded a single dead *A. rufa* from Barmouth, its only other known locality in Britain.

Threats Urbanisation of coastal dunes and the development of golf courses.

Author R. C. Welch.

Aphodius brevis

A dung beetle   **ENDANGERED**

Order **Coleoptera**   Family **Scarabaeidae**

Aphodius (Ammoecius) brevis Erichson, 1848.

Identification Britton (1956), p.22 and fig.42.

Distribution Known from Southport and Birkdale (Merseyside), Matlock (Derbyshire), Bewdley (Hereford & Worcester), and Pool (West Yorkshire). Very localised but may be abundant.

Habitat and ecology *A. brevis* is said to live on rabbits' dung and to excavate burrows about 4 cm long, into which it retreats in dry weather. Also recorded from partly dry cow dung. Recorded from coastal dunes and sandy localities inland.

Status	First taken at Southport in May 1859 and certainly locally common on that coast up until 1913. Johnson (1962b) commented that the rabbit population had greatly diminished but was of the opinion that *A. brevis* probably still occurred at Southport but was most likely very localised. Fowler & Donisthorpe (1913) attribute the Matlock and Bewdley localities to Blatch. These are included by Joy (1932) but omitted by Britton (1956). Flint (1957) provides a more recent inland record of a single specimen collected on 6 May 1956 from a sand-bank on the River Wharfe at Castley Ford, near Pool, West Yorkshire.
Threats	Loss of dune areas due to urban development, and the stabilisation of turf for golf courses.
Author	R. C. Welch.

Aphodius niger

A dung beetle   **ENDANGERED**

Order **Coleoptera**   Family **Scarabaeidae**

Aphodius (Nialus) niger (Panzer, 1796).

Identification	Britton (1956), p.22.
Distribution	Only known from the Brockenhurst area of the New Forest (Hampshire).
Habitat and ecology	In mud at the sides of ponds frequented by cattle and horses.
Status	First recorded by D. Sharp from the New Forest in 1909, and taken the same year on the banks of a pond at Brockenhurst by G. C. Champion. It was present at the same locality spasmodically for at least thirty years. I have a specimen collected by W. West in June 1918, and the most recent records I know of are those of A. M. Massee from Balmer Lawn on 1 September 1931 and 10 April 1938, although it has almost certainly been taken there since. Hallett (1952) recorded *A. niger* from Treago Castle (Hereford & Worcester) in May 1942 and from flood refuse by the River Wye in 1946. Johnson (1962a) has since examined the specimens in the R. W. Lloyd collection and found the above two specimens and one labelled "22 September 1946 Ross flood" all to refer to *A. pusillus* (Herbst).
Author	R. C. Welch.

Psammodius porcicollis

Order **Coleoptera**   Family **Scarabaeidae**

Psammodius porcicollis (Illiger, 1803).

Identification   Britton (1956), p.23 and fig.51.

Distribution   Known only from Whitsand Bay (Cornwall) and Pyle (Mid Glamorgan).

Habitat and ecology   Sandy places on the coast, under stones, in vegetable debris and at the roots of low herbage, e.g. rest-harrow *Ononis*. Biology unknown.

Status   J. J. Walker and others found a few specimens last century (1875-97) at Whitsand Bay, 6km from Devonport. One previous specimen was known from the Kirby collection mixed with *P. sulcicollis* (Illiger), but bearing no data (Fowler, 1887-91, 4:38). The only other known locality is in South Wales at Pyle, where J. R. le B. Tomlin recorded the species (Fowler & Donisthorpe, 1913). *P. porcicollis* does not appear to have been found in Britain for the past seventy years.

Author   R. C. Welch.

Diastictus vulneratus

VULNERABLE

Order **Coleoptera**   Family **Scarabaeidae**

Diastictus vulneratus (Sturm, 1805).

Identification   Britton (1956), p.11; Harde (1984), fig. 237:3.

Distribution   Near Brandon (?west Suffolk), near Icklingham, Foxhole Heath and Knettishall Heath (west Suffolk). Populations possibly cover substantial areas of open Breckland but are unlikely to be very large.

Habitat and ecology   Restricted to sandy situations in mostly dry, open, heathy areas. Also sometimes found (in Continental Europe) on sandy river banks. Most British specimens have been collected from the entrances to rabbits' burrows or by pitfall trapping, but the species is also to be found under stones, in moss and ground litter. Several Continental records specify an association with the ant *Formica fusca* L., but an obligatory relationship with this ant would seem unlikely. Adults have been collected in Britain in the months April-June and September.

Status	The first British find of this species was in 1902 at a site near Brandon. Further specimens were collected at the same site in 1906 and 1907, and two more were collected "near Brandon" in 1912. A single individual (the seventh British specimen) was found at Knettishall Heath in 1939. There appear to be no further British records until 1962, when M. G. Morris collected a single individual near Icklingham (for review of records to that date see Morris, 1963). The same collector trapped several individuals at Foxhole Heath in 1964. *D. vulneratus* is widely distributed in Continental Europe, but its overall range is of the 'Continental' type. In Britain, like several other beetle species of this type, it is probably restricted to the Breckland area.
Threats	Any threat to the remaining areas of open Breckland in west Suffolk and west Norfolk.
Conservation	Measures to conserve areas of open Breckland are needed.
Author	P. M. Hammond.

Copris lunaris

Horned Dung Beetle **ENDANGERED**

Order **Coleoptera**   Family **Scarabaeidae**

Copris lunaris (L., 1758).

Identification	Britton (1956), p.9 and fig.12; Harde (1984), fig. 233:4. Larva: van Emden (1941), p.122.
Distribution	Most recent records come from the North Downs of Surrey (the Godalming/Guildford area, 1903-17, and two or three sites in the Box Hill area, 1939-55), with two records from the Abingdon area of Oxfordshire (Tubney in 1913, Frilford Heath in 1942). Older records included several localities in south London (including Richmond Park), Shoreham and Chatham (Kent), Bungay and Ipswich (Suffolk), Bournemouth (Dorset), Bath (Avon), and Whitmore (Staffordshire) (Fowler, 1887-91, 4:10; Fowler & Donisthorpe, 1913, p.270). Colonies can be quite extensive, but it is many years since the species was found "in plenty" (Stephens, 1827-35, 3:171).
Habitat and ecology	Occurs on well-drained, unploughed pastures, on either chalky or sandy soil. *C. lunaris* belongs to a group of scarabs remarkable for the parental care that they exhibit. The adults cooperate in excavating an oblique or vertical tunnel up to 10-20cm deep, under cow (or horse) dung, leaving a large cast on the surface. A large terminal brood chamber is prepared and furnished with four to seven brood balls of dung, and only one egg is laid on each ball. The female remains in the brood chamber until the new adults emerge three to four months later (Klemperer, 1982a, 1982b). Adults are usually seen in mid to late May (to July) and fly at dusk on warm evenings.

Status	The sites in the Box Hill area are well-documented (Allen, 1956b), beginning with a specimen taken by A. M. Easton in 1939. In May 1948 L. S. Whicher and A. A. Allen took six adults in the same field, in the vicinity of shallow burrows in hard, chalky ground, and took a few more a few days later in another field in the area. On revisiting the site in subsequent years Allen and others failed to find further specimens. At 10.30pm on 27 May 1955 a male was taken in flight indoors at the nearby Juniper Hall Field Centre, but it appears that none have been recorded in Britain since that date. Like many scarabs, *C. lunaris* is much commoner in southern Europe and is on the edge of its range in Britain.
Threats	Allen (1956b) cites the ploughing-up of its habitats, and drought rendering the ground too hard for burrowing. Over-collecting was discounted in view of the difficulty of extracting specimens at depth in stony soil.
Conservation	If colonies are located the sites should be protected from ploughing. Grazing could be encouraged on unploughed downland such as Box Hill itself (a National Trust property), as the supply of dung is probably inadequate there at present (Allen, 1956b).
Author	D. B. Shirt.

Gnorimus variabilis

A chafer **ENDANGERED**

Order **Coleoptera** Family **Scarabaeidae**

Gnorimus variabilis (L., 1758).

Identification	Britton (1956), p.27; Harde (1984), fig. 243:8. Larva: van Emden (1941), p.126.
Distribution	Known only from the London area up to 1908: Brixton, Penge, Tooting Common, Purley, Lee and Balham. There are recent records only from Windsor Forest (Berkshire). Has been recorded in considerable numbers at Brixton and Windsor, although such populations are very localised and may be restricted to a single tree.
Habitat and ecology	Adults have been taken on flowers, but the larvae feed in black wood mould in the forks and hollow centre of old oaks *Quercus* and beeches *Fagus*.
Status	First recorded from Penge in 1806, and 150 specimens were taken at Brixton in 1849. A damaged specimen was found on a path at Balham in 1898 and it was still present at Lee, Woolwich, around the turn of the century. In 1908 E. C. Bedwell rediscovered a quantity of larvae under the bark of one of the Purley oaks. *G. variabilis* was first taken at Windsor about 1811, then not again until 1898, and Donisthorpe found it for the first time on 24 July 1925.

Subsequently he found all stages in considerable numbers. The larva was collected at Windsor in June 1930. For a review of pre-war records see Allen (1960a). In May 1972 A. A. Allen and G. Shephard found larvae in a hollow beech in the High Standing Hill area of Windsor Forest. Larvae were also found by J. A. Owen in April 1984.

Threats The removal of ancient rotten oaks and beeches.

Conservation The Crown Estates Commissioners are aware of the importance of old trees at Windsor, both standing and fallen.

Author R. C. Welch.

Curimopsis nigrita

A pill beetle — **ENDANGERED**

Order **Coleoptera** Family **Byrrhidae**

Curimopsis nigrita (Palm, 1934).

Identification Johnson (1978).

Distribution Only known in Britain from Thorne Waste, South Yorkshire. In Europe its known distribution is restricted to southern Sweden, Denmark and northern parts of Germany and Poland.

Habitat and ecology Apparently confined to lowland peat bogs in the presence of heather *Calluna*, unlike *Bembidion humerale* Sturm (also Endangered and known from Thorne Moors), which requires bare peat.

Status Known from a single female sieved from "vegetational debris in a boggy situation with heather and peat" on 15 April 1977 (Buckland & Johnson, 1983).

Threats Drainage and commercial peat extraction have greatly reduced what was the largest area of lowland peat bog remaining in England, and the threat persists.

Conservation Part of the moor is an NNR, although it is very doubtful whether management for such a localised species is possible.

Author R. C. Welch.

Normandia nitens

A riffle beetle — **VULNERABLE**

Order **Coleoptera** Family **Elmidae (Elminthidae)**

Normandia nitens (Mueller, 1817).

Identification Holland (1972), p.24, figs 15 and 16.

Distribution	The only confirmed records are from the River Severn catchment. For map see Holland (1980), p.10. Isolated populations at low densities: only single specimens have ever been captured.
Habitat and ecology	Freshwater rivers. The larvae and adults are aquatic. Pupates in the river bank at the water's edge. The adults are flightless, and have been collected in the months July-September.
Status	Prior to the publication of Holland (1972) all identifications have been made on the basis of unreliable external features. Examination of the genitalia of museum material has so far failed to confirm any old records. Modern records are limited to localities in Hereford & Worcester: the River Teme at Knightsford Bridge in 1965 and 1971, the River Wye at Symonds Yat in 1977, and again in the Teme near Bransford in 1980.
Threats	Always under threat from accidental pollution to the river. There will be a long-term decline in water quality if present standards are not maintained.
Conservation	The sites are not known to be specially protected. Normal water quality standards are maintained by Severn-Trent Water Authority.
Author	D. G. Holland.

Stenelmis canaliculata

A riffle beetle

VULNERABLE

Order **Coleoptera**

Family **Elmidae (Elminthidae)**

Stenelmis canaliculata (Gyllenhal, 1808).

Identification	Holland (1972), p.22, figs 13 and 14; also larva p.34 and pupa p.40.
Distribution	Lake Windermere (Cumbria), the River Nene (Cambridgeshire), the River Lymn/Steeping (Lincolnshire), and the River Wye (Powys). For map see Holland (1980), p.11. Thinly distributed on the exposed shores of Lake Windermere. The river populations are probably at low density.
Habitat and ecology	Stony lake shores and freshwater rivers. The larvae and adults are aquatic. The adults are flightless.

Status	First recorded at Windermere in 1960 and taken on several occasions from then until the latest capture in 1978. Population numbers are apparently on the decline, as only three specimens were taken in 1978. The River Wye locality was found in 1983.
Threats	Windermere is under threat of long-term eutrophication. River sites are always under threat of accidental pollution and long-term decline in water quality if present standards are not maintained.
Conservation	The sites are not known to be specially protected. Normal water quality standards are maintained by the water authorities.
Author	D. G. Holland.

Anthaxia nitidula

A jewel beetle **ENDANGERED**

Order **Coleoptera** Family **Buprestidae**

Anthaxia nitidula (L., 1758).

Identification	Levey (1977), p.4; Harde (1984), fig.181:8, 9.
Distribution	Only recorded from the Brockenhurst and Lyndhurst areas of the New Forest (Hampshire). The most recent record is 1954. It appears to be a very localised species.
Habitat and ecology	Larvae develop beneath the bark of blackthorn *Prunus spinosa* and some other woody Rosaceae. Adults frequent the flowers of hawthorns *Crataegus*, roses *Rosa*, and buttercups *Ranunculus*. Adults have been collected from mid-May to late July.
Status	At the extreme edge of its range in south-east England. The last three specimens were taken off hawthorn in June 1954 (Allen, 1955b).
Threats	Changes to open areas of the New Forest with abundant woody Rosaceae, such as afforestation, would probably eliminate this species.
Conservation	Preservation of the open nature of such areas as Balmer Lawn would probably favour this species.
Author	B. Levey.

Agrilus pannonicus

A jewel beetle　　　　　　　　　　**VULNERABLE**

Order **Coleoptera**　　　　　　　　Family **Buprestidae**

Agrilus pannonicus (Piller & Mitterpacher, 1783), formerly known as *A. biguttatus* (F.).

Identification　　Levey (1977), p.4; Harde (1984), fig.183:4.

Distribution　　Sherwood Forest, near Ollerton, Nottinghamshire (last record in 1940); Bishops Wood, Batchworth, Hertfordshire (1953); Windsor Forest, Berkshire (1972 and 1984); Kingspark Wood, West Sussex (1977); and Richmond Park and Hampstead Heath, Greater London (both in 1984). There are old records from Darenth Wood (Kent), Cuckfield (Surrey), and the New Forest (Hampshire). The populations appear to be very localised.

Habitat and ecology　　The larvae develop in and under the bark of oaks *Quercus*. They appear to attack mainly old, dying and dead trees, and are probably confined to old woods with oaks. The adults have been collected in June and early July.

Status　　A widespread European species. It is probably confined to England in Britain, but its occurrence as far north as Sherwood Forest suggests that it is not at the edge of its range in Britain. Probably a restriction in habitat accounts for its localisation. The lack of recent records suggests that some of its former strongholds may have become unsuitable. Its present status needs to be investigated.

Threats　　Any threats to ancient forest, especially those containing oaks. The removal of dead timber and dying trees.

Conservation　　The conservation of ancient woodland.

Author　　B. Levey.

Agrilus sinuatus

A jewel beetle　　　　　　　　　　**VULNERABLE**

Order **Coleoptera**　　　　　　　　Family **Buprestidae**

Agrilus sinuatus (Olivier, 1790).

Identification　　Levey (1977). p.6 and fig.6; Harde (1984), fig.183:5.

Distribution　　South-eastern counties. The main strongholds appear to be the New Forest, Hampshire (last recorded in 1931), and Windsor Forest, Berkshire (last recorded in 1972). There are more recent records from various localities, e.g. Richmond Park, Greater London (1984). This appears to be a localised species. However, it may be overlooked because of the limited time that the adults are about in any one year.

Habitat and ecology	The larvae develop in hawthorns *Crataegus*. The adults are mainly collected by beating hawthorns, and occur mainly in July and August.
Status	This species is probably near the edge of its range in south-east England. Its rarity may be more apparent than real. It does not appear to be associated with old woodlands in particular.
Threats	Since hawthorns are very widespread there does not appear to be any major threat to the species.
Author	B. Levey.

Agrilus viridis

A jewel beetle   **VULNERABLE**

Order **Coleoptera**   Family **Buprestidae**

Agrilus viridis (L., 1758).

Identification	Levey (1977), pp.4-6, figs 2 and 7.
Distribution	The New Forest, Hampshire (recorded again in 1984); Ham Street Woods, Kent (last recorded in 1950); Capite Wood, Ashington, West Sussex (1978); and Wood Fidley (locality not known to me). Some other old records need confirmation. The populations appear to be localised.
Habitat and ecology	The larvae develop in willows *Salix* and oaks *Quercus*. The adults have been collected in Britain from common sallow *Salix cinerea* from June to early August. The species is probably confined to areas with old sallows.
Status	A widespread European species. It is probably confined in Britain to southern England. The reasons for its rarity are unknown.
Threats	Any threats to areas with old sallow trees.
Conservation	The conservation of areas containing sallows.
Author	B. Levey.

Lacon querceus

A click beetle   **ENDANGERED**

Order **Coleoptera**   Family **Elateridae**

Lacon querceus (Herbst, 1784), formerly known as *Adelocera quercea* or *Agrypnus varius* (Olivier).

Identification	Allen (1936). Larva: van Emden (1945), p.15.
Distribution	Only known in Britain from Windsor Forest, Berkshire. Very localised, but occasionally fairly numerous in individual trees.

Habitat and ecology	Breeds exclusively in red-rotten oak *Quercus*, in dead trunks (both standing and fallen) and large boughs, but apparently not in stumps. The adults may be nocturnal.
Status	Stephens (1830) mentions one specimen taken at Windsor by J. H. Griesbach, a record treated with some doubt until Allen (1936) found a single specimen in a standing oak in Windsor Park on 12 September 1936. Van Emden (1945) used a larva collected by Donisthorpe that same month in constructing his key. It used to be found regularly over a wider area of the Park, but was not found in the Forest until Allen and Massee found many larvae and adults in an old log near High Standing Hill on 26 March 1951. After this *L. querceus* appears to have become rarer. In April 1972, P. Cook (in litt.) found two specimens in the same area of the Forest in a red-rotten oak bough which had fallen from 5m up the tree, where he found a further specimen in July.
Threats	The loss of ancient, over-mature oaks, and the lack of suitable replacements. A survey in 1971 showed that all the old oaks in which *L. querceus* had been known to breed had been felled and burnt.
Conservation	The known breeding area is within an SSSI notified in 1973. The Crown Estate Commissioners are aware of the value of ancient oaks. Excessive removal of dead wood, fallen boughs and ancient standing oaks should be prevented.
Author	R. C. Welch, using information from Donisthorpe (1939, p.80), Allen (1966), and Welch (1972).

Ampedus cardinalis

A click beetle   **VULNERABLE**

Order **Coleoptera**   Family **Elateridae**

	Ampedus cardinalis (Schioedte, 1865), formerly known as *Elater cardinalis* or *E. coccinatus* Rye, and much confused with *A. praeustus* (F.).
Identification	Freude, Harde & Lohse (1964-83), 6:109-113. Larva: van Emden (1945), p.22 (as *E. praeustus*).
Distribution	The Windsor area, Berkshire, is the chief station for this species in Britain today. It has been recorded this century from very few other localities, including Moccas Park (Hereford & Worcester), Parham Park (West Sussex), and Richmond Park (London).
Habitat and ecology	In decayed oaks *Quercus*, mostly breeding in red-rotten wood. The adults remain in the pupal cells from September to April, and have been collected free from May to July.

Status	Fowler (1887-91, 4:90) records it from Kensington Gardens (London), and Windsor and Sherwood Forests. Fowler & Donisthorpe (1913, p.274) add Waltham Abbey, Essex, but this locality has since been destroyed. In February 1928 Donisthorpe (1939) reared this species from larvae collected from Windsor in 1925, the first since 1867. P. Cook and A. A. Allen (in litt.) found adults and larvae independently in the same oak log in 1971. J. A. Owen (pers. comm.) considers that it is probably present in most old oaks with red-rotten wood in the Forest and Park. Elsewhere there are fairly recent records from Moccas Park, Parham Park (?1983), and Richmond Park (1983-84). Not apparently recorded from the New Forest or Epping Forest.
Threats	The removal of ancient over-mature oaks and the lack of a suitable replacement generation.
Conservation	The Windsor Forest (an SSSI) and Moccas Park (an NNR) sites have some protection. The removal of dead and fallen timber and the felling of over-mature oaks should be prevented.
Author	R. C. Welch, using information from Allen (1966).

Ampedus nigerrimus

A click beetle   **ENDANGERED**

Order **Coleoptera**   Family **Elateridae**

Ampedus nigerrimus (Lacordaire, 1835), formerly known as *Elater nigerrimus*.

Identification	Joy (1932), p.447. Larva: van Emden (1945), p.22.
Distribution	Only known in Britain from Windsor Forest, Berkshire.
Habitat and ecology	Breeds exclusively in decayed oaks *Quercus*, chiefly when red-rotten, in the trunks, logs, large boughs and stumps.
Status	Hammond (1979) lists *A. nigerrimus* as found in Epping Forest since 1950. Van Emden (1945) based his larval description on two larvae, one from Windsor, 9 February 1867, and one from Mytchett, Hampshire, December 1942, from birch (E. A. J. Duffy). The latter is clearly not this species. Allen (1966) rejects any records outside the Windsor area with the exception of the old record of *A. nigrinus* (Herbst) collected by S. Stevens on Tooting Common (Fowler, 1887-91, 4:92), which he believes may have been *A. nigerrimus*. First discovered in Windsor Forest on 7 March 1841 by T. Desvigues and later that century by Charles Turner, it was not seen again until Donisthorpe (1939) found three adults and many larvae on 26 October 1925 in an old decayed oak. He also beat one from hawthorn and found one on an elder stem. Allen took it freely in two stumps, an old log, and a large standing oak in

the spring of 1951. Only one specimen has been found in the Park by C. Johnson (Allen, 1966). It appears to have increased slightly in numbers during the past thirty years or so (Allen, in litt.) and I have a specimen from the Cranbourne Chase area of the Forest collected on 7 April 1972. J. A. Owen (pers. comm.) took the species from an oak stump in the Forest in 1980-82, and from hawthorn blossom at another site in June 1982.

Threats
The removal of ancient oaks and fallen timber.

Conservation
The known breeding area is within an SSSI notified in 1973. Excessive removal of dead wood and ancient oaks should be prevented.

Author
R. C. Welch.

Ampedus ruficeps

A click beetle   **ENDANGERED**

Order **Coleoptera**   Family **Elateridae**

Ampedus ruficeps (Mulsant & Guillebeau, 1855), formerly known as *Elater ruficeps*.

Identification
Allen (1938). Larva: van Emden (1945), p.21.

Distribution
Only known from a single adult and larva from Windsor Great Park, Berkshire.

Habitat and ecology
Only known in Britain from a single decayed oak *Quercus*, but recorded from beech *Fagus* on the Continent. It breeds in wood mould in hollow oaks.

Status
One adult and one larva were collected from wood mould in a cavity high in an oak in Windsor Park on 3 April 1938 by Allen (1938). This larva was used for the description by van Emden (1945). Allen (1966) searched the area for further specimens in succeeding years without success. I revisited the site with Allen in 1972 and could find no suitably rotten oaks in the vicinity, but it is always possible that it will be rediscovered elsewhere in the Forest.

Threats
The original tree no longer exists.

Conservation
Measures to conserve other Elateridae of old timber within the SSSI at Windsor may also protect this species. Further removal of ancient over-mature oaks should be prevented.

Author
R. C. Welch.

Ampedus rufipennis

A click beetle   **VULNERABLE**

Order **Coleoptera**   Family **Elateridae**

Ampedus rufipennis (Stephens, 1830), formerly known as *Elater rufipennis*.

Identification	Joy (1932), p.448. Larva: van Emden (1945), p.23.
Distribution	Known only from very few scattered localities where its occurrence is erratic. In Windsor Forest and Great Park (Berkshire) it is widespread and may be fairly numerous. Elsewhere it is known from Moccas Park (Hereford & Worcester), and Great and Little Chart, Godmersham and Eastwell Park (Kent).
Habitat and ecology	Breeds in decaying and rotten beech *Fagus*; occasionally in elm *Ulmus*, birch *Betula* and ash *Fraxinus*; in the trunks, logs and boughs, and more rarely in stumps. Once beaten from hawthorn blossom *Crataegus*.
Status	Early records, as with many members of this genus, are confused and unreliable. Allen (1966) believes that Fowler's (1887-91, 4:89-90) record of *Elater lythropterus* Germar from Windsor may refer to this species, but credits N. H. Joy with the first genuine record about 1923; subsequently recorded by Donisthorpe (1939). P. Cook (in litt.) found adults and a number of larvae in a beech log at High Standing Hill, Windsor, in 1971 and 1973. J. A. Owen (pers. comm.) considers that it is probably present in most dead beech trees in the Forest and Park. Elsewhere it has been recorded at Moccas Park as recently as September 1968 by F. A. Hunter and P. Skidmore (Welch & Cooter, 1981). I know of no recent captures from any of the Kent localities.
Threats	The removal of ancient trees, particularly over-mature beech.
Conservation	The Windsor Forest area (an SSSI) and Moccas Park (an NNR) should afford some protection for this species. Excessive felling and removal of old trees should be prevented.
Author	R. C. Welch.

Procraerus tibialis

A click beetle   **VULNERABLE**

Order **Coleoptera**   Family **Elateridae**

Procraerus tibialis (Boisduval & Lacordaire, 1835).

Identification	Joy (1932), p.449. Larva: van Emden (1945), p.17.
Distribution	Found in scattered localities from the New Forest (Hampshire) to Sherwood Forest (Nottinghamshire) and

188

Moccas Park (Hereford & Worcester). Also known from localities in the following counties: Buckinghamshire, Devon, Essex, Hertfordshire, Leicestershire, Northamptonshire, Surrey, Sussex and Wiltshire. It has always been very rare except at Windsor.

Habitat and ecology Breeds in hollow and decayed oaks *Quercus* and beeches *Fagus*.

Status This species has always been rare or very rare at all sites except Windsor Forest, where it is widespread. The larva upon which van Emden (1945) based his description was taken by Allen at Windsor in 1938. Donisthorpe (1939) recorded as many as fourteen specimens in a felled beech. It has apparently been recorded from many of the counties listed above during the past thirty years (Allen, in litt.), and most recently at Yardley Chase, Northamptonshire, by A. B. Drane on 2 June 1983.

Threats The loss of ancient trees and the lack of a suitable replacement generation.

Conservation There is some protection of the habitat at Moccas Park (an NNR) and Windsor Forest (an SSSI). Excessive loss of ancient trees in sites such as Windsor and Moccas should be prevented.

Author R. C. Welch, using additional information from Allen (1966, 1971b).

Megapenthes lugens

A click beetle

ENDANGERED

Order **Coleoptera**

Family **Elateridae**

Megapenthes lugens (Redtenbacher, 1842).

Identification Joy (1932), p.445. Larva: van Emden (1945), p.17.

Distribution There are old records from Highgate (London), and Box Hill, Stockwell and Mickleham (Surrey). There are records this century from the New Forest (Hampshire), Tewkesbury (Gloucestershire), Windsor (Berkshire) and Epping Forest (Essex).

Habitat and ecology Breeds in decaying elm *Ulmus* and probably also beech *Fagus*. The larvae feed in harder, drier wood than *Ampedus* species, etc. The adults are more often found on flowers, chiefly hawthorn *Crataegus*, once on holly *Ilex*, and once on nettles *Urtica* in flower.

Status	The earliest British specimen dates from 1838, when C. Griesbach found it in Windsor Forest (Allen, 1964a). Of the 19th century records listed by Fowler (1887-91, 4:93-94), only at Highgate were about half-a-dozen specimens collected. All other records are of one or two individuals. This century Donisthorpe (1939) found *M. lugens* twice at Windsor in the 1930s and Allen (1964a, 1966) found two in their pupal cells in a wind-blown elm in Windsor Great Park on 5 March 1938. In 1970-71 P. Cook (in litt.) took several specimens on hawthorn blossom in the High Standing Hill area of Windsor Forest, and Allen reared one from a larva found in elm from the same locality in 1973. *M. lugens* has been recorded from the New Forest three times: Lyndhurst, May 1915, one on holly bloom (D. Cumming); Ashurst, 25 May 1946, two specimens (C. W. Henderson); and P. Cook saw one in Mallard Wood in 1971 on a beech on which *Eucnemis capucina* Ahrens (also Endangered) was found. H. W. Forster beat a single male from hawthorn blossom at High Beech, Epping Forest, in 1943 (Allen, 1964a). Allen also relates how G. H. Ashe mentioned seeing a specimen on an ash stump near Tewkesbury in the early 1950s. I have not heard of any recent records from the glut of felled elm available throughout southern Britain, confirming the rarity and localised nature of *M. lugens*.
Threats	The widespread removal of dead elms in recent years following the epidemic of Dutch elm disease may well have destroyed unknown colonies, and certainly resulted in a loss of potential breeding sites.
Conservation	The main locality at Windsor is offered some protection by the SSSI notification. Excessive removal of dead timber and over-mature trees should be prevented.
Author	R. C. Welch.

Limoniscus violaceus

A click beetle   **ENDANGERED**

Order **Coleoptera**   Family **Elateridae**

Limoniscus violaceus (Mueller, 1821).

Identification	Allen (1937b). Larva: van Emden (1945).
Distribution	Now only known in Britain from Windsor Forest (Berkshire), and recently only from a single tree. A 1939 record from Tewkesbury (Gloucestershire) has been confirmed recently by H. Mendel. The adults emerge in late April or early May, and are nocturnal until July. The larvae are predatory.
Habitat and ecology	Breeds in wood-mould in the bases of ancient hollow beech trees *Fagus*.

First recorded in Britain by Allen (1937b) from a single specimen collected in an old prostrate beech at High Standing Hill in Windsor Forest on 17 May 1937. In April 1947 A. A. Allen and B. A. Cooper found several larvae and a few adults in an adjoining part of the forest. All were in a mixture of wood and leaf-mould in hollow beech trees. These were later felled, sawn up and removed, and *L. violaceus* was not seen again until May 1972 when Allen and G. Shephard discovered larvae and one adult in wood-mould in the base of a hollow beech in the same area of the Forest. P. Cook (in litt.) found three larvae in the same tree later that year, to which he returned on a later visit but found none. J. A. Owen found single larvae in July 1981 and March 1983, and two adults in pupal chambers in a dead beech in February 1984.

Threats

Several old beech trees in which *L. violaceus* had been known to breed have since been destroyed.

Conservation

The location of the tree housing the only known breeding site of this species was notified in 1972. Further loss of ancient over-mature beech trees, particularly from the High Standing Hill area of Windsor Forest, should be prevented.

Author

R. C. Welch.

Anostirus castaneus

A click beetle **ENDANGERED**

Order **Coleoptera** Family **Elateridae**

Anostirus castaneus (L., 1758), formerly known as *Corymbites castaneus.*

Identification

Joy (1932), p.449. Larva: van Emden (1945), p.20.

Distribution

There are old records, mostly of single specimens, from Mousehold Heath (Norfolk), the Isle of Wight, near Monmouth and the Forest of Dean (Gloucestershire), the Northumberland and Durham Coast, and Pateley Bridge and Harrogate (North Yorkshire). The only recent records of *A. castaneus* are from Luccombe Chine, Isle of Wight, and from near Harrogate (1984).

Habitat and ecology

Under stones, on grasses, low plants, bushes, etc, and on bare sandy ground. The site near Harrogate consists of sandy areas between rocky outcrops at the top of gritstone crags. The larvae have been found in sand at the roots of isolated tufts of grass. There are several coastal records but it has also been found inland. Larvae have been fed on sprouting corn in captivity (Appleton, 1974).

Status	There is an indication from old records that *A. castaneus* was, and may still be, established on the Northumberland/ Durham coast and in the Monmouth/Forest of Dean area. Fowler & Donisthorpe (1913) record it from Shanklin and Sandown on the Isle of Wight, and on 21 March 1972 Appleton (1974) found a single female on damp sand at the foot of some cliffs on the south-east coast of the island (Luccombe Chine). In the following week he found two larvae at the roots of grass tufts, one near to where the adult was found and one on the top of the cliff. On 4 May he returned and found a dozen males crawling over the bare ground and on a grass tuft on a patch of bare undercliff just above high-tide mark. The species was still present at this site in 1977 and in April 1983, and it is thought likely that other very localised colonies exist on the island (Allen, in litt.).
Threats	The area of the Harrogate site is being 'tidied up' by the local authority.
Conservation	A section of the cliffs at Luccombe is owned by the National Trust.
Author	R. C. Welch.

Elater ferrugineus

A click beetle **ENDANGERED**

Order **Coleoptera** Family **Elateridae**

Elater ferrugineus L., 1758, formerly known as *Ludius ferrugineus.*

Identification	Joy (1932), p.445. Larva: van Emden (1945), p.18.
Distribution	Old records indicate that *E. ferrugineus* was once more widely distributed in southern Britain. Fowler (1887-91, 4:94-95) gives Hyde Park and Richmond Park (London), Darenth Wood (Kent), Windsor (Berkshire), Clengre (?), Bottisham, Cambridge, Grantchester and Chesterton (Cambridgeshire), and Swansea (West Glamorgan). Fowler & Donisthorpe (1913) add Santon Downham (Suffolk). Only known this century from Windsor, where larvae may be locally common, and possibly Rochester (Kent) (see van Emden, 1945, p.34).
Habitat and ecology	Breeds in decayed and rotten wood and mould in the interiors of old trees (trunks and boughs), chiefly elm *Ulmus*, beech *Fagus* and ash *Fraxinus*. Larvae are often found in rot-holes where there has been a nest. P. Cook (in litt.) found no evidence of larval carnivory.

Status	Said by Stephens to have been taken at Windsor by Dr Leach; rediscovered there by Donisthorpe (1939) when he found eight larvae in the wood-mould of a felled ash on 23 July 1926. At present only found in Windsor Forest and the Great Park, but apparently widespread and well-established. Rarely found as an adult. On 4 August 1958 P. S. Tyler found a damaged specimen walking on a path. P. Cook has found adult fragments in wood-mould, and in 1975 found one adult and two pre-pupae with ninety larvae in recently-felled dead elms in Windsor Park, showing how difficult it is to assess the occurrence of such species. Some half-a-dozen adults were seen flying at midday on 31 July 1982 in a garden at West Windsor (Verdcourt, 1983). J. A. Owen (pers. comm.) found larvae in some numbers in wood-mould in a fallen beech in the Park in February 1984, and an adult in the Cranbourne Park area later in 1984.
Threats	The felling and removal of old trees is evidently the greatest threat, as most records are of larvae in felled trees. P. Cook (*in litt.*) found five larvae in a heap of wood-mould which had been left after the tree had been sawn up and removed.
Conservation	P. Cook reared adults from the larvae collected in 1975 and hoped to be able to reintroduce specimens into suitable habitats in Windsor Forest. Excessive removal of fallen and over-mature trees should be prevented.
Author	R. C. Welch, using additional information from Allen (1966) and H. Mendel (pers. comm.).

Eucnemis capucina

ENDANGERED

Order **Coleoptera**   Family **Eucnemidae**

Eucnemis capucina Ahrens, 1812.

Identification	Joy (1932), p.443; Harde (1984), fig. 177:6. Larva: van Emden (1943), p.218 and fig.19.
Distribution	Only known from the New Forest (Hampshire) and Windsor Forest (Berkshire), in very small localised populations.
Habitat and ecology	Under the bark and in rotten wood of beech *Fagus* and other deciduous trees. Allen (1968) found pupae in March (the adults emerged in April) in mould beneath a fallen beech branch.
Status	Long known from the New Forest, where most early specimens were collected from one old beech tree (Allen, 1966). Appleton (1972) refers to one taken in the New Forest by P. Harwood in 1936, and records two in June 1968, one in June 1969 and two in July 1971, all from inside the same rotten beech tree. Donisthorpe (1939) found it in Windsor Forest in June and August, one in an old ash tree, one by

sweeping and one in a hollow beech tree. P. Cook (in litt.) found four specimens running over freshly-sawn beech logs on 16 June 1973.

Threats The destruction and removal of ancient decaying trees.

Author R. C. Welch.

Hylis cariniceps

ENDANGERED

Order **Coleoptera** Family **Eucnemidae**

Hylis cariniceps (Reitter, 1902), formerly known as *Hypocoelus cariniceps*.

Identification Allen (1969b).

Distribution Only known in Britain from one specimen from the New Forest, Hampshire.

Habitat and ecology Probably associated with ancient dead beeches *Fagus* like its Rare congener *H. olexai* (Palm).

Status The only British specimen, a female, was swept by D. Appleton near some old beech trees near Lyndhurst, New Forest, on 2 July 1966 (Allen, 1969b).

Threats The removal of standing and fallen old dead beech trees.

Conservation Ancient dead beech trees should be retained *in situ* as long as possible.

Author R. C. Welch.

Phosphaenus hemipterus

A glow-worm **ENDANGERED**

Order **Coleoptera** Family **Lampyridae**

Phosphaenus hemipterus (Goeze, 1777).

Identification Joy (1932), p.424; Harde (1984), fig. 165:6. Unlike the common glow-worm, *Lampyris noctiluca* (L.), the male has very short elytra and is flightless.

Distribution Mainly confined to East Sussex (Lewes, Hastings, Buxted and Chelwood Gate), though also known from Hampshire (Southampton). The populations must be small, as several years generally elapse between records.

Habitat and ecology Usually recorded in gardens and churchyards, where it frequents walls, rockeries, kerbs, etc. Most records refer to the male, which can be active by day; the larviform female is rarely seen, being located only by its faint luminescence

	at dusk. As in the common glow-worm, both adults and larvae are believed to be predatory on snails. Adults are seen in June and early July.
Status	The species was first discovered in Britain in Lewes in 1868, and for some years was only known from gardens there and in Hastings. One was found near Southampton in 1894, and seventy males were taken in a garden at Shirley Warren nearby on 21-25 June of the following year. There appears to be a gap of fifty years until 1946, when Cribb (1946) took one in the churchyard of St Margaret's, Buxted. A series collected there in subsequent years is now in the Brighton Museum (P. Hodge, pers. comm.). The most recent record consists of two males taken in a garden at Chelwood Gate in Ashdown Forest on 3-6 July 1961 (Airy Shaw, 1961). The species is on the edge of its range in Britain.
Conservation	If a new colony is located, collecting should be discouraged.
Author	D. B. Shirt.

Platycis cosnardi

ENDANGERED

Order **Coleoptera** Family **Lycidae**

Platycis cosnardi (Chevrolat, 1829), formerly known as *Dictyopterus cosnardi*.

Identification	Airy Shaw (1944); Freude, Harde & Lohse (1964-83), 6:12.
Distribution	Only known from near Goodwood (West Sussex) and near Monmouth (in Gloucestershire).
Habitat and ecology	Under bark or in rotten wood.
Status	Known in Britain from only three specimens: Airy Shaw (1944) recorded two specimens taken in the garden of a house on the Staunton road, one mile or so east of Monmouth, on 6 and 29 May 1944. What may have been a third specimen was seen flying through the garden on 26 June. On 25 May 1969 Cooter (1973) took a single specimen in Red Copse, near Goodwood. The Monmouth site is on the periphery of the Forest of Dean with large oaks and beeches nearby, and the West Dean woodlands are close to the West Sussex locality.
Threats	The Goodwood site was revisited in 1970 and found to have been clear-felled, sprayed and replanted with conifers.
Author	R. C. Welch.

Globicornis nigripes

Order **Coleoptera**   Family **Dermestidae**

Globicornis nigripes (F., 1792).

Identification   Fowler & Donisthorpe (1913), p.134.

Distribution   Only known from two sites, half a mile apart, on the periphery of Windsor Great Park, Berkshire (Allen, 1945 and 1947b), Slough (Woodroffe) and Tewkesbury, Gloucestershire (Fowler & Donisthorpe).

Habitat and ecology   Adult beetles have been collected on various flowers from May to July and may be pollen feeders. Woodroffe (1971) bred this species on a mixture of fishmeal, dried yeast and cholesterol and a piece of cotton flock. Mature larvae were present by early November.

Status   First recorded by Curtis in 1837 near Windsor. Blatch provided what Fowler & Donisthorpe (1913) believed to be the first possible indigenous record when he swept one at the side of a wood near Tewkesbury (date not known), but this species was not included by Joy (1932). In 1944 Allen found single females on 19 May and 11 June by sweeping under oaks in Windsor Forest. In 1946, within half a mile of the 1944 locality, he caught one male on 22 May and one female on 11 July, by sweeping the umbels of hogweed *Heracleum sphondylium* growing nearby under an oak. Allen (pers. comm.) took a series on 14 May 1948 by sweeping "hedge-parsley" (?*Anthriscus sylvestris*) flowers in a lane just outside Windsor Park. Further specimens were taken in Windsor Forest by Donisthorpe in 1949 and by Massee in 1950. On 5 June 1970 Woodroffe took thirteen specimens on the flowers of *Spiraea* and other shrubs in the grounds of the Pest Infestation Laboratory at Slough, Berkshire. The last specimen was taken by A. A. Allen off an old oak in Cranbourne Park, Windsor, in June 1971.

Author   R. C. Welch.

Gastrallus immarginatus

Order **Coleoptera**   Family **Anobiidae**

Gastrallus immarginatus (Mueller, 1821), formerly misidentified as *G. laevigatus* (Olivier).

Identification   Donisthorpe (1936); Freude, Harde & Lohse (1964-83), 8:43; Harde (1984), fig. 213:2.

Distribution   Only known in Britain from Windsor Forest, Berkshire.

Habitat and ecology	Presumed to breed in small dead twigs of field maple *Acer campestre*, on which it has also been found in Sweden. Adults have been recorded in July and early August.
Status	First recorded in Britain by Donisthorpe and Allen on a stack of oak, elm and beech logs. Donisthorpe (1936) notes that the beetle seemed to prefer to rest on the elm logs. Six specimens were found on 19 July 1936 and 18 more two days later. Allen (1954) beat one from the dead twigs of a field maple and swept two others in the vicinity of other maple trees. He later (Allen, 1956a) reports beating *Gastrallus* repeatedly from maple both in the Great Park and in Windsor Forest. Additional specimens were also obtained by sweeping beneath them. In an editorial footnote to Donisthorpe's (1936) paper, J. J. Walker states that there is a male *G. immarginatus* on an "English" pin in the Hope Collection at Oxford but bearing no data label.
Threats	The removal of old field maple.
Author	R. C. Welch.

Dorcatoma dresdensis

ENDANGERED

Order **Coleoptera**   Family **Anobiidae**

Dorcatoma dresdensis Herbst, 1792.

Identification	Joy (1932), p.461.
Distribution	Only known this century from Windsor Forest (Berkshire), the New Forest (Hampshire), East Malling (Kent), Earith and Linton (Cambridgeshire), and Brighton (East Sussex).
Habitat and ecology	Larvae in a tinder bracket fungus *Fomes fomentosus* collected off an old oak in April produced adults the following June.
Status	E. W. Janson considered that this species was incorrectly recorded as British by Stephens, but K. G. Blair regarded the specimen in the Stephens Collection as *D. dresdensis* (pre-1858). Two specimens were collected by Power at Esher, Surrey, on 9 July 1870 and 8 July 1871. Donisthorpe (1928) reared a number of specimens in June 1925 from a bracket fungus collected in Windsor Forest on 22 April 1924. There are a further two specimens in the British Museum (Natural History) collection labelled "bred 6.38, Windsor". A. Massee bred three specimens from *Polyporus* from East Malling, Kent, on 10 June 1942, and there is a male from Enfield, London, collected by D. Sharp. A. A. Allen (in litt.) notes its occurrence near Cambridge (? Donisthorpe) and the New Forest (Forster, ex Massee). A specimen was taken at Linton, Cambridgeshire, on 7 May 1944 (P. S. Hyman, pers. comm.). G. B. Alexander took a series indoors at

Brighton in July 1955 (Booth Museum). J. A. Owen (pers. comm.) took specimens at Earith, Cambridgeshire, in June 1974, and in Windsor Forest in June 1982.

Threats   The removal of dead oaks.

Author   R. C. Welch.

Caenocara affinis

ENDANGERED

Order **Coleoptera**   Family **Anobiidae**

Caenocara affinis (Sturm, 1837), formerly misidentified as *C. subglobosa* Mulsant & Rey.

Identification   Joy (1932), p.461.

Distribution   Only known from Barton Mills (Suffolk); Joy gives Norfolk in error.

Habitat and ecology   In the puff-ball fungus *Lycoperdon perlatum* (=*L. gemmatum*).

Status   Only known from three males and five females bred from larvae in puff-balls collected at Barton Mills, Suffolk, on 9 September 1917 (Donisthorpe, 1918).

Author   R. C. Welch.

Ostoma ferrugineum

ENDANGERED

Order **Coleoptera**   Family **Peltidae**

Ostoma ferrugineum (L., 1758).

Identification   Lloyd (1953); Freude, Harde & Lohse (1964-83), 7:17. Larva: van Emden (1943), p.215.

Distribution   Only known from the ancient Caledonian relict pinewood areas at Guisachan (Inverness, Highland) and Mar (Deeside, Grampian). Possible larval borings and adult exit holes have been seen at one or two other highland sites but the presence of *Ostoma* there has not, as yet, been confirmed.

Habitat and ecology   The larvae feed in the heartwood and sapwood of Scots pines *Pinus sylvestris* that have been extensively rotted by the fungus *Phaeolus schweinitzii*. Larvae collected in early April pupated in late May. The adults are also to be found under pine bark in April and May.

Status	Originally discovered by A. M. Robertson under the bark of a pine at Linn O'Dee, Braemar, Deeside, on 18 May 1952 (Lloyd, 1953). It has since been found between 1965 and 1969 by F. A. Hunter, C. Johnson and P. Skidmore to be well-established in large dead pines in Glen Quoich, Glen Derry and Glen Lui on the Mar Estate, and a single adult was found in Guisachan by Hunter in a recently-felled pine together with signs of much larval boring. *Ostoma* appears to have poor powers of dispersal and requires dead pines which have been left long enough for the associated fungus to rot the heartwood. Since any dead or fallen timber is viewed by most foresters as a potential source of insect pests, most is removed before it has reached a stage suitable for the larval development of this species. The shape of the exit holes is characteristic and the presence of the species at a site may be confirmed without destroying the habitat in searching for specimens.
Threats	The removal of ancient rotten pines.
Conservation	Estate owners and managers have been made aware of conservation requirements through meetings of the Native Pinewoods Discussion Group. Large fallen pines should be allowed to remain *in situ* to rot.
Author	R. C. Welch, using additional information from Hunter (1977).

Hypebaeus flavipes

ENDANGERED

Order **Coleoptera**   Family **Melyridae**

Hypebaeus flavipes (F., 1787), formerly misidentified as *Ebaeus abietinus* Abeille.

Identification	Donisthorpe & Tomlin (1934); Blair & Donisthorpe (1943); Freude, Harde & Lohse (1964-83), 6:58; Harde (1984), fig. 169:4.
Distribution	Only known from Moccas Park, Hereford & Worcester.
Habitat and ecology	Associated with red-rotten oaks *Quercus*. Recorded from hornbeam *Carpinus* in Germany.
Status	Originally described from three female specimens taken by J. R. le B. Tomlin on 26 June 1934 by sweeping under oaks at Moccas Park. In 1943 G. H. Ashe donated two pairs (from the same locality) from which Blair (1943) was able correctly to identify the species. In June and July 1975, using a sketch map indicating the position of the 'Ashe' oak, J. Cooter (1976) found *H. flavipes* to be reasonably common in the same tree some forty years after its discovery. Cooter has also beaten four specimens from two other oaks in Moccas Park but is of the opinion that, in addition to the 'Ashe' oak, it may be breeding in one other red-rotten oak in the southern end of the Park.

Threats	The availability of suitable alternative host trees. The species is very vulnerable to bad weather, overcollecting, and tree damage/natural death (Cooter, pers. comm.).
Conservation	The site is an NNR protected by a nature reserve agreement. Existing ancient oaks in Moccas Park should be retained, coupled with a policy of allowing some younger oaks to become over-mature.
Author	R. C. Welch, using additional information from Welch & Cooter (1981).

Axinotarsus pulicarius

VULNERABLE

Order **Coleoptera**　　　　　　　　Family **Melyridae**

Axinotarsus pulicarius (F., 1777).

Identification	Joy (1932), p.434; Harde (1984), fig. 169:9; Allen (1971d). This species is very difficult to distinguish from the common *A. marginalis* Lap., a recent addition to the British fauna.
Distribution	Restricted to the south-east of England: the London area, Surrey, East Sussex, Kent and Essex. Formerly local and occasionally in numbers, but there are no recent records.
Habitat and ecology	In open grassy areas, waste ground near the sea or inland, on herbage, flowers, etc.
Status	Fowler (1887-91, 4:157) records *A. pulicarius* as local and not common from Wandsworth, Peckham and Walworth (London), Claygate (Surrey) and Charlton (Kent), but it has not been found there since. Fowler & Donisthorpe (1913, p.278) add Rye and near Hastings, East Sussex. E. C. Bedwell also took it at Lydd/Camber (Kent) in the 1920s or 1930s, and found 32 specimens at Wivenhoe near Colchester (Essex) on 30 June 1923 (Allen, in litt.).
Author	R. C. Welch.

Lymexylon navale

VULNERABLE

Order **Coleoptera**　　　　　　　　Family **Lymexylidae**

Lymexylon navale (L., 1758).

Identification	Joy (1932), p.429; Harde (1984), fig. 171:9. Larva: van Emden (1943), p.261 and fig.29.
Distribution	There are recent records only for the Windsor Forest area (Berkshire), Richmond Park (London), the New Forest

200

(Hampshire), Hatfield (Hertfordshire), and Moccas Park (Hereford & Worcester). Local populations are often restricted to individual oaks.

Habitat and ecology	Found in living and dead oak *Quercus* (Fowler, 1887-91, 4: 178). The larvae bore into the dead seasoned timber of dead standing oaks, usually at some distance above the ground.
Status	At the end of the last century *L. navale* was common in Dunham Park, Manchester, and was also recorded from Bowden and Stretford, Manchester (Fowler, 1887-91). C. Johnson (1977) has collected extensively in Dunham Park in recent years but has not found *L. navale*. There is an old record from Portsmouth (Fowler, 1887-91) which may have been an import. Van Emden's larvae were described from specimens in imported oak. The species has been known from Windsor Forest since 1829. Recent records are from Silwood Park, near Ascot (Berkshire) in July 1963 (R. C. Welch). The latest record from Windsor is July 1981, by J. A. Owen, who also took the species in Richmond Park in August 1980. *Lymexylon* was first recorded in the New Forest in 1905, and has been taken in at least three localities there by D. Appleton between 1968 and 1974. P. Roche (1964a) caught a single specimen at Hatfield on 18 August 1963. J. Cooter (1976) caught a single gravid female at Moccas Park on 5 August 1975, the first record from this well-studied site, but the specimen recorded from Brampton Bryan Park in June 1981 (Cooter, 1981c) later proved to be *Hylecoetus dermestoides* (L.). This species may be under-recorded owing to its habit of frequenting dead wood well above ground level. The adults fly in the evening and may have a very short flight period.
Threats	The felling and removal of dead standing old oaks.
Conservation	The protection of stag-headed old oaks.
Author	R. C. Welch, using additional information from Bedwell (1926).

Rhizophagus oblongicollis

ENDANGERED

Order **Coleoptera**   Family **Rhizophagidae**

Rhizophagus oblongicollis Blatch & Horner, 1892, formerly misidentified as *R. simplex* Reitter.

Identification	Peacock (1977), pp. 8-9 and 11, figs 11, 21 and 33.
Distribution	Known from eight counties: Richmond Park (London), Epping Forest (Essex), Hatfield (Hertfordshire), Windsor Forest (Berkshire), Blenheim Park (Oxfordshire), Sherwood Forest (Nottinghamshire), Bagots Park (Staffordshire), and Ashstead Common (Surrey). The populations are very small and localised.

Habitat and ecology	Under the bark of oak *Quercus* stumps or logs, or in fungi on stumps. There is one record from beech *Fagus*. Often recorded as single specimens, twice in colonies of *Rhizophagus ferrugineus* (Paykull).
Status	*R. oblongicollis* has been recorded from only four localities this century. H. W. Forster (1955) found one in Epping Forest on 12 July 1943; A. A. Allen (1955a) records one from Blenheim Park on 18 April 1954 and mentions that the last time he found it in Windsor Forest was in 1953 where Donisthorpe (1939) had recorded it earlier. P. Roche (1964b) found six specimens at Hatfield on 14 September 1963. Allen again found several under bark in Windsor Forest and Park in July 1972. J. A. Owen (pers. comm.) took the species on Ashtead Common in April 1979 and at Windsor in March 1982.
Author	R. C. Welch, using additional information from Tozer (1973).

Uleiota planata

VULNERABLE

Order **Coleoptera**   Family **Cucujidae**

Uleiota planata (L., 1761).

Identification	Joy (1932), p.486.
Distribution	Known from only five localities this century: Liss (Hampshire); Braemar (Deeside, Grampian); Silwood Park, near Ascot, and Swinley Park, near Bracknell (Berkshire); and Richmond Park (London).
Habitat and ecology	Typically under the bark of beech *Fagus*, but recorded from birch *Betula* in Hampshire and one under pine *Pinus* bark in Deeside. The larvae have been found in August and September, and the teneral adult in late September.
Status	The first record of *Uleiota* in Britain is of three specimens taken at Blackheath by J. W. Douglas, some time prior to E. C. Rye, who recorded adults and larvae under the bark of a large dead beech at Putney (?1866). Several specimens were recorded on imported timber at Carlisle by Day in 1906. On 19 February 1952 S. E. Allen found five specimens under the loose dry bark of a fallen dead silver birch *Betula pendula* near Liss, Hampshire, and two more specimens were collected a week later (Allen, 1953). On 25 May 1952 A. M. Robertson found a single specimen under the bark of a dead standing pine at Linn o'Dee, Braemar. On 21 September 1962 a male and female together with two larvae were found at Silwood Park, under the bark of a large beech felled in 1960. Four days later a further two males, five females and five larvae were collected from the same tree. On 15 August 1963 a single larva was found.

On 19/20 June 1982 H. Mendel found one under sycamore *Acer pseudoplatanus* bark in Richmond Park (Cooter, 1982). J. A. Owen (pers. comm.) found four specimens under the bark of a beech stump in Swinley Park in May 1983.

Threats The removal of large dead timber in ancient forest areas.

Author R. C. Welch, using additional information from Welch (1963).

Laemophloeus monilis

ENDANGERED

Order **Coleoptera**   Family **Cucujidae**

Laemophloeus monilis (F., 1787).

Identification Champion & Lloyd (1909); Joy (1932), p.487; Lefkovitch (1959).

Distribution Known only from Arundel Park (West Sussex) and Streatley (Berkshire), in extremely local populations.

Habitat and ecology All English specimens have been taken from under the bark or cut ends of beech *Fagus*. On the Continent *L. monilis* is also found under the bark of plane *Platanus*. Lefkovitch states that it has been recorded from the cones of conifers, in the burrows of the bark beetle *Taphrorychus bicolor* (Herbst), on lime trees *Tilia* and under the bark of dead lime.

Status First found in Britain at Streatley by Joy and Chitty in October 1905. About a dozen specimens were taken from under beech bark and a few subsequently from the same tree. Ashe (1944) recorded *L. monilis* from a fallen beech in Arundel Park in October 1943; Allen (1950) found one there on 9 August 1949, and with A. Massee collected a further ten specimens on 12 September 1949. P. Hodge (pers. comm.) found it numerous under beech bark in Arundel Park on 16 July 1978.

Threats The removal of fallen and felled large beech trees.

Author R. C. Welch.

Leptophloeus clematidis

VULNERABLE

Order **Coleoptera**   Family **Cucujidae**

Leptophloeus clematidis (Erichson, 1846), formerly known as *Laemophloeus clematidis*.

Identification Joy (1932), p.488; Lefkovitch (1959).

Distribution Only recorded this century from Higham (Kent) and near Ipswich (Suffolk).

Habitat and ecology	A predator upon the bark beetle *Xyclocleptes bispinus* (Duftschmid) in small dead stems of traveller's joy *Clematis vitalba*.
Status	*L. clematidis* is known from old records for Gravesend and Dartford (Kent) and Henley (Oxfordshire) (Fowler, 1887-91, 3:299). Since J. J. Walker recorded it from Higham, Kent (Fowler & Donisthorpe, 1913, p.262), the only known locality is at Little Blakenham, near Ipswich, Suffolk. D. R. Nash (1980) collected twenty individuals on 17 April 1977 with its scolytid host, in 1cm-thick dead stems of *Clematis*. On 30 April 1978 one was found dead in a spider's web and three specimens were collected on 18 April 1979, all from the same site. Nash reports that both A. A. Allen and A. Massee failed to find this species in Kent, and he believes that it may be extinct in that county.
Author	R. C. Welch.

Cryptophagus badius

VULNERABLE

Order **Coleoptera**   Family **Cryptophagidae**

Cryptophagus badius Sturm, 1845.

Identification	Coombs & Woodroffe (1955a), pp.260-261, figs 40, 76 and 120.
Distribution	Only known from a 25km stretch of the Spey Valley (Highland Region), from Aviemore to Grantown-on-Spey. The population is small and extremely localised.
Habitat and ecology	The only authentic British specimens are from the dreys of red squirrels *Sciurus vulgaris* and the nests of a sparrowhawk *Accipiter nisus*, an osprey *Pandion haliaetus* and an owl. The larva is unknown.
Status	All early records refer to *C. postpositus* Sahlberg, short-haired *C. pilosus* Gyllenhal, or some other species (Coombes & Woodroffe, 1955a). In 1955 the only known British specimens were those collected by P. Harwood from red squirrels' dreys between September 1924 and July 1925 at Nethy Bridge, Loch Garten, Boat of Garten and Aviemore (Welch, 1979a). There are also specimens from Aviemore dated June 1930 and one later specimen from Kincraig dated 28 August 1952. Small numbers were extracted from a sparrowhawk's nest collected at Polchar, near Aviemore, on 6 September 1966 (Welch, 1979a); five were obtained from osprey nest material collected at Loch Garten in November 1979, and one from an owl's nest nearby in July 1979 (Carter *et al*, 1980). J. A. Owen (pers. comm.) continued finding specimens at Loch Garten up to 1983. Recent examination of a number of sparrowhawks' nests from Dumfries & Galloway,

Anglesey and Windsor Forest (Berkshire) has failed to produce further specimens.

Conservation   The Loch Garten population is well protected by RSPB wardening of the osprey nest site.

Author   R. C. Welch.

Cryptophagus falcozi

Order **Coleoptera**   Family **Cryptophagidae**

Cryptophagus falcozi Roubal, 1927, formerly known as *C. westi* Bruce.

Identification   Coombs & Woodroffe (1962); Freude, Harde & Lohse (1964-83), 7:128.

Distribution   Only found three times out-of-doors in Britain, in Windsor Forest (Berkshire).

Habitat and ecology   In fungus, on the infected wood of dead beech *Fagus*.

Status   First recorded in Britain from a single male found alive in one of six new insect store-boxes delivered to the Pest Infestation Laboratories at Slough (Berkshire) from a North London manufacturer in the summer of 1962. On 29 January 1981 J. A. Owen (1982a) found one male and four females in an old beech trunk in Windsor Forest. He took further specimens in the Park in June 1982 and in the Forest in August 1982 (pers. comm.). The specimens of *C. westi* described by Bruce from four females collected in Denmark in 1940 were found in fungi on dead rotting beech. Owen considers that the Windsor specimens represent an old forest relict and not a recent introduction.

Threats   The removal of dead timber.

Conservation   The preservation of ancient beech and oak in Windsor Forest.

Author   R. C. Welch.

Cryptophagus labilis

Order **Coleoptera**   Family **Cryptophagidae**

Cryptophagus labilis Erichson, 1846.

Identification   Coombs & Woodroffe (1955a), p.251, figs 18, 60 and 103.

Distribution   Only known in Britain from Moccas Park (Hereford & Worcester), and from Cambridge.

Habitat and ecology	Under bark and in rotten wood and old stumps. The larva is unknown.
Status	Coombs & Woodroffe (1955a) give Moccas Park (G. H. Ashe) and Cambridge, Trinity Fellows' Garden, under bark (University Museum collection) as the only known localities. However, in a later paper (1955b) they state "a few examples from Moccas Park, Herefordshire (Coll. G. H. Ashe) and an occasional specimen in other collections". Massee (1964), presumably referring to the Ashe records, describes *C. labilis* as very local, under bark and in old stumps.
Conservation	Moccas Park is now an NNR, and the importance of dead wood to its insect fauna is known by the present owner.
Author	R. C. Welch.

Cryptophagus lapponicus

VULNERABLE

Order **Coleoptera**   Family **Cryptophagidae**

Cryptophagus lapponicus Gyllenhal, 1827.

Identification	Coombs & Woodroffe (1955a), p.255, figs 30, 83 and 117.
Distribution	Only known from the Aviemore area of Speyside (Highland). The population is very small.
Habitat and ecology	The only authentic British specimens are from the dreys of red squirrels *Sciurus vulgaris*, the nest of a sparrowhawk *Accipiter nisus*, and possibly in fungi. The larva is unknown.
Status	Most early specimens examined by Coombs & Woodroffe (1955a) proved to be *C. subfumatus* Kraatz, but they found a long series in the P. Harwood collection taken between September 1924 and July 1925 from red squirrels' dreys at Aviemore. Although Coombs & Woodroffe state "This remarkable series consisted of about equal numbers of *badius* and *lapponicus*", C. O'Toole has been unable to find any specimens of *C. lapponicus* in the Hope Department, Oxford. The Harwood collection in the British Museum (Natural History) contains three specimens, two from A. M. Massee's collection from Boat of Garten (7 September 1924) and one from Aviemore (June 1930). Coombs & Woodroffe also identified a single specimen from Aviemore in the G. C. Champion collection (Welch, 1979a). On 6 September 1966 small numbers of *C. lapponicus* were extracted from a sparrowhawk's nest collected at Polchar, near Aviemore. With the subsequent deaths of W. O. Steel and G. E. Woodroffe it has not been possible to trace specimens in their collections and the only extant specimen is in my collection (Welch, 1979a). A number of

sparrowhawks' nests have since been examined from Dumfries & Galloway, Anglesey and Windsor Forest, Berkshire, but no further specimens have been found.

Author R. C. Welch.

Atomaria reitteri

ENDANGERED

Order **Coleoptera**   Family **Cryptophagidae**

Atomaria (Anchisera) reitteri Loevendal, 1892.

Identification Allen (1968); Freude, Harde & Lohse (1964-83), 7:141-147. Confused in collections with *A. atra* (Herbst).

Distribution Known in Britain from Wicken Fen (Cambridgeshire) and Yarnton (Oxfordshire). Only found singly, on four occasions.

Habitat and ecology A northern European species of marsh litter and pond margins.

Status The earliest known British specimen was taken by Dr Crotch near Cambridge last century as *A. atra* (Herbst), which was misspelt as *A. atrata* in the Omer-Cooper & Tottenham (1932) list of Coleoptera from Wicken Fen (if that indeed was where it was found). P. Harwood found it at Wicken Fen on 10 November 1912 and in April 1925. The only other known specimen was collected by J. Collins in a marshy place at Yarnton (Allen, 1968).

Conservation Wicken Fen is a property of the National Trust.

Author R. C. Welch.

Clitostethus arcuatus

A ladybird   **ENDANGERED**

Order **Coleoptera**   Family **Coccinellidae**

Clitostethus arcuatus (Rossi, 1794).

Identification Pope (1952), p.4; H. Fuersch *in* Freude, Harde & Lohse (1964-83), 7:256.

Distribution The only old (pre-1900) record is from Shenton Hall, near Market Bosworth, Leicestershire, 24 August 1872 (a single specimen collected by Wollaston and quoted by Fowler (1887-91, 3:172)). Post-1900 records are: Stonor Park, Berkshire, 6 August 1915 (six specimens in the Donisthorpe collection, BM(NH)); Henley-on-Thames, Oxfordshire, 1915 (seven specimens collected by H. F. Perry and in the BM(NH)); and Oxford in 1979 and 1980. The populations are probably very small and extremely local as a rule, with occasional upsurges as in 1979 and 1980.

Habitat and ecology Recorded in Britain on old ivy *Hedera* (Fowler, 1887-91), and on bushes of *Viburnum tinus* infested with whitefly (Mills, 1981). Most host records from the Continent (Horion, 1961) refer to ivy, but Reitter (1911) says that it is found, both as larva and adult, feeding on woolly apple aphid *Eriosoma lanigerum* (Hausmann) on apple and other fruit trees, a statement viewed with some suspicion by the present author.

Status Very small and may easily be overlooked. Britain may represent the northernmost limit of its distribution. The only record in recent years is by Mills (1981 and pers. comm.), who recorded breeding colonies at Oxford in 1979 and 1980, but they were not found by him in 1981.

Author R. D. Pope.

Nephus quadrimaculatus

A ladybird

VULNERABLE

Order **Coleoptera**

Family **Coccinellidae**

Nephus quadrimaculatus (Herbst, 1783).

Identification Pope (1973), pp.12-14; H. Fuersch *in* Freude, Harde & Lohse (1964-83), 7:253.

Distribution Old (pre-1900) records are: Woodditton, Cambridgeshire, 1827; Norfolk, 1895; Coddenham, Suffolk, 1894 and 1895; and near Manchester, 1869. Recent (post-1900) records are: Frostenden, near Southwold, Suffolk, 1934 and 1938, and near Stowmarket, Suffolk, 1981. The populations are probably very small as a rule, with very rare upsurges.

Habitat and ecology Recorded in Britain on pine *Pinus* in 1894 and 1895, and on ivy *Hedera* in 1937 and 1981. Horion (1961) associates the species with oak *Quercus* in southern Europe and ivy in France, and gives as a prey species the coccid bug *Phenacoccus aceris* (Signoret).

Status Small and easily overlooked other than during specialist collecting. The only record in recent years is by H. Mendel (pers. comm.), who found the species in profusion on ivy at Badley Church near Stowmarket on 5 September 1981. The species is said to be very common in France (Gourreau, 1974) and is generally distributed throughout the southern Palaearctic (Horion, 1961).

Author R. D. Pope.

Lycoperdina succincta

Order **Coleoptera**   Family **Endomychidae**

	Lycoperdina succincta (L., 1767).
Identification	Joy (1932), p.496.
Distribution	The Barton Mills district and Mildenhall (Suffolk); near Thetford (Norfolk) and Thetford Heath (Suffolk). There is now probably only a single Breckland population, of limited size.
Habitat and ecology	The adults and larvae are found in various puffball fungi, on which they feed. The only British record for a named fungus cites *Lycoperdon gemmatum*; in Continental Europe *L. succincta* has been found in *Bovista nigrescens*, as well as *Lycoperdon* species. Larvae and pupae have been found at the beginning of May, with adults emerging in early June, and larvae and pupae have also been found in October. The adults are known to overwinter in decaying puffballs. Adults have been collected in Britain in the months September to November.
Status	*L. succincta* was first collected in Britain by G. W. Nicholson, who found fifteen specimens at Barton Mills in 1916. The species was taken there again in 1917 and has been found in the same district as recently as 1981. Other captures may have been made at Barton Mills in the intervening years. *L. succincta* has also been collected at three other Breckland sites: Mildenhall, October 1923 (C. E. Stott) and October 1924 (E. C. Bedwell); near Thetford, 1943 (S. O. Taylor); Thetford Heath, 1979, in numbers (H. Mendel). The general distribution of this species is of the 'Continental' type; there are no records for Norway, Belgium or western France. In Britain it is probably confined to the Breckland area, where several beetle species of this type have their north-western outpost.
Threats	Any threat to the remaining areas of open Breckland in west Suffolk and west Norfolk.
Conservation	Measures to conserve open areas of Breckland.
Author	P. M. Hammond.

Enicmus rugosus	VULNERABLE

Order **Coleoptera**	Family **Lathridiidae**

Enicmus rugosus (Herbst, 1793).

Identification Joy (1932), p.511.

Distribution Formerly recorded on a number of occasions from Sherwood Forest (Nottinghamshire) and Epping Forest (Essex) but there are few recent records for England. It is probably more widespread in the ancient Caledonian pine forests of Scotland (a similar distribution to the Endangered ptiliid beetle *Ptinella limbata* (Heer)).

Habitat and ecology Found under bark or associated with powdery fungi on old trees, mainly oak *Quercus*, but also recorded from ash *Fraxinus* and beech *Fagus* in England, and alder *Alnus* and pine *Pinus* in Scotland.

Status Fowler (1887-91, 3:284) records *E. rugosus* as very rare from Loughton (Essex), Sherwood (Nottinghamshire), Salford Priors (Warwickshire), Cannock Chase (Staffordshire) and Aviemore on Speyside, Scotland. Hammond (1979) notes post-1950 records from Epping Forest. Although it is not listed by Donisthorpe (1939), C. Johnson (in litt.) includes Windsor Forest as a locality, and A. A. Allen took it there in October 1971. J. A. Owen (pers. comm.) found it in Windsor Great Park in August 1981 and at Wisley Common (Surrey) in February 1984. Apparently not recorded from the New Forest. It has always been rare but may have declined in England. In Scotland, it may be widespread in the older forests of the Highlands (Ashe, 1952; Hunter, 1977). P. Hodge (pers. comm.) records it from a plantation near Dulnain Bridge on Speyside, 10 July 1979, and J. A. Owen (pers. comm.) has taken it at Loch Garten, Speyside, 1979-83.

Threats The removal of ancient trees.

Author R. C. Welch.

Corticaria fagi	VULNERABLE

Order **Coleoptera**	Family **Lathridiidae**

Corticaria fagi Wollaston, 1854, formerly known as *C. aequidentata* Allen.

Identification Johnson (1974).

Distribution Only known in Britain from Windsor Forest (Allen, 1937a).

Habitat and ecology Its biology is unknown, but it is probably associated with the old mouldy dead wood of broadleaved trees.

Status	Known in Britain only by the unique type of *C. aequidentata* which Allen collected in July 1936 by sweeping round a stack of cut timber in the evening. Johnson regards it as "an extremely rare species of wide but sporadic occurrence" throughout Europe.
Threats	The removal of dead wood and decaying ancient trees.
Conservation	Maintenance of ancient forest areas with over-mature trees and dead wood.
Author	R. C. Welch.

Corticarina latipennis

ENDANGERED

Order **Coleoptera**   Family **Lathridiidae**

Corticarina latipennis (Sahlberg, 1871), formerly known as *C. fowleriana* (Sharp).

Identification	A. von Peez *in* Freude, Harde & Lohse (1964-83), 7: 88-189.
Distribution	Only known by three specimens from Braemar, Deeside (Grampian Region).
Habitat and ecology	Associated with ancient Scots pine *Pinus sylvestris*, and spruce *Picea* in Scandinavia.
Status	Originally described as *Corticaria fowleriana* by D. Sharp from a specimen collected at Braemar in June 1871. On 22/23 July 1970 C. Johnson (1976b) sieved two males from refuse at the side of a burn in Glen Lui, Braemar. In Scandinavia it is known to have a north-eastern distribution, as it is not found south of 69° 30' N or west of 23° E.
Author	R. C. Welch.

Teredus cylindricus

ENDANGERED

Order **Coleoptera**   Family **Colydiidae**

Teredus cylindricus (Olivier, 1790), formerly known as *T. nitidus* (F.).

Identification	Joy (1932), p.517.
Distribution	Only known from the Windsor Forest area (Berkshire) and Sherwood Forest (Nottinghamshire). The populations are very localised but it may be relatively common where found.
Habitat and ecology	Under the bark of old oaks *Quercus*, sweet chestnut *Castanea* and other trees. It is often found in association with

nests of the ant *Lasius brunneus* (Latreille), or borings of the bark beetle *Dryocoetinus villosus* (F.) and various anobiid beetles, etc.

Status

T. cylindricus was recorded twice from Sherwood Forest, in 1839 by Stephens, and again in 1884 by Blatch (Carr, 1916), before its discovery in July 1925 in Windsor Forest by Bedwell and Donisthorpe (Donisthorpe, 1939). On 24 June 1964 one was found in the bark of a large wind-blown oak at Silwood Park, near Ascot, Berkshire. Many specimens were subsequently collected at night on the cut ends of the trunk and main branches. A single specimen was also found on 23 June 1971 under the bark of a felled sweet chestnut in Windsor Forest (R. C. Welch), a host tree noted by Donisthorpe, and J. A. Owen (pers. comm.) has taken it from old and dead oaks in the Great Park, 1982-84. There are no recent records known from Sherwood but it is probably widely distributed in the Windsor Forest area.

Threats

The removal of dead wood and the felling of ancient oaks, etc.

Author

R. C. Welch.

Diaperis boleti

VULNERABLE

Order **Coleoptera**   Family **Tenebrionidae**

Diaperis boleti (L., 1758).

Identification

Brendell (1975), p.11; Harde (1984), fig. 227:9.

Distribution

There are early records (pre-1891) from Hastings, East Sussex; Barham, east Suffolk; Sherwood, Nottinghamshire; and Dalston, Cumbria (also 1907). It was rediscovered in the area of the Hampshire-Dorset border (Ringwood district 1952, Soply 1956 and West Parley 1953-55). At the time of its rediscovery small local populations were apparently quite well-established. It was found in Cambridgeshire in 1985 (R. S. Key, pers. comm.).

Habitat and ecology

In brackets of the fungus *Piptoporus betulinus* on birch *Betula*. On the Continent it has been found in a number of other Polyporaceae such as *Fomes fomentarius*, *Laetiporus sulphureus*, *Polyporus squamosus* and *Coriolus versicolor* on beech *Fagus*, oak *Quercus* and conifers. The adults and larvae apparently feed on the soft fleshy part of the fungus just above the gills. Pupation takes place in a roomy excavation within the fungus. The larva has been observed to construct this chamber and to use the debris of excavation to reseal the exit hole which it makes for later use. Pupae are found in late summer and winter, and development takes one year.

Status	Sankey collected fifteen examples in June 1956, A. M. Massee ten examples in August 1953, and "good series" were reported by Basker in 1952 and by Harwood in June 1953.
Threats	Habitat destruction and over-collecting.
Conservation	The preservation of dead and dying trees. Public access should be limited. The most recent records are from an NNR.
Author	M. J. D. Brendell, using additional information from Sankey (1956), Benick (1952) and Palm (1959).

Platydema violaceum

ENDANGERED +

Order **Coleoptera**   Family **Tenebrionidae**

Platydema violaceum (F., 1790).

Identification	Brendell (1975), p.11.
Distribution	In the New Forest, Hampshire, up until 1901. At Juniper Hall Field Centre near Dorking, Surrey, a single example was taken at light by J. Sankey in August 1957.
Habitat and ecology	In fungi (*Auricularia auricula-judae* and *A. mesenterica*) on elder *Sambucus* and elm *Ulmus*. Also under the fungoid bark of rotten beech *Fagus* and oak *Quercus* and especially in fungi on the latter. In Britain the only records are from under the bark of oak and at light. The larvae and adults are found in the outer, more rotten parts of *Auricularia*, the fungus appearing eaten away at the edge. Pupation takes place in the fungus.
Status	Believed extinct. Historically found in the New Forest, it was rediscovered there by Donisthorpe and Gorham, who found seven examples under the bark of a felled oak in August 1901. It has not been found there since.
Conservation	Preservation of the localities in which this species has been found. The removal of dead and fungoid timber from recorded localities should be controlled.
Author	M. J. D. Brendell, using additional information from Fowler & Donisthorpe (1913), p.295, Allen (1958), Benick (1952) and Palm (1959), p.299.

Prionychus melanarius

VULNERABLE

Order **Coleoptera**   Family **Tenebrionidae**

Prionychus melanarius (Germar, 1813), formerly misidentified in Britain as *P. fairmairei* Reiche.

Identification
Buck (1954), p.5.

Distribution
Ollerton, Nottinghamshire, in a remnant of Sherwood Forest; Staverton Park and neighbouring Rendelsham Forest, Suffolk; Arundel Park, West Sussex; and Norton, Gloucestershire. Very local but well-established.

Habitat and ecology
A nocturnal, ancient forest species. The adults and larvae are found in dry frass under loose bark and in the rotten wood of old oak *Quercus* and birch *Betula*. It has also been found in numbers in an old ash *Fraxinus* and in elm *Ulmus*. Usually found as larvae.

Status
Confined to ancient forest remnants in four of the localities given above. It is still plentiful at Ollerton and Staverton Park. The records from Rendelsham are based on reared adults collected as larvae in May 1961 and June 1962. These were found in a rotten birch stump that remained after the existing woodland had been felled and planted with conifers. The continued presence of the species at Rendelsham is therefore doubtful. The records from Norton are also based on larvae, taken by J. A. Owen in August 1983 and July 1984 and reared to adult.

Threats
The destruction of ancient forest and the removal of old, dead or dying oaks and birches.

Conservation
Some of the sites are already protected and suitably managed. More protected areas are required, and dead and dying oaks and birches should be retained.

Author
M. J. D. Brendell, using additional informtion from Bedwell (1923), Johnson (1976a), Mendel (1979 and pers. comm.) and Nash (1982, misidentified as *P. ater* (F.)).

Omophlus rufitarsis

ENDANGERED

Order **Coleoptera**   Family **Tenebrionidae**

Omophlus rufitarsis (Leske, 1785).

Identification
Buck (1954), pp.4-5.

Distribution
Only known from Chesil Beach, Portland and Weymouth, in Dorset.

Habitat and ecology	Found on the flowers of thrift *Armeria maritima* in June and July. (At variance with observations in Britain, it is recorded from southern and central Europe occurring on "flowering bushes" and "ears of corn".)
Status	The last record had been in 1926 (C. E. Tottenham), until C. Johnson found a pupa at Weymouth some years ago (P. Hodge, pers. comm.).
Threats	Environmental disturbance.
Conservation	The protection of Chesil Beach and cliffs from disturbance.
Author	M. J. D. Brendell, using additional information from Fowler (1887-91, 5: 32) and Freude, Harde & Lohse (1964-83, 8: 227-229).

Abdera affinis

ENDANGERED

Order **Coleoptera**   Family **Melandryidae**

Abdera affinis (Paykull, 1799).

Identification	Buck (1954), p.9.
Distribution	Known in Britain only from Strathspey, Highland Region.
Habitat and ecology	In fungus on trees (pines?).
Status	Originally taken by C. G. Lamb in July 1905 in fungus on trees at Nethy Bridge, and subsequently at the same locality by Col. Yerbury.
Author	R. C. Welch, using additional information from Fowler & Donisthorpe (1913, p.176).

Hypulus quercinus

VULNERABLE

Order **Coleoptera**   Family **Melandryidae**

Hypulus quercinus (Quensel, 1790).

Identification	Buck (1954), p.8.
Distribution	Known this century in Britain only from Bickleigh (Devon), Darenth Wood (Kent), and Monks Wood (Cambridgeshire).
Habitat and ecology	In the decaying wood of oak *Quercus*, hazel *Corylus* and birch *Betula*. The larvae have also been recorded from ash *Fraxinus* on the Continent.
Status	Although rare in the last century it had been recorded widely over southern England: Darenth Wood (Kent); Coombe Wood and Godstone (Surrey); Colney Hatch

215

(London); Plumstead Wood, Woolwich (London); Rusper, near Horsham (West Sussex); Woodditton (Cambridgeshire); Leigh Woods, Bristol; and Dorset (A. Ford); but not, surprisingly, from the New Forest or Windsor Forest. Allen (1947a) reports how Mitchell swept one from a hedge at Bickleigh, south Devon, on 26 May 1917, the first record since 1880. Tozer (1947) describes how K. J. Clark beat a single *H. quercinus* from a half-rotten hazel branch lying on the ground. In 1946 Allen collected two specimens in Darenth Wood, Kent, by beating young saplings, one off birch on 7 June and one off oak, a few hundred yards away on 14 June. On 6 June 1975 a single specimen was swept beneath an ash in a narrow ride in Monks Wood (Welch, 1977).

Threats	The removal of dead wood and the loss of ancient hazel coppice.
Author	R. C. Welch.

Melandrya barbata

ENDANGERED

Order **Coleoptera**   Family **Melandryidae**

Melandrya barbata (F., 1787), formerly misidentified in Britain as *M. dubia* (Schaller).

Identification	Buck (1954), p.7, fig. 7.
Distribution	Only known in Britain from the New Forest (Hampshire) and Chiddingfold (Surrey).
Habitat and ecology	In decaying timber, mainly oak *Quercus* and beech *Fagus*.
Status	*M. barbata* has occurred in the New Forest at wide intervals of time since it was first discovered there in June 1823. Fowler & Donisthorpe (1913, pp.175-176) reported that about six specimens had been taken in 1901 by various collectors. Buck (1952) clarifies the inclusion of *M. dubia* by Joy (1932) based on a J. J. Walker specimen collected at Burley Lodge (New Forest) on 26 May 1923, now in the G. C. Champion collection. Buck considers Joy's record for Berkshire to be an error since no specimens exist in his collection. Similarly Allen (1973) rejects the Oxfordshire locality for *M. barbata* given by Buck (1954). Allen (1973) mentions a specimen in the Power Collection taken by C. Waterhouse at Brockenhurst in 1902. Allen (1973) recounts how in 1935 Walker told him he had taken a few specimens that year in Denny Wood. On 31 May 1971 P. J. Hodge caught a single specimen on a nettle leaf in the wooded district of Chiddingfold, Surrey (Allen, 1973).
Threats	The removal of dead timber.
Author	R. C. Welch.

Anaspis schilskyana

ENDANGERED

Order **Coleoptera**   Family **Scraptiidae**

Anaspis schilskyana Csiki, 1915.

Identification   Allen (1975), but confused with *A. garneysi* Fowler.

Distribution   Known in Britain only from Blenheim (Oxfordshire) and Moccas Park (Hereford & Worcester).

Habitat and ecology   Adults have been beaten from old oaks *Quercus* but may occur on flowers of such shrubs as hawthorn *Crataegus* with other members of the genus. In Denmark larvae have been found in half-dry, red-rotten, oak wood in January.

Status   Originally recognised as British by Allen (1975) from a specimen collected by G. H. Ashe at Blenheim on 1 June 1953, almost certainly from Blenheim Park where Ashe is known to have collected. On 8 June 1980 J. A. Owen (1982b) collected a male and a female *A. schilskyana* at Moccas Park. They were mixed with other *Anaspis* species and he was uncertain as to their precise origin. On 7 June 1981 he returned to Moccas and beat a further male and female from the bough of an old oak tree in the park.

Threats   The loss of ancient park woodland.

Conservation   Ancient oaks at the above sites should be preserved, and their eventual replacement should be assured.

Author   R. C. Welch.

Chrysanthia nigricornis

ENDANGERED

Order **Coleoptera**   Family **Oedemeridae**

Chrysanthia nigricornis (Westhoff, 1881).

Identification   Skidmore (1973); Harde (1984), fig. 219:2.

Distribution   Only known from one site in Glen Tanar, Deeside (Grampian). The population is presumably very small since the adult is fairly large and brightly coloured.

Habitat and ecology   Adults have been swept from heather *Calluna* in open canopy pine forest. Larvae have been found in the heart-wood of a sodden old pine branch (5cm thick) lying beneath tufts of moss and *Calluna*.

Status   Possibly confined to a local Deeside population in the Caledonian Pine Forest.

Threats   The removal of dead timber.

Conservation	The site is within an NNR.
Author	R. C. Welch.

Ischnomera cinerascens

VULNERABLE

Order **Coleoptera**　　　　　　　Family **Oedemeridae**

Ischnomera cinerascens (Pandelle, 1867).

Identification	Skidmore & Hunter (1981).
Distribution	Duncombe Park near Helmsley, North Yorkshire (June 1979), and Moccas Park, Hereford & Worcester (May 1965) (Skidmore & Hunter, 1981).
Habitat and ecology	Open deciduous parkland with old trees where there is believed to have been long continuity of this woodland type. It probably breeds in decaying wood. The adults have been collected by beating.
Status	It apparently occurs in much smaller numbers than either *I. caerulea* (L.) or *I. sanguinicollis* (F.). There are six specimens from Duncombe Park, and one specimen from Moccas Park.
Threats	The removal of old trees and dead wood.
Conservation	Moccas Park is an NNR where the importance of the dead-wood fauna is fully recognised. Duncombe Park is an SSSI.
Author	P. T. Harding.

Apalus muralis

ENDANGERED

Order **Coleoptera**　　　　　　　Family **Meloidae**

Apalus muralis (Forster, 1771), formerly known as *Sitaris muralis*.

Identification	Joy (1932), p.305; Buck (1954), p.26; Harde (1984), fig. 223:5.
Distribution	There are 19th century records from Hammersmith and Chelsea (London), the New Forest (Hampshire), Devon, Warwickshire, and Weston-on-the-Green near Oxford. Early this century it was taken from Chobham (Surrey), Gloucester and the Oxford district, where it was taken up until the 1930s, occasionally common locally.

Habitat and ecology	In and about the nests of mason bees and others, mostly in old walls, where the larva feeds on the bee's brood. In Britain it is probably chiefly associated with *Anthophora plumipes* (Pallas) and *A. retusa* (L.) but it has been recorded from a *Bombus terrestris* (L.) nest.
Status	Although taken in plenty at times in the Iffley/Littlemore/ Cowley/Wheatley/Wolvercote areas around Oxford in the earlier years of this century up to the mid-1940s, it has not been seen since. J. J. Walker noted that the intensely hot and dry summer of 1911 greatly reduced its numbers and it had scarcely been seen since. However A. A. Allen (in litt.) was told in 1944 that *A. muralis* still occurred most years at Iffley and Cowley. It may not be extinct, as the mason-bee which used to support it still abounds about Oxford (and in other parts of the country). The beetles spend most of their time inside the burrows and are seldom seen (Allen, in litt.).
Threats	The old walls near Oxford where it used to be established have long been demolished.
Conservation	If the species is rediscovered, any old walls or banks in which its host is burrowing will require protection.
Author	R. C. Welch, using additional information from Fowler (1887-91, 5: 98-100) and Fowler & Donisthorpe (1913, p.300).

Acmaeops collaris

A longhorn beetle **ENDANGERED**

Order **Coleoptera** Family **Cerambycidae**

Acmaeops collaris (L., 1758).

Identification	Duffy (1952), p.6; Harde (1984), fig. 251:6. Immature stages: Duffy (1953).
Distribution	Formerly widespread but very local in the Midlands and south, especially Kent (see Kaufmann, 1948). Now probably confined to the Wyre Forest district of Hereford & Worcester/Salop. It is probably restricted to small isolated populations.
Habitat and ecology	Broad-leaved woodland, especially on steep slopes on sandy soil. It breeds in dead exposed rotten roots, especially of oaks *Quercus*, where the larvae occur under loose dry bark. The larvae do not construct galleries and can move actively on the surface of branches. They pupate in the soil. Not associated with sweet chestnut *Castanea* hop poles as sometimes claimed.
Status	Very infrequently seen by coleopterists recently (and the adult is conspicuous and occurs on flowers).

Threats	The removal of very old oak hedges on field boundaries bordering woodland; the clearance of woodland; and reafforestation, especially where conifers are used.
Conservation	The Wyre Forest is an NNR. The actual breeding sites need to be identified and given enhanced status.
Author	F. A. Hunter.

Pyrrhidium sanguineum

A longhorn beetle **VULNERABLE**

Order **Coleoptera** Family **Cerambycidae**

Pyrrhidium sanguineum (L., 1758).

Identification	Duffy (1952), p.11; Harde (1984), fig. 261:4.
Distribution	Breeding has been confirmed at six sites: Moccas Park and Brampton Bryan Park (Hereford & Worcester), Llanfair Waterdine (Salop) and three sites in Powys. Adults have also been recorded in Gwent. There are probably small isolated populations. That at Moccas Park has been known since 1949, the others are more recently discovered.
Habitat and ecology	Open canopy woodland with oaks *Quercus*. Breeds in recently dead, fallen branches of oaks.
Status	Apparently confined to the southern Welsh borders, and confirmed as breeding in this area in 1949 and 1986. Earlier records were from ports and sawmills, suggesting introductions from abroad.
Threats	The removal of fallen dead wood, the clearance of woodland, and reafforestation.
Conservation	Moccas Park is an NNR, Brampton Bryan Park is an SSSI and one Powys site is a reserve of the Herefordshire and Radnorshire Nature Trust. Management proposals have been made for these sites. The other sites are not known to be protected but the site in Gwent has not been revealed by the author of the record. Other sites should be identified, notified and managed to retain dead wood.
Author	P. T. Harding, using information from Allen & Lloyd (1951), Horton (1980), Cooter (1981a), Welch & Cooter (1981) and R. S. Key (pers. comm.).

Lamia textor

A longhorn beetle

VULNERABLE

Order **Coleoptera**

Family **Cerambycidae**

Lamia textor (L., 1758).

Identification	Duffy (1952), p.13 and fig.27; Harde (1984), fig. 265:4.
Distribution	Recorded from England, Scotland and Wales, but only found occasionally, usually as single adults in widely separated localities (see Kaufmann, 1948). It is probably restricted to very small isolated populations.
Habitat and ecology	Associated with aspen *Populus tremula* and sallow *Salix* in damp areas, usually in or near continuous woodland. The larvae develop in living healthy roots or boles and often leave scant evidence above ground of their presence.
Status	The species is cryptic in both coloration and habits and is crepuscular, so it could easily be overlooked.
Threats	The clearance of sallows for drainage or reafforestation purposes.
Conservation	There is an urgent need to identify actual breeding sites and to afford these protection.
Author	F. A. Hunter.

Oberea oculata

A longhorn beetle

ENDANGERED

Order **Coleoptera**

Family **Cerambycidae**

Oberea oculata (L., 1758).

Identification	Duffy (1952), p.15 and fig.30; Harde (1984), fig. 271:2. Larva: Duffy (1953), pp.295-297 and cf. figs 283-285.
Distribution	Known only from Wicken Fen in Cambridgeshire this century. In the early 19th century it was "not uncommon" in the fens, and was also recorded from Cumbria (Barnwood, Carlisle). A specimen was taken near Romney in Kent in 1883. Kaufmann (1948) added west Norfolk, west Suffolk and Oxfordshire, and believed that an old "Scottish" record from Solway may have referred to a specimen once reported from Cumbria. It is occasionally seen "in good numbers" at Wicken Fen.
Habitat and ecology	In fenland, usually associated with sallows and willows *Salix*. The species has also been recorded on buckthorn *Rhamnus*, alder *Alnus*, sea buckthorn *Hippophae rhamnoides* and umbellifers (Kaufmann, 1948). The eggs are laid on the smooth bark of twigs and slender stems of living healthy sallow bushes, and the larva bores a straight gallery in the

pith channel 30cm or more in length, or in sapwood in wider stems (Duffy, 1953). It sometimes causes damage in commercial osier-beds on the Continent. An accumulation of ejected frass clinging to the twigs is the only external indication that larvae are present. Adults are seen in July and August (June-September), usually sitting alert and motionless on the upper branches of sallows but sometimes flying very actively in sunny conditions.

Status

The species had not been observed in Britain for some fifty years when one was taken on sea buckthorn on the coast of Romney Marsh in 1883 – a previously unrecorded plant association and locality. Since 1890 it has apparently been confined to Wicken Fen. Although a conspicuous and attractive insect it can be difficult to locate while sitting amongst the foliage, and it is said to be very difficult to catch. There were no recent records until August 1983, when one was photographed at Wicken Fen by C. R. Munford and later identified by H. Mendel (pers. comm.).

Threats

Has been seriously affected in the past by the drainage of fens and the associated removal of sallows, though this is not a problem at Wicken Fen.

Conservation

Wicken Fen is a property of the National Trust.

Author

D. B. Shirt.

Donacia obscura

A leaf beetle

VULNERABLE

Order **Coleoptera**

Family **Chrysomelidae**

Donacia obscura Gyllenhal, 1813.

Identification

Joy (1932), p.392.

Distribution

Recorded from localised, widely separated sites in Britain. England: Windsor (Berkshire), Sutton Broad (Suffolk), Wareham (Dorset), and near Penrith (Cumbria); Scotland: Dumfries and Lochinvar (Dumfries & Galloway), the Glasgow district and Loch Tromlee, Argyll (Strathclyde); Aviemore, and single sites in Inverness and Ross & Cromarty (Highland); Wales: Bryn Pyde W. and Llyn Parc, Betws-y-coed (Gwynedd), and near Newbridge on Wye (Powys). The total population is probably small, since it never occurs in high numbers in the above localities.

Habitat and ecology

A species occurring in lakes on uplands, in fens and woodland. The adults have been recorded from water-lilies (Nymphaeaceae) and sedges *Carex* during April-July. The larvae probably develop at the roots of the host plants during the autumn, winter and spring.

Status	There are recent records for Scotland and Wales. The species occurred in high numbers at Llyn Parc, Betws-y-coed, on 27 April 1980 (P. Kirby), two were taken at Aberithon Turbary, Newbridge on Wye, in 1982 (R.S. Key), and it is regularly recorded near Loch Garten (J.A. Owen *et al*).
Threats	The draining of lakes and broads for agricultural purposes.
Conservation	Aberithon Turbary is a reserve of the Herefordshire and Radnorshire Nature Trust, and Loch Garten is a reserve of the RSPB.
Author	M. L. Cox.

Zeugophora flavicollis

A leaf beetle

ENDANGERED

Order **Coleoptera**　　　Family **Chrysomelidae**

Zeugophora flavicollis (Marsham, 1802).

Identification	Joy (1932), p.392.
Distribution	Recorded from the following localities in England: Colchester, and Great Monk Wood and High Beech in Epping Forest (Essex); Matley Bog in the New Forest (Hampshire); Bexley (Kent); Laughton (East Sussex); near Kidderminster (Hereford & Worcester); Kendal (Cumbria); and Bricket Wood (Hertfordshire). In addition Fowler (1887-91, 4:280) recorded this species from Ashford (Kent), Seal Wood (Leicestershire), Kimpton (Hampshire) and the Manchester district. The total population is probably small, since it never occurred in high numbers in the above localities.
Habitat and ecology	A woodland species in which the adults occur on the leaves of aspen *Populus tremula* during May, June, July and again in September and October. They probably overwinter, whilst the larvae mine the leaves of aspen during the summer.
Status	Not recorded in the above localities since 1946.
Threats	The clearing of natural woodland.
Author	M. L. Cox, using additional information from Cox (1947), Buck (1955), and P.S. Hyman (pers. comm.).

Labidostomis tridentata

A leaf beetle

ENDANGERED

Order **Coleoptera**

Family **Chrysomelidae**

Labidostomis tridentata (L., 1758).

Identification	Joy (1932), p.396.
Distribution	Recorded from several widely separated sites in England as follows: Darenth Wood near Dartford, Oaken Wood near East Malling, and Ham Street Woods near Ashford (Kent); Abbot's Wood near Hailsham (East Sussex); Pamber Forest near Basingstoke (Hampshire); Wyre Forest (Hereford & Worcester); and Roseberry Topping near Great Ayton (Cleveland). In addition Fowler (1887-91, 4:285) recorded it from Coombe Wood (Surrey) and Bewdley (Hereford & Worcester). The total population is presumably small, since the adults are usually collected in low numbers. However, they occurred in profusion at Oaken Wood, East Malling, in May 1945.
Habitat and ecology	The adults have been collected from young birches *Betula* about five years old in rough open ground in woodland during May, June and July. The larvae frequent the nests of ants and require at least a year to complete development.
Status	The last records are for Ham Street Woods in July 1951 (van Emden, unpubl.), and for Abbot's Wood in the mid-1950s (J. Cribb collection: P. Hodge, pers. comm.)
Threats	The clearing of woodland.
Author	M. L. Cox, using additional information from Massee (1945).

Gynandrophthalma affinis

A leaf beetle

ENDANGERED

Order **Coleoptera**

Family **Chrysomelidae**

Gynandrophthalma affinis (Illiger, 1794).

Identification	Joy (1932), p.395.
Distribution	Recorded from Wychwood Forest near Witney, Oxfordshire, and from thickets by the River Windrush, 20km from Wychwood Forest. The total population is probably small since it is present in low numbers during the years of its occurrence in the above localities.
Habitat and ecology	Adults have been taken from hazel *Corylus* in deciduous woodland during June and, rarely, in May. The larvae probably develop inside the nests of ants.
Status	Not recorded since 1965, and confined to one or two populations in Oxfordshire.

Threats	The clearing of woodland.
Conservation	Wychwood is an NNR.
Author	M. L. Cox, using information from Champion & Lloyd (1910) and Atty (1970).

Cryptocephalus biguttatus

A leaf beetle **VULNERABLE**

Order **Coleoptera** Family **Chrysomelidae**

Cryptocephalus biguttatus (Scopoli, 1763).

Identification	Joy (1932), p.394.
Distribution	Occurring in several extremely localised, widely separated populations in the following English counties: Devon (Totnes); Dorset (Parley Common near Bournemouth, and Studland); Berkshire (Wellington College at Crowthorne, and Wokingham); Buckinghamshire; Hampshire (Silchester Common, Eversley, Bournemouth and Lyndhurst); Surrey (Esher, Chobham Common, and Thursley or Hankley Common); Kent (Chatham and Walmer); West Sussex (Lavington Common near Petworth); and Staffordshire (Chartley Moss). Uncommon and very local, although not particularly rare on Parley or Lavington Commons.
Habitat and ecology	Adults have been swept from cross-leaved heath *Erica tetralix*, its foodplant, and heather *Calluna vulgaris* on boggy heaths and moors during June and July. The larvae probably occur in ants' nests and probably require at least a year to achieve full development.
Status	The last published record was from Chobham Common in 1969 but it apparently also occurred on Thursley or Hankley Common in 1974, and was taken by P. S. Hyman on Lavington Common in July 1983 (K. N. A. Alexander, pers. comm.).
Conservation	Studland Heath and Thursley Common are NNRs, and Lavington Common is a property of the National Trust.
Author	M. L. Cox, using information from Nicholson (1921), Donisthorpe (1922), Allen (1970d) and P. S. Hyman (pers. comm.).

Cryptocephalus coryli

A leaf beetle · ENDANGERED

Order **Coleoptera** · Family **Chrysomelidae**

Cryptocephalus coryli (L., 1758).

Identification	Joy (1932), p.394.
Distribution	There are old records from several localised, widely separated sites in England and one in Scotland. The English records are as follows: Cobham near Gravesend, Darenth near Dartford, and Westerham (Kent); Box Hill near Mickleham (Surrey); Stockgrove near Leighton Buzzard (Bedfordshire); and Sherwood Forest (Nottinghamshire). The Scottish record is from Inverness (Highland). The adults occurred in low numbers in the above localities so that the populations are presumably small.
Habitat and ecology	The adults occur on young birch *Betula* and oak *Quercus* trees in natural woodland during May and June. However, they have also been collected by beating hawthorn *Crataegus* blossom. The larvae are probably myrmecophiles, living in association with ants and requiring at least a year to achieve complete development.
Status	The last record was in 1958, when it was collected from Box Hill by R. J. Bartell.
Threats	The clearing of woodland.
Author	M. L. Cox.

Cryptocephalus decemmaculatus

A leaf beetle · VULNERABLE

Order **Coleoptera** · Family **Chrysomelidae**

Cryptocephalus decemmaculatus (L., 1758), also written as *C. 10-maculatus*.

Identification	Joy (1932), p.395.
Distribution	Occurring in several extremely localised, widely separated populations from the following localities: Comachgowran, Loch Rannoch (Tayside); Deeside, not far from Braemar (Grampian); Chartley Moss and Burnt Woods (Staffordshire); and Abbot's Wood near Hailsham (East Sussex). Probably small, isolated populations.
Habitat and ecology	Adults have been swept from dwarf sallows *Salix* and birch *Betula* in deciduous woodland during June. The larvae occur in ants' nests and probably require at least a year to achieve full development.

Status	Probably surviving as small isolated populations. Plentiful at Chartley Moss during 1978-79, and taken at Rannoch in July 1983 (J. A. Owen, pers. comm.).
Threats	The destruction of natural woodland.
Author	M. L. Cox, using information from Allen (1960b and 1970d).

Cryptocephalus exiguus

A leaf beetle   **ENDANGERED**

Order **Coleoptera**   Family **Chrysomelidae**

Cryptocephalus exiguus Schneider, 1792.

Identification	Joy (1932), p.395.
Distribution	Occurring in several extremely localised, widely separated populations from the following localities in eastern England: Oulton Broad, Barton Mills, and Lakenheath (Suffolk); Horning Fen and Woodbastwick (Norfolk); Eaton Common (?); and Freshney Bog near Grimsby (Humberside). Probably small, isolated populations.
Habitat and ecology	Adults have been beaten from birch *Betula* and common sallow *Salix cinerea* in bogs and fens during June and July. The larvae probably occur in ants' nests and probably require at least a year to achieve full development.
Status	Not recorded since 1908, until taken at Pashford Poors' Fen, Lakenheath, on 15 June 1980 (H. Mendel, pers. comm.).
Threats	The drainage of fens and bogs.
Conservation	Pashford Poors' Fen is an SSSI.
Author	M. L. Cox, using information from Fowler & Donisthorpe (1913, p.287).

Cryptocephalus nitidulus

A leaf beetle   **ENDANGERED**

Order **Coleoptera**   Family **Chrysomelidae**

Cryptocephalus nitidulus F., 1787.

| Identification | Joy (1932), p.394. |
| Distribution | There are old records for several localised, widely separated sites in the Midlands and southern England: Cobham near Gravesend, and Darenth Wood near Dartford (Kent); Box Hill near Mickleham (Surrey); Bournemouth (Dorset); the New Forest (Hampshire); Oxford and Wychwood Forest (Oxfordshire); Colesbourne (Gloucestershire); and Sherwood Forest (Nottinghamshire). |

The adults occurred in low numbers in the above localities, so populations are presumably small.

Habitat and ecology   The adults occur on young birches *Betula* in natural woodland during May, June and early July. The larvae are probably myrmecophiles, living in association with ants and requiring at least a year to complete development.

Status   The last record is for Colesbourne in 1944.

Threats   The clearing of woodland.

Author   M. L. Cox.

Cryptocephalus primarius

A leaf beetle   **ENDANGERED**

Order **Coleoptera**   Family **Chrysomelidae**

Cryptocephalus primarius Harold, 1872.

Identification   Joy (1932), p.394.

Distribution   It has been recorded from widely separated localities in three English counties as follows: the western slope of Rodborough Hill (Gloucestershire); Cholsey (Oxfordshire); and the Gogmagog Hills (Cambridgeshire). Probably usually in small isolated populations; however, Fletcher (1944) recorded it as not uncommon in one localised area on Rodborough Hill.

Habitat and ecology   Adults have been taken on warm, sheltered, dry hillsides with grasses, hawkweeds *Hieracium*, rockroses *Helianthemum*, etc. They have also been swept from common rockrose *H. nummularium* or collected at the roots during May and June. The larvae are probably associated with ants and require at least a year to complete development.

Status   The last record was in 1944.

Author   M.L. Cox.

Cryptocephalus querceti

A leaf beetle   **VULNERABLE**

Order **Coleoptera**   Family **Chrysomelidae**

Cryptocephalus querceti Suffrian, 1848.

Identification   Joy (1932), p.395.

Distribution   There are old records for three localised widely separated sites in England: Sherwood Forest (Nottinghamshire); Windsor Forest (Berkshire); and the New Forest

(Hampshire). The adults occur in low numbers in the above localities, so the populations are presumably small.

Habitat and ecology   The adults occur on oaks *Quercus* and hawthorn *Crataegus* in natural woodland during June and July. The larvae are probably myrmecophiles, living in association with ants and requiring at least a year to achieve complete development.

Status   The only post-war specimens taken were obtained by beating oak branches in the Cranbourne Park area at Windsor in June-July 1981 and June 1983 (J.A. Owen, pers. comm.).

Threats   The clearing of woodland.

Author   M.L. Cox, using additional information from Bedwell (1909).

Cryptocephalus sexpunctatus

A leaf beetle   **VULNERABLE**

Order **Coleoptera**   Family **Chrysomelidae**

Cryptocephalus sexpunctatus (L., 1758).

Identification   Joy (1932), p.394.

Distribution   It has been collected from widely separated localities in England and Scotland. The English localities are as follows: Salisbury (Wiltshire); Wool (Dorset); Lords Wood near Southampton (Hampshire); Hollington (East Sussex); Darenth Wood near Dartford, Cobham near Gravesend, Pilgrims Way near Ryarsh, East Malling, and Swanscombe (Kent); Grays chalk pit and Colchester (Essex); near Kidderminster (Hereford & Worcester). Those in Scotland are: Scarwater (?Dumfries & Galloway); Dalry Wood (?Strathclyde). The adults occur in low numbers in the above localities, so the populations are presumably small.

Habitat and ecology   The adults occur on hazel *Corylus*, birch *Betula*, aspen *Populus tremula* and crack willow *Salix fragilis* in natural woodland during May, June and early July. In addition, they have also been collected from wood spurge *Euphorbia amygdaloides* blossoms. The larvae are probably myrmecophiles, living in association with ants and requiring at least a year to achieve complete development.

Status   A single specimen was taken at Grays in 1978.

Threats   The clearing of woodland.

Author   M.L. Cox.

Bromius obscurus

A leaf beetle

ENDANGERED

Order **Coleoptera**   Family **Chrysomelidae**

Bromius obscurus (L., 1758), formerly known as *Adoxus obscurus.*

Identification

Portevin (1934); Freude, Harde & Lohse (1964-83), 10; Harde (1984), fig. 275:8.

Distribution

Occurring only as a single colony alongside the River Dane at Hugbridge near Bosley, Cheshire. The population is probably small but difficult to estimate, since willow-herbs are found in dense stands which are difficult to sweep and the beetles are easily alarmed and drop from the plants.

Habitat and ecology

Adults have been taken on various willow-herbs (*Epilobium* species) and especially the rose-bay willow-herb *Chamerion angustifolium*. The beetle seems to prefer light sandy soil alongside rivers. On the Continent it was recognised as a pest of the grape vine *Vitis vinifera* as early as the 15th century. According to Balachowsky (1963, pp. 593-597) this species is parthenogenetic and only the female is known. The adults start to emerge from the soil during May. Oviposition commences in early June and continues up to August, and the adults may survive for nearly three months. The bright yellow, 1.0 x 0.5mm ova are laid in batches of 20-40. They are laid either in the soil near the host plants or at the base of the stem, slightly above the root neck under the old sloughed-off epidermis. The larvae feed in groups on the roots, decorticating them and thus removing the epidermis and even sometimes the superficial wood. They eat either linear or irregular incisions, the latter resembling the damage caused by certain scarabaeid larvae. The larvae develop slowly during the autumn and winter and penetrate deep into the earth. Pupation occurs in an earthen cocoon during March or early April and the adults emerge 20-30 days later. The adults feed on the foliage of the host plants.

Status

This beetle was apparently very common in Britain during the mild phase about 11,000-12,000 years ago. Stephens (1827-35, 4:363) is perhaps the only British author to include this amongst the reputed British species. He referred to a specimen in the collection of the British Museum which was said to have been taken in Lincolnshire, but no subsequent record has since been reported, the species being expunged from the British list. It was 'rediscovered' by P. Kendall (1982), who found several specimens by the River Dane on 29 August 1979.

Author

M.L. Cox.

Chrysolina cerealis

"Rainbow Leaf Beetle" **ENDANGERED**

Order **Coleoptera** Family **Chrysomelidae**

Chrysolina cerealis (L., 1767).

Identification Joy (1932), p.398; Harde (1984), fig. 277:2.

Distribution Recorded from several sites on and at the foot of Mount Snowdon, Gwynedd, and in the surrounding district. The population is probably small, since it only occurs in low numbers.

Habitat and ecology Adults occur on and at the base of wild thyme *Thymus praecox* plants. The adults are present from June to October, and according to Balachowsky (1963, p.640) overwintering occurs in this stage in the mountains. Oviposition probably occurs in the spring and the larvae feed on the leaves of thyme during the summer. At lower altitudes the larvae may overwinter and resume their activity the following spring.

Status It has been recorded recently from Snowdon by J. Parry, who will be publishing his findings on the biology of this species. In a research project in 1980-81, P. King found it on Snowdon and in Cwm Idwal but not at other sites (A. Buse, pers. comm.).

Threats The destruction of stands of the host plant by burning, etc.

Conservation This species is listed on Schedule 5 of the Wildlife and Countryside Act 1981 and should not be collected. Part of the area is owned by the National Trust.

Author M.L. Cox.

Chrysolina latecincta

A leaf beetle **VULNERABLE**

Order **Coleoptera** Family **Chrysomelidae**

Chrysolina latecincta (Demaison, 1896), formerly confused with the commoner *C. sanguinolenta* (L.) which only occurs in England.

Identification Joy (1932), p. 399.

Distribution There are old records for the Scottish mainland: the Clyde area near Glasgow, and Glen Noe (Strathclyde), and Sutherland (Highland). It has also been recorded from the Shetland Islands, and several sites on the Orkneys. It usually occurs in low numbers.

Habitat and ecology	In dry grassy places and sandy hills in maritime situations. At Yesnaby (Orkney) it occurred very locally along about half a mile of Atlantic cliff top. Adults occurred in sunshine among stunted grasses, none more than 50m from the cliff edge (I. Lorimer, pers. comm.). The adults occur mainly on toadflax *Linaria* during January, April, May and September, and probably overwinter. The larvae are external feeders on the same host and probably occur during the summer months. Drummond (1956) collected the larvae on the normal and hairy forms of sea plantain *Plantago maritima* growing in crevices at the top of sea cliffs on Black Craig to the west of Stromness (Orkney) on 22 July 1956. In captivity they also fed on the plantains *P. lanceolata*, *P. major* and *P. coronopus* and on yellow toadflax *Linaria vulgaris*.
Status	The species was found to be very common at Yesnaby (Orkney) in April and May 1984 (I. Lorimer, pers. comm.).
Author	M. L. Cox.

Chrysomela tremula

A leaf beetle

ENDANGERED

Order **Coleoptera**　　　　Family **Chrysomelidae**

Chrysomela tremula F., 1787.

Identification	Joy (1932), p.398.
Distribution	There are numerous old records from the Midlands and southern England: Ham Street Woods near Ashford, and Darenth Wood and Wilmington near Dartford (Kent); Barnthorpe Woods near Effingham, Box Hill, Esher Common, and Godstone (Surrey); Warley Common near Brentwood, Ongar Park Wood, Waltham Abbey, and High Beech in Epping Forest (Essex); Knebworth Great Woods, Broxbourne Woods, and Haileybury near Hertford (Hertfordshire); Windsor Forest (Berkshire); Brasenose Wood at Shotover (Oxfordshire); Gamlingay, Cambridge, and Monks Wood (Cambridgeshire); Flitwick Moor and Kings Wood (Bedfordshire); Hartlebury and Rous Lench (Hereford & Worcester); and Knowle (West Midlands). The adults occurred in reasonable numbers in the above localities.
Habitat and ecology	The adults, larvae and pupae occur on aspen *Populus tremula*, poplars (*Populus* species) and sallows (*Salix* species), on commons and in woodland. The biology has been studied by Bromley (1947). The dirty white ova are laid in clusters of about 25 on the underside of leaves of the host plants in May and June. The larvae are rather inactive during the first two instars but in the last instar roam from the foodplant. The full-grown larvae leave the foodplant and ascend the stems of low herbage to a height of about 30cm,

where they pupate. The adults emerge from the pupae in about 6-7 days. They occur from May to the end of September, when they enter over-wintering sites. The larvae probably occur in the field during June and July and there is one generation annually.

Status	The last record is for Ongar Park Wood in 1951.
Threats	The clearing of woodland
Author	M.L. Cox.

Galeruca interrupta

A leaf beetle   **ENDANGERED**

Order **Coleoptera**   Family **Chrysomelidae**

Galeruca interrupta Illiger, 1802, formerly known as *G. oelandica* Boheman.

Identification	Joy (1932), p.403.
Distribution	Very little is known concerning the distribution. One was taken at Sherborne, Dorset, whilst Stephen (in Fowler) records it from the borders of Whittlesea Mere, Cambridgeshire, during June and July. In addition Blatch recorded it in numbers in Wicken Fen, Cambridgeshire, in August 1878. It probably occurred in reasonable numbers.
Habitat and ecology	According to Fowler (1887-91, 4:331) it occurs on sallows *Salix* in marshy places. However, abroad the host plant is a crucifer or the composite field southernwood *Artemisia campestris*. It has also been recorded from creeping willow *Salix repens*. The adults oviposit in the spring and the larvae occur in early summer.
Status	There have been no records since July 1919, when one was taken on the wing at Sherborne by E.J. Pearce, and it is therefore possibly extinct.
Author	M.L. Cox.

Longitarsus nigerrimus

A flea beetle   **ENDANGERED**

Order **Coleoptera**   Family **Chrysomelidae**

Longitarsus nigerrimus (Gyllenhal, 1827).

Identification	Kevan (1967).
Distribution	Occurring in southern and eastern England as far north as Cleveland: Greathide (?); Studland and Hurn (Dorset); Ringwood, Setley Plain near Ringwood, and the New Forest (Hampshire); Grantham (Lincolnshire); Grimsby and near Cleethorpes (Humberside); and Middlesbrough (Cleveland).

(The last four records probably refer to *L. plantagomaritimus* Dollman.) Reasonable numbers of this species may occur, since a series of eight were taken at Hurn on 21 June 1929 (coll. G.W. Nicholson).

Habitat and ecology   Adults have been swept from greater bladderwort *Utricularia vulgaris*, rushes *Juncus* and *Sphagnum* moss in ponds and peaty bogs during February, May, June, September and October. The adults apparently overwinter and the new generation emerges in late September and October, so that the immature stages probably develop during the summer at the roots of their host plant.

Status   Last recorded in 1933. However, A.A. Allen thinks that it must still occur in the New Forest area.

Threats   The drainage of ponds and bogs.

Author   M.L. Cox, using information from Tomlin & Joy (1908), Tomlin & Sharp (1912) and Harwood (1928).

Longitarsus rutilus

A flea beetle   **VULNERABLE**

Order **Coleoptera**   Family **Chrysomelidae**

Longitarsus rutilus (Illiger, 1807).

Identification   Kevan (1967).

Distribution   Recorded from the following localites in England: the Lizard, Wacca Bridge near Antony, near Saltash, Porthcothan, and Trevone (Cornwall); Torquay and Seaton (Devon); Swanage, and Tadden Withy Beds near Wimborne Minster (Dorset); Southsea and Hayling Island (Hampshire); Halstow (Kent); Eaton in south-west Norwich (Norfolk); and Tresco (Scilly Isles). Fowler (1887-91, 4:352) recorded this species from Weybridge (Surrey) and Hastings (East Sussex).

Habitat and ecology   Adults have been swept from figworts *Scrophularia auriculata* and *S. scorodonia* by streams during March to June, August and December. They probably overwinter and the developmental stages probably occur at the roots of the host plants.

Status   This species occurs in reasonable numbers in some of the above localities. In 1981 it was obtained on the Lizard, a new locality. Several specimens were collected at Tadden Withy Beds, Dorset, on 14 June 1983 by P. S. Hyman.

Threats   The filling in, diversion or drying-up of streams as well as water pollution.

Conservation   There is an NNR on the Lizard. Tadden Withy Beds is a property of the National Trust.

Author   M. L. Cox, using information from Allen (1979) and P.S. Hyman (pers. comm.).

Dibolia cynoglossi

A flea beetle **ENDANGERED**

Order **Coleoptera** Family **Chrysomelidae**

Dibolia cynoglossi (Koch, 1803).

Identification Joy (1932), p.421.

Distribution Recorded from several widely distributed localities in England: Burwell Wood (Lincolnshire); Chatteris (Cambridgeshire); Pevensey Bay and Rye Harbour (East Sussex); and Fordlands and Dawlish Warren (Devon). This species occurred in low numbers in the above localities.

Habitat and ecology Adults occur on the hemp-nettle *Galeopsis* and hound's-tongue *Cynoglossum officinale* in woodland, sometimes near the coast, from May to September. They probably overwinter and the larvae probably mine the leaves of the above host plants during the summer.

Status The only post-war record is a specimen taken by K. Side in Rye Harbour in July 1973 (P. Hodge, pers. comm.).

Author M.L. Cox, using information from Fryer & Fryer (1923b) and Carey Riggall (1944).

Psylliodes hyoscyami

A flea beetle **ENDANGERED**

Order **Coleoptera** Family **Chrysomelidae**

Psylliodes hyoscyami (L., 1758).

Identification Joy (1932), p.411.

Distribution The foodplant, henbane, is very local, and sporadic, though widely scattered, and thus the beetle is seldom found but doubtless occurs far more widely than the records would suggest. *P. hyoscyami* has been recorded from the following localities: Cleveland (Hartlepool); North Yorkshire (York); the Manchester district; Leicestershire (Gumley); Berkshire (Aldworth and Streatley); Cambridgeshire (St. Neots); Oxfordshire (Oxford, Wychwood Forest and Wytham Hill); London (Shirley near Croydon, and Merton); Hertfordshire (Hitchin); and in Scotland from Dalmeny near Edinburgh (Lothian). It may occur in quite large numbers where the host plant is grown commercially.

Habitat and ecology Adults have been swept from April to August from henbane *Hyoscyamus niger*, which grows in sandy waste places, especially near the sea. The following notes on the biology are taken from a detailed study by Newton (1934). The adults hibernate in long grass and appear in the field at the end of April. Oviposition commences in early May and continues during June, and incubation requires about two weeks. The entire larval life is passed within the plant, the leaf stalks of which are mined almost to the leaf tip. Mines may also be found in the leaf blade, the pith of the main stem and the tap roots. The first pupae occur in late June and the new generation adults at the end of July. There appears to be only one generation a year.

Status	Not recorded since 1930 but probably surviving as small isolated populations.
Author	M.L. Cox, using additional information from Fowler & Donisthorpe (1913, p.294).

Psylliodes luridipennis

A flea beetle   **ENDANGERED**

Order **Coleoptera**   Family **Chrysomelidae**

Psylliodes luridipennis Kutschera, 1864, formerly regarded as a variety of *P. chrysocephala* (L.). Also listed in Category 5 (Endemic).

Identification	Joy (1932), p.412; Shute (1975).
Distribution	Confined to Lundy Island (off north Devon), where it has been recorded from several sites including Quarry Beach. The population is presumably small since the adults never occur in high numbers on Lundy.
Habitat and ecology	Adults have been swept from Lundy cabbage *Rhynchosinapis wrightii* on sand dunes from April to August. The larvae probably occur during the winter at the roots or mining the roots of the host plant.
Status	The beetle is endemic to Lundy Island and probably survives in low numbers in several localities on Lundy. It was last recorded in 1979.
Author	M.L. Cox.

Otiorhynchus auropunctatus

A weevil   **ENDANGERED**

Order **Coleoptera**   Family **Curculionidae**

Otiorhynchus auropunctatus Gyllenhal, 1834.

Identification	Fowler & Donisthorpe (1913), pp.184-185.
Distribution	Known only from one site, Stac Polly, Ross & Cromarty (Highland). (It is often common on the east coast of Ireland.)

Habitat and ecology	The adults occur on a variety of shrubs and herbs on roadsides and in waste places in Ireland. The larvae are root-feeders.
Status	Probably an outlier of a 'Lusitanian' distribution, but it should be looked for elsewhere on the British west coast.
Conservation	The site is part of an NNR. There is little practical conservation to be undertaken. Monitoring is desirable.
Author	M. G. Morris.

Otiorhynchus ligustici

A weevil   **VULNERABLE**

Order **Coleoptera**   Family **Curculionidae**

Otiorhynchus ligustici (L., 1758).

Identification	Fowler (1887-91), 5:172-179; Joy (1932), p.181; Harde (1984), fig. 287:9.
Distribution	Recorded from several very well scattered sites in England and Scotland, but from only Shropshire and the Isle of Wight in recent years. The Isle of Wight colony is persistent.
Habitat and ecology	Rough grasslands, including maritime cliff slopes. It feeds on a variety of plants, but shows an association with kidney-vetch *Anthyllis vulneraria* at the main British site. The larvae are root-feeders. The species is parthenogenetic, so small populations are probably quite usual and viable.
Status	A rare native species, existing as small populations. Recorded near Ventnor, Isle of Wight, in April 1980 and July 1981 (P. Hodge, pers. comm.).
Threats	Development for holiday facilities, and the erosion of some sites.
Conservation	The Isle of Wight site is well known, but its status must be checked.
Author	M. G. Morris.

Cathormiocerus attaphilus

A weevil   **ENDANGERED**

Order **Coleoptera**   Family **Curculionidae**

Cathormiocerus attaphilus Brisout, 1880, formerly known as *Trachyphloeus attaphilus.*

Identification	Keys (1921); Joy (1932), p.180.
Distribution	Known only from the Lizard (Cornwall) and Wembury near Plymouth (Devon).

Habitat and ecology	Coastal cliffs. The larvae are root-feeders. The adults are probably not closely associated with a particular plant, and are ground-living. (They have been taken in moss-traps.)
Status	A rare native species in a genus markedly maritime and extremely localised, even within its restricted range in western Europe (France, Spain, etc.).
Threats	Degradation of the sites through uncontrolled public pressure: wear on the coastal grassland in the Lizard area is very severe. No information is available about the Wembury site.
Conservation	The Lizard is well-known as a very important locality for invertebrate conservation and has an NNR. NCC regional staff are aware of this. Some rehabilitation of the worst-eroded sites has taken place. Recent work at the Lizard has failed to locate *C. attaphilus*, and confirmation that the weevil is still present in the area is necessary. The British sites are important internationally.
Author	M. G. Morris.

Cathormiocerus britannicus

A weevil **ENDANGERED**

Order **Coleoptera** Family **Curculionidae**

Cathormiocerus britannicus Blair, 1934.

Identification	Blair (1934).
Distribution	Known only from sites on the Lizard in south Cornwall, from Kynance to Rinsey, but probably not looked for in many potential areas further north. There is one old record from Tintagel (north Cornwall).
Habitat and ecology	Coastal cliff grassland. The larvae are root-feeders and probably feed on a variety of plants. The adults, which are ground-living, seem to be particularly associated with ribwort *Plantago lanceolata*.
Status	A rare species in a markedly 'Lusitanian' genus, once thought to be endemic but recently found in northern France. It is a species with a very narrow range for which British conservationists have a particular responsibility.
Threats	Erosion and degradation of the habitat through severe over-use by the public.
Conservation	The well-known Kynance (Lizard) site is an important SSSI and conservation area (National Trust). NCC regional staff are aware of the importance of the area to rare species generally. The Porthleven site is also National Trust land,

but the Rinsey locality appears to lie between Trust properties, though this should be checked. Practical conservation is probably unnecessary; the avoidance of heavy wear to the cliffs is the main consideration.

Author   M. G. Morris.

Cathormiocerus socius

A weevil   **VULNERABLE**

Order **Coleoptera**   Family **Curculionidae**

Cathormiocerus socius Boheman, 1843.

Identification   Fowler (1887-91), 5:185-6; Joy (1932), p.181.

Distribution   Known only from the south coast of the Isle of Wight, from Freshwater almost to Bembridge. Very local but not extremely rare.

Habitat and ecology   Occurs in maritime grasslands and sparsely-vegetated clifftops, etc. Its biology is not well known. The larvae are root-feeders, perhaps associated with plantains (*Plantago* species).

Status   A very local native species, extremely limited in its total range. Very rare in France and known only from Spain (Sierra Nevada) otherwise.

Threats   Holiday development and the erosion of habitat by tourists. Possibly some sites are inaccessible.

Conservation   Both NCC and the National Trust are aware of the importance of some sites of occurrence.

Author   M. G. Morris.

Sitona gemellatus

A weevil   **ENDANGERED**

Order **Coleoptera**   Family **Curculionidae**

Sitona gemellatus Gyllenhal, 1834.

Identification   Fryer & Fryer (1923a); Donisthorpe & Walker (1931), p.77; Joy (1932), p. 177; Kevan (1959).

Distribution   Originally recorded from the Sidmouth-Branscombe area of south Devon; it is not known whether a colony is extant there. It was discovered at Eype's Mouth near Bridport (Dorset) in 1982 and there is an apparently thriving colony there.

Habitat and ecology	Coastal undercliffs and disturbed areas. In Britain the weevil is associated mainly with restharrow *Ononis repens* and black medick *Medicago lupulina*, but on the Continent large birdsfoot-trefoil *Lotus uliginosus* and meadow vetchling *Lathyrus pratensis* are quoted as foodplants. The larvae are root-feeders.
Status	A rare native species, the range of which needs to be ascertained with much greater accuracy. It possibly occurs at other localities along the south coast. Not widespread on the Continent and absent from mid-Europe.
Threats	Not well-documented. Cliff falls are likely to affect populations, at least temporarily, but public pressure leading to habitat degradation is probably slight.
Conservation	The Eype site is on National Trust land. No practical conservation is required but the species should be surveyed and monitored.
Author	M.G. Morris.

Lixus algirus

A weevil   **ENDANGERED**

Order **Coleoptera**   Family **Curculionidae**

Lixus algirus (L., 1758).

Identification	Fowler (1887-91), 5:241-244; Joy (1932), p.218.
Distribution	In Britain, apart from the early 19th century records, it is restricted to a few coastal sites in East and West Sussex, but it has not been seen recently.
Habitat and ecology	In Britain the best-known localities are marshy, wet grasslands, but on the Continent it is not restricted to such places. The larvae feed in the stems of thistles (*Cirsium* and *Carduus* species predominantly), and also in the stems of other plants such as common mallow *Malva sylvestris*. The adults congregate on the foodplants, which may afford them some protection from predators.
Status	A common and abundant species on the Continent, probably on the edge of its range in Britain and unlikely to survive either on agricultural land or in conventional nature reserves.
Threats	Mainly agricultural. Thistles and weeds (the field thistle, *Cirsium arvense*, is a statutory 'noxious weed') are not often allowed to persist. In any case, the ploughing and drainage of pasture has caused much destruction of habitat.
Author	M. G. Morris.

Lixus paraplecticus

A weevil

ENDANGERED

Order **Coleoptera**   Family **Curculionidae**

Lixus paraplecticus (L., 1758).

Identification Fowler (1887-91), 5:241-243; Joy (1932), p.218.

Distribution Formerly widely distributed in southern England, especially in the East Anglian fens. Recorded from many sites in the 19th and early 20th centuries. The most recent records are from Somerset (c. 1950) and west Kent (1940s), but no localities in either county have been confirmed in the last ten years. There are no recent records from East Anglia.

Habitat and ecology Watersides, marshes and fens. The larvae feed in the stems of semi-aquatic Umbelliferae, particularly greater water-parsnip *Sium latifolium* and fine-leaved water dropwort *Oenanthe aquatica* (and hemlock water dropwort, *O. crocata*?). The adults occur on the foodplants and in litter, etc.

Status A native species highly susceptible to land-use changes and which is unlikely to survive unless a colony can be found and protected. The species is likely to be dependent on a large area of foodplant, and the carrying capacity of existing sites is probably low.

Threats The draining of fens and marshes, commercial development (at the Kent site), the canalisation of rivers, and land-use changes generally. The threats are generally very severe, as demonstrated by the history of the species in the 19th and 20th centuries.

Conservation The first essential is rediscovery of a colony of the weevil, with immediate protection and management.

Author M. G. Morris.

Lixus vilis

A weevil

ENDANGERED

Order **Coleoptera**   Family **Curculionidae**

Lixus vilis (Rossi, 1790), formerly known as *L. bicolor* Olivier.

Identification Fowler (1887-91), 5:241-244; Joy (1932), p.218.

Distribution At the Deal and Sandwich sand dunes (Kent) until the end of the 19th century, and just possibly still there, though more probably extinct. There are other records either of long-extinct colonies or casuals only.

Habitat and ecology	Sandy places, especially near the coast; not on acid sands. The larvae feed in the stems of common storksbill *Erodium cicutarium*. The adults are usually found on or near the foodplants.
Status	A rare native species occurring in a biotope which is particularly threatened, both here and abroad.
Threats	Use of sand dunes by the public. It is likely that the large plants (?semi-perennial) needed to support the weevil get little chance to develop under modern conditions of land-use.
Conservation	The last recorded site is a well-known conservation area, possibly included in a reserve of the Kent Trust for Nature Conservation. However, conservation is impracticable until it is established that the species is not extinct.
Author	M. G. Morris.

Hypera pastinacae

A weevil   **ENDANGERED**

Order **Coleoptera**   Family **Curculionidae**

Hypera pastinacae (Rossi, 1790), formerly known as *Phytonomus pastinacae* or *H. tigrina* Boheman.

Identification	Fowler (1887-91), 5:229-234; Joy (1932), pp.228-229.
Distribution	One known site in east Kent. (A Dorset record is almost certainly erroneous.)
Habitat and ecology	On cliff grassland in Britain. The larvae feed externally on the foliage (and flowers?) of wild carrot *Daucus carota*; the adults are associated with the same plant.
Status	A very localised native species.
Threats	Development and public pressure. Possibly cliff falls.
Conservation	At least part of the area of occurrence is on National Trust land. A modern survey of the status of the weevil is required.
Author	M. G. Morris.

Limobius mixtus

A weevil   **VULNERABLE**

Order **Coleoptera**   Family **Curculionidae**

Limobius mixtus (Boheman, 1834).

Identification	Fowler (1887-91), 5:228; Joy (1932), p.228.
Distribution	South Devon (very old records); Chesil Beach, Dorset (no recent records); the Sandwich/Deal sandhills, Kent; and Rye Harbour, East Sussex.

Habitat and ecology	The host-plant is common storksbill *Erodium cicutarium*, confined to sandy areas (but not on very acid sands). The larvae feed externally. The known British sites are all maritime.
Status	A very local native species, with no recent records except from the Kent and East Sussex localities.
Threats	Development and public pressure. Rye Harbour has been threatened by the establishment of a leisure centre.
Conservation	The Kent Trust for Nature Conservation has a nature reserve in which the species may occur. Rye Harbour is an important SSSI. A survey of the weevil's status would be desirable.
Author	M. G. Morris.

Liparus germanus

A weevil **VULNERABLE**

Order **Coleoptera** Family **Curculionidae**

Liparus germanus (L., 1758).

Identification	Fowler (1887-91), 5:248-250; Joy (1932), p.187.
Distribution	Kent (?only). Widely distributed throughout Kent. There are old (early 19th century) records from near Hastings, East Sussex, but there are no recent Sussex occurrences.
Habitat and ecology	Roadsides, waste places, the edges of agricultural land, etc., in tall herb communities. The larvae feed in the rootstocks of hogweed *Heracleum sphondylium*, and the adults are almost invariably associated with the same plant.
Status	A native species on the edge of its range, probably best described as local and restricted, rather than rare. The species is the largest British weevil.
Threats	All kinds of development and land-use changes, particularly on roadside verges and agricultural land. It is one of the species to which collecting might be a threat. It is also vulnerable to senseless killing, particularly on roadsides, by the ignorant (cf. the stag beetle, *Lucanus cervus* (L.)).
Conservation	Not fully known. Several colonies are in or near nature reserves. A survey of sites for the weevil and those with formal protection needs to be co-ordinated.
Author	M. G. Morris.

Anchonidium unguiculare

A weevil | **VULNERABLE**

Order **Coleoptera** | Family **Curculionidae**

Anchonidium unguiculare (Aube, 1850).

Identification
Donisthorpe & Walker (1931), pp.78-79; Joy (1932), p.208.

Distribution
The first British specimen was found in flood refuse near Plymouth (Keys, 1916), but since 1932 the weevil has been taken freely at Gweek Wood, west Cornwall. It has recently been taken in neighbouring woods.

Habitat and ecology
Occurs in leaf litter and mosses in oak *Quercus* woodland on acidic soil. Its biology is unknown.

Status
A very local native species, rare over much of its range in Europe. The population size seems to vary but it is often fairly numerous in the best-known site.

Threats
Development and other land-use changes, particularly felling of the woodland habitat.

Conservation
NCC (South-West Region) has been informed of the Gweek Wood site. Recent searches (April 1984) for the weevil in woodlands along the Helford River have been successful. One of the new sites is on National Trust land and the Trust's agent has been informed; the other new site is an SSSI.

Author
M. G. Morris.

Dryophthorus corticalis

A weevil | **ENDANGERED**

Order **Coleoptera** | Family **Curculionidae**

Dryophthorus corticalis (Paykull, 1792).

Identification
Donisthorpe (1925); Donisthorpe & Walker (1931), pp.84-85, pl. H:6.

Distribution
Known only from Windsor Forest, Berkshire, where there have been good recent records. The weevil is fairly widespread as a Flandrian fossil in Britain.

Habitat and ecology
In red-rotten wood of deciduous trees, notably oak *Quercus*, often in association with the ant *Lasius brunneus* (Latreille). The larvae feed on wood. The species is an 'Urwaldtier', associated only with old relict forest (see below).

Status
An important species of relict forest, almost certainly very much reduced in range by the inexorable destruction of hardwood trees and the clearance of woodland areas. There are several recent records from Windsor Forest (J. A. Owen *et al*, pers. comm.).

Threats	Over-zealous forestry practice, particularly clearing of the dead wood in which the weevil lives and breeds.
Conservation	NCC regional staff have been alerted and fully briefed, and the Crown Estate staff have been informed. Further consultation between the NCC and the Crown Estate is necessary.
Author	M. G. Morris.

Bagous argillaceus

A weevil **VULNERABLE**

Order **Coleoptera** Family **Curculionidae**

Bagous (*Bagous*) *argillaceus* Gyllenhal, 1836.

Identification	Fowler (1887-91), 5:285-289; Joy (1932), pp.210-211; Dieckmann (1964).
Distribution	Recorded from only five vice-counties. The main area of occurrence is the Thames marshes (Kent and Essex).
Habitat and ecology	In brackish ditches and ponds; maritime in Britain (but inland on haline soils on the Continent). The foodplants and larval biology are unknown.
Status	An uncommon and very local native species, vulnerable to habitat loss.
Threats	Drainage, reclamation, conversion of brackish dykes to freshwater, agricultural intensification and industrial development. The habitat is extremely vulnerable.
Conservation	Some sites have been notified as SSSIs, but a good modern survey of the species is a priority. Recorded from Scolt Head NNR, Norfolk, though this requires confirmation.
Author	M. G. Morris.

Bagous binodulus

A weevil **ENDANGERED +**

Order **Coleoptera** Family **Curculionidae**

Bagous (*Bagous*) *binodulus* (Herbst, 1795).

Identification	Fowler (1887-91), 5:285-289; Newbery (1902); Joy (1932), pp.210-211; Dieckmann (1964).
Distribution	Reliably known probably only from the Norfolk Broads, and not recently. There are older records from the London area and ?Sussex. Possibly extinct. The foodplant is restricted in range, but the Norfolk Broads population of the plant has recently increased in size through management of dykes.

Habitat and ecology	Feeds on water soldier *Stratiotes aloides*, the larvae occurring on the fleshy leaves. In broads, ditches, ponds, etc.
Status	A rare native species, possibly extinct. Newbery (1902) knew of only four British specimens.
Threats	The foodplant has been declining, mainly owing to pollution and possibly drainage, but has recently increased.
Author	M. G. Morris.

Bagous brevis

A weevil   **ENDANGERED**

Order **Coleoptera**   Family **Curculionidae**

Bagous (Bagous) brevis Gyllenhal, 1836.

Identification	Newbery (1902); Fowler & Donisthorpe (1913), pp. 186-189; Joy (1932), pp. 210-212; Dieckmann (1964).
Distribution	Known from the Horsell area of Surrey (?no recent records) and the New Forest, Hampshire (two recent records). More doubtfully recorded from Sheerness, Kent (Fowler & Donisthorpe, *loc. cit.*), but no colony is known and it has not been recorded from Kent for the last fifty years. It is seldom taken in numbers, so populations may be small.
Habitat and ecology	Virtually unknown. Occurs in and on the banks of ponds. Associated with lesser spearwort *Ranunculus flammula* by Lohse *in* Freude, Harde & Lohse (1964-83), 11.
Status	A very rare species both here and in northern Europe generally, including Ireland. Recorded from two sites in the New Forest in May 1978 and June 1983 by P. Hodge (pers. comm.).
Threats	Drainage of ponds and other land-use changes; and possibly natural succession.
Conservation	The Forestry Commission should be informed of the New Forest sites, and monitoring, and if necessary management, of the sites should be initiated.
Author	M. G. Morris.

Bagous cylindrus

A weevil

VULNERABLE

Order **Coleoptera**

Family **Curculionidae**

Bagous (Cyprus) cylindrus (Paykull, 1800).

Identification

Fowler (1887-91), 5:285-288; Joy (1932), pp.210; Dieckmann (1964).

Distribution

Recorded from seven vice-counties, all in south-east England. The main area of occurrence is the Thames marshes (Kent and Essex). Numbers are often large where the weevil occurs.

Habitat and ecology

Dykes, ditches and ponds. The host plants are grasses, including *Glyceria plicata* and orange foxtail *Alopecurus aequalis*. The larval feeding habits are unknown.

Status

An uncommon native species: not very rare, but under considerable pressure because of its threatened habitat. Recorded near Tenterden, Kent, in May 1981 and on the Lewes Levels, East Sussex, in 1983 (P. Hodge, pers. comm.).

Threats

Drainage, agricultural intensification, and all kinds of development. The habitat is extremely vulnerable.

Conservation

Some sites have been notified as SSSIs. The weevil probably occurs in at least one nature reserve.

Author

M. G. Morris.

Bagous czwalinai

A weevil

ENDANGERED

Order **Coleoptera**

Family **Curculionidae**

Bagous (Bagous) czwalinai Seidlitz, 1891, formerly known as *B. tempestivus* var. *heasleri* Newbery.

Identification

Newbery (1902); Fowler & Donisthorpe (1913), pp.186-189; Joy (1932), pp.210-211; Dieckmann (1964).

Distribution

Known only from the New Forest (Hampshire), in the Lyndhurst area. There is one precisely known and one indefinite locality. The weevil is seldom taken and its populations may be small.

Habitat and ecology

In small *Sphagnum* bogs. Its biology is unknown, either here or abroad.

Status

A very rare native species. Also very uncommon throughout its known range (north and eastern Europe, not widely distributed).

Threats

Drainage and inadvertent land-use changes; drying out, and succession.

Conservation	The Forestry Commission has been informed of the importance of the better-known site and suitable management procedures have been agreed. Recent monitoring of the site has revealed some deterioration due to trees overgrowing the bog and to drying out. Monitoring should continue.
Author	M. G. Morris.

Bagous diglyptus

A weevil		ENDANGERED
Order **Coleoptera**		Family **Curculionidae**

Bagous (Bagous) diglyptus Boheman, 1845.

Identification	Fowler (1887-91), 5:285-291; Dieckmann (1964).
Distribution	Recorded from East Anglia (the Norfolk Broads, and near Ipswich, Suffolk), and Burton-upon-Trent, Staffordshire. All records are old; there are no recent occurrences known.
Habitat and ecology	Apparently mainly on dry soils (in contrast to most species of *Bagous*), but the British localities give contradictory evidence on this point. The hostplants and larval biology are unknown.
Status	A rare, vulnerable, native species whose biology is very poorly known.
Threats	Land-use changes, but as the habitat is poorly known it is difficult to be precise.
Conservation	The location of a colony and study of the weevil's biology are the first requirements.
Author	M. G. Morris.

Bagous frit

A weevil		ENDANGERED
Order **Coleoptera**		Family **Curculionidae**

Bagous (Bagous) frit (Herbst, 1795).

Identification	Blair (1935); Dieckmann (1964).
Distribution	Known from the New Forest, Hampshire (only two small sites known), Studland, Dorset (the locality is said to have been destroyed), and Sutton Broad, Norfolk (no recent records). The only known existing colonies are those in the New Forest.
Habitat and ecology	Occurs in small *Sphagnum* bogs. The biology is unknown.
Status	A very rare native species which is also very uncommon throughout its European range. The weevil was not uncommon within one of its very small areas of occurrence

(1960-71) but could not be found in 1983, when it was discovered at another site.

Threats	Drainage, clearance, inadvertent interference during forestry operations, and natural succession.
Conservation	There has been full consultation with the Forestry Commission, and management procedures have been agreed. Monitoring has shown deterioration of the main site in the period 1971-83.
Author	M. G. Morris.

Bagous longitarsis

A weevil **ENDANGERED**

Order **Coleoptera** Family **Curculionidae**

Bagous (Bagous) longitarsis Thomson, 1868, formerly known as *B. tomlini* Sharp.

Identification	Sharp (1917); Joy (1932), pp.210-212; Dieckmann (1964).
Distribution	Known only from the New Forest, Hampshire, and Romney Marshes, Kent. There is a recent record from the latter area.
Habitat and ecology	In ponds and possibly ditches. Its biology is unknown, though it is perhaps associated with water-milfoils (*Myriophyllum* species).
Status	A rare species, very rare in Britain. Occasionally taken in numbers on the Continent of Europe. It was taken near Snargate, Romney, in September 1982 (P. Hodge, pers. comm.).
Threats	Drainage, and associated damage; land-use changes (especially in the Romney Marshes).
Conservation	The general importance of the localities is known but there have been no specific suggestions for practical conservation.
Author	M. G. Morris.

Bagous nodulosus

A weevil **ENDANGERED**

Order **Coleoptera** Family **Curculionidae**

Bagous (Bagous) nodulosus Gyllenhal, 1836.

Identification	Fowler (1887-91), 5:285-289; Joy (1932), pp.210-211; Dieckmann (1964).
Distribution	Recorded from eight vice-counties, but certainly extinct in one (Huntingdon). In the Somerset Levels, and from Sussex to Suffolk. Mostly in maritime counties, but the weevil itself is not coastal.

Habitat and ecology	In and near ditches, dykes, ponds, etc. The foodplant is flowering rush *Butomus umbellatus*. The larvae feed in the stems.
Status	A very local native species. The species was common in a 50m length of rhyne in Somerset in April and June 1983, in a large stand of flowering rush (A. P. Foster, pers. comm.).
Threats	Drainage, management of watercourses, agricultural intensification, eutrophication, and land-use changes of all kinds. The habitat is particularly vulnerable.
Conservation	No conservation work has been done and the presence or absence of the weevil in protected sites has not been determined. This species could be conserved in conjunction with the foodplant (a widely-distributed but declining species). The Somerset site is on a proposed SSSI. A survey of the weevil's present status is desirable.
Author	M. G. Morris.

Bagous puncticollis

A weevil **ENDANGERED**

Order **Coleoptera**   Family **Curculionidae**

Bagous (*Abagous*) *puncticollis* Boheman, 1845.

Identification	Fowler & Donisthorpe (1913), pp.186-189 (as *B. glabrirostris* Herbst var. *major*); Dieckmann (1964).
Distribution	Recorded from a few sites in Kent, Sussex and Surrey, but the exact distribution is not known because of confusion with other species. There is a recent record from near Pevensey, East Sussex.
Habitat and ecology	Occurs in ponds, etc., and watersides. The biology is scarcely known; it perhaps feeds on a variety of water plants.
Status	A rare native species, Endangered by virtue of its habitat.
Threats	Drainage and land-use changes generally. Perhaps natural succession.
Conservation	No conservation of this species is known to have been attempted, but the general threats to its habitat are well-known. Existing (and new) sites should be assessed against formal protection in the form of SSSI or nature reserve status.
Author	M. G. Morris.

Dorytomus affinis

A weevil

VULNERABLE

Order **Coleoptera**

Family **Curculionidae**

Dorytomus affinis (Paykull, 1800).

Identification Fowler (1887-91), 5:272-278.

Distribution There are old records from a number of localities, many of them in error through confusion with other species. There are reliable recent records from two small areas only: Ham Street, Kent, and Monks Wood, Cambridgeshire.

Habitat and ecology In oak *Quercus*, or mixed oak, woodland. Associated with aspen *Populus tremula*, the larvae feeding in the catkins, predominantly the female ones. The latest of the three aspen *Dorytomus* species to emerge.

Status A rare native species, which occurs in good numbers in both of its restricted areas.

Threats Afforestation with exotics, especially conifers; the removal of aspen in forestry and management operations.

Conservation One site is an NNR, and NCC knows of the importance of the other area. Encouragement of aspen growth is essential in both areas.

Author M. G. Morris.

Pachytychius haemato-cephalus

A weevil

ENDANGERED

Order **Coleoptera**

Family **Curculionidae**

Pachytychius haematocephalus (Gyllenhal, 1836).

Identification Fowler (1887-91), 5:267; Joy (1932), p.227.

Distribution Known from a restricted site at Gosport, Hampshire, for over a hundred years. There are other records from Devon, Wiltshire and Dorset, but the last two, in particular, are dubious and the Dorset occurrence is not localised.

Habitat and ecology Coastal grassland, in association with birdsfoot-trefoil *Lotus corniculatus*. The larvae develop in the pods, feeding on the unripe seeds.

Status A very local native species. Despite feeding on a very common plant, it has not been reliably recorded except at its one Hampshire locality.

Threats Obviously Endangered because of threats to the site from any kind of land-use change.

Conservation Protection of the site is required.

Author M. G. Morris.

Ceutorhynchus insularis

A weevil   **ENDANGERED**

Order **Coleoptera**   Family **Curculionidae**

Ceutorhynchus insularis Dieckmann, 1971.

Identification   Dieckmann (1971), pp.581-583.

Distribution   Known in Britain so far only from the remote island of St Kilda.

Habitat and ecology   Coastal grasslands or sea shores in a few north European islands. The weevils live on scurvy-grass *Cochlearia*; the larval biology is unknown.

Status   A recently-described species (1971), known elsewhere only from a few islands off the southern coast of Iceland. Probably a relict species, perhaps pushed into a restricted range and hostile environment by competition (?with *C. contractus* Marsham).

Conservation   The only known British site is an NNR. The weevil and its habitat should be surveyed/monitored whenever practicable.

Author   M. G. Morris.

Ceutorhynchus pilosellus

A weevil   **VULNERABLE**

Order **Coleoptera**   Family **Curculionidae**

Ceutorhynchus pilosellus Gyllenhal, 1837.

Identification   Fowler (1887-91), 5:340-350; Joy (1932), pp.195-198.

Distribution   Recorded from a number of scattered localities in the south of England and Wales, both on the coast and inland. The distribution is from Cornwall to Kent, and northwards to Surrey, Berkshire and Glamorgan. However, the only records in the last fifty years are from South Wales. It was said in 1936 to be common in the Gower and has recently been rediscovered in Mid Glamorgan.

Habitat and ecology   All the published records are from sandy localities. The biology is very little known, either in Britain or abroad. The host-plant appears to be a sand-dune species of dandelion *Taraxacum*. The larvae probably feed in the capitula, as species in this group (subgenus *Glocianus*) are all feeders in the capitula of various dandelions or other yellow-flowered composites.

Status   A native species which has probably always been very local, but which has been rare this century. Recorded from Merthyr Mawr, Mid Glamorgan, in May 1983 (P. Hodge, pers. comm.).

Vulnerable to development of all kinds. Coastal sites are threatened by holiday developments and inland ones (if they still exist) by building, agriculture and afforestation.

Conservation

Monitoring of the very restricted site of occurrence is needed.

Author

M. G. Morris.

Ceutorhynchus querceti

A weevil

VULNERABLE

Order **Coleoptera**

Family **Curculionidae**

Ceutorhynchus querceti (Gyllenhal, 1813), formerly known as *Coeliodes querceti.*

Identification

Fowler & Donisthorpe (1913), pp.195-197; Joy (1932), p.202.

Distribution

Known in Britain only from the Norfolk Broads.

Habitat and ecology

The sides of broads, ponds, etc., especially where winter-standing water dries out in summer. On marsh yellow-cress *Rorippa islandica* (?also great yellow-cress *R. amphibia*). The larvae feed in the stems.

Status

A very local native species, but with good-sized populations.

Threats

Drainage, eutrophication and land-use changes.

Conservation

The weevil possibly occurs within nature reserves, but it should be ensured that the species is known to local conservationists and reserve managers. A survey of distribution and status would be helpful.

Author

M. G. Morris.

Rhinoncus albicinctus

A weevil

ENDANGERED

Order **Coleoptera**

Family **Curculionidae**

Rhinoncus albicinctus Gyllenhal, 1837.

Identification

Dieckmann (1972), p.25; Allen (1974a).

Distribution

Known only from the Berkshire shore of Virginia Water. The area of occurrence is restricted.

Habitat and ecology

Lakesides; a semi-aquatic species. The adult weevils rest on the floating leaves of amphibious bistort *Polygonum amphibium* f. *natans*; the larvae feed in the stems of the same plant. The adults overwinter on dry land, usually on banks of the lakes in which the foodplant grows.

Status	Certainly a breeding species in Britain, but whether overlooked or accidentally introduced cannot be determined with any certainty. It is clearly very localised and rare. It was still present at Virginia Water in 1982 (P. Hodge, pers. comm.).
Threats	The clearance of banks and shallow water for lake maintenance and in the interests of angling. Also suffers in severe, stormy weather.
Conservation	Although the site is not likely to be threatened, too drastic removal of vegetation is to be avoided. Other sites for the species should be sought.
Author	M. G. Morris.

Baris analis

A weevil   **ENDANGERED**

Order **Coleoptera**   Family **Curculionidae**

Baris analis (Olivier, 1790).

Identification	Fowler (1887-91), 5:381; Joy (1932), p.217.
Distribution	Known in Britain only from the Isle of Wight. Originally taken near Ryde (Fowler, *loc. cit.*) by several collectors, it was later found near Sandown by Champion in 1887. Thought to be extinct, it was rediscovered near Sandown by D. Appleton in 1984.
Habitat and ecology	Low cliffs and damp, open places where the foodplant grows. The larvae feed in the lower stems and rootstocks of fleabane *Pulicaria dysenterica*.
Status	A very rare resident species. Two specimens were taken by D. Appleton in 1984, on 31 March and 26 April respectively.
Threats	Mainly accidental destruction of habitat by land-use changes, including increased tourism.
Author	M. G. Morris, using additional information from D. Appleton (pers. comm.).

Tychius quinque- punctatus

A weevil   **VULNERABLE**

Order **Coleoptera**   Family **Curculionidae**

Tychius quinquepunctatus (L., 1758).

Identification	Fowler (1887-91), 5:296-298; Joy (1932), p.219; Harde (1984), fig. 307:5.
Distribution	There are scattered records throughout southern England from Devon to Sussex, and north to Norfolk. Always very

local and with few recent records. The New Forest, Hampshire (Woodfidley area), was a well-known locality. Extinct in many former localities. Recently discovered as a strong colony at Kenfig, Mid Glamorgan.

Habitat and ecology   Wood edges, open areas, etc. It occurs on species of vetch (*Lathyrus* and *Vicia*) abroad. One of the main hosts in Britain is bitter vetch *Lathyrus montanus*. The larvae feed in the pods.

Status   A rare native species, which has declined in many areas. There are no known records from the New Forest since 1967. It was recorded as "very common" on sand dunes at Kenfig in May 1983, and was new to Wales (P. Hodge, pers. comm.).

Threats   Over-grazing of the foodplant by ponies in the New Forest. Development and land-use changes elsewhere.

Conservation   Although it possibly still occurs in an area supposed to be conserved, unrestrained grazing by ponies has greatly threatened its continued existence in the New Forest. Temporary fencing from stock would be useful if an extant colony can be relocated there. The Kenfig colony should be monitored.

Author   M. G. Morris.

Ernoporus caucasicus

A bark beetle   **ENDANGERED**

Order **Coleoptera**   Family **Scolytidae**

Ernoporus caucasicus Lindemann, 1876.

Identification   Allen (1970c). Confused in earlier collections with *E. tiliae* Panzer (a Rare species).

Distribution   Known from four sites: Moccas Park (Hereford & Worcester), Bedford Purlieus (Cambridgeshire), Swithland Wood (Leicestershire) and Rockingham Castle Park (Northamptonshire). It is extremely localised and is only ever recorded in small numbers.

Habitat and ecology   In the bark of dead, thick branches of limes (*Tilia* species), mainly small-leaved lime *T. cordata*, but recently found in common lime *T.* x *vulgaris*.

Status   Originally known only from specimens from one small-leaved lime in Moccas Park, which blew down in January 1976 and was cut up and removed the following June. The last recorded capture from this tree was in June 1954. On 27 May and 8 June 1980 several specimens were collected from two common limes in the Park. J. Cooter (1981b) examined specimens collected by D. Tozer off small-leaved lime from two east Midland localities. Those from Bedford Purlieus, Wansford, Cambridgeshire, taken in June 1934 and July 1935 were all *E. caucasicus*, as was one specimen collected in Swithland Wood, near Leicester, on 12 February 1950, together with *E. tiliae*. Eight specimens were beaten from common limes in Rockingham Castle Park in June 1983 (Drane, 1985).

Threats

The destruction and replanting of ancient small-leaved lime sites.

Conservation

Moccas Park is now an NNR. With the acceptance of common lime as an alternative host plant, this population may be secure. Part of Bedford Purlieus has some protection as a local Trust reserve. The closure of the Corby steelworks has removed the main threat to the wood from ironstone quarrying. Ancient small-leaved lime sites in other Midland and Lincolnshire localities should be maintained.

Author

R. C. Welch, using additional information from Harding (1982).

HYMENOPTERA: PARASITICA

The Parasitic Wasps

Although accounting for about a quarter of our insect fauna (with about 5600 species), the parasitic Hymenoptera are among the least understood insects in Britain and, at a time when the ecology – and indeed taxonomy – of so many remains obscure, it is difficult to single out the species and groups whose populations are most at risk. Impressions of declining abundance or distribution can only be sought in the most conspicuous or striking groups, since only these have been even moderately well collected and identified over the years. Among the Ichneumonidae belonging in this category a continuous decline of many species appears to have taken place this century, to the point at which several species common in old collections are now rarely or no longer encountered in the field. Examples include many of the larger Ichneumoninae (e.g. some *Amblyteles* and *Callajoppa* species), some *Banchus* species (notably *B. falcatorius* (F.)), and *Metopius dentatus* (F.): in these cases the host species (if known) have remained more or less abundant to the present day. Presumably similar declines have taken place among the less conspicuous species as well, and it is clear that parasitic Hymenoptera in general will tend to be especially vulnerable to changes and instabilities in the environment because of their extreme trophic positions. Although no hard data demonstrating these declines in Britain are available, Thirion (1976, 1981) has analysed the history of distribution and abundance of many Ichneumoninae in Belgium and shown that numerous striking declines have apparently taken place, particularly in the 30 years after 1950.

Those parasitic Hymenoptera which are effectively or locally host-specific, as many are, tend to be considerably less abundant than the insect species they parasitise. It follows that any recession, whether numerical or spatial, in the host population would be expected to have a corresponding or even greater impact on the associated parasitic Hymenoptera, some of which will be unable to compensate by attacking alternative hosts. Thus all parasites known to be dependent on restricted or declining hosts should be treated as at risk. These include the ichneumonids *Trogus lapidator* (F.) (parasitic on the Swallowtail *Papilio machaon* L.), *Cotiheresiarches* (=*Zimmeria*) *dirus* (Wesmael) (on the Small Eggar *Eriogaster lanestris* (L.)), and *Lissonota setosa* (Geoffroy) (on the Goat Moth *Cossus cossus* (L.)). Similarly, within the context of habitat destruction, parasitic Hymenoptera always occupy a particularly precarious position. The widespread pollution or draining of ponds, for example, will threaten parasites such as the already rare *Chalcis* species (Chalcididae) even more acutely than their hosts, flies of the genus *Stratiomys*.

Many parasitic Hymenoptera have been collected on only one or two occasions in Britain but, in view of our ignorance of their origins and host associations and the paucity of collectors, it is probably advisable to ignore all of these as candidate species until ecological knowledge enables surveys to be made with respect to their host populations. One example of a rare oligophagous parasite of abundant, widespread and often-collected hosts is the braconid *Rogas pulchripes* (Wesmael), which attacks the Grey Dagger moth *Acronicta psi* (L.) and related species, but has been found in Britain only at Chat Moss (near Manchester). In general, however, there is rarely sufficient information to apportion species found only once or twice in Britain to categories reflecting their true distribution and abundance.

M. R. Shaw

HYMENOPTERA: ACULEATA

The Ants, Bees and Wasps

The aculeate Hymenoptera number some 580 species in Britain, and, with the Parasitica, constitute the suborder Apocrita. They have not had a great following in the past, perhaps due in part to the lack of adequate identification guides (though the situation is improving). Many people are familiar with the social ants, bees and wasps, including bumblebees and honeybees, but most aculeates are solitary species whose presence attracts little attention. Many of them are economically important as pollinators or predators, and they are of great interest to the biologist in view of their advanced behaviour patterns and wide variety of life cycles. There are many examples of parasitism and 'cuckoo' relationships (brood parasites), 'cuckoo' species being specifically dependent upon a host species which may itself be rare.

The Red Data Book includes 37 Endangered, 12 Vulnerable and 97 Rare species. At least eight of the Endangered species are believed to be extinct, and a further 18 species are listed in the Appendix (extinct before 1900). The total number listed is 164, representing 28% of the British aculeate fauna – the highest proportion of threatened species in any group. This is due to the precise habitat requirements of many species, which make them very sensitive to environmental change, and the low population levels at which they normally occur.

Suitable nesting sites are the first requirement, many species favouring sunny banks on dry sandy soils for the excavation of their burrows. Others nest above ground, burrowing in dead wood and other plant material or in old walls. Threats to nesting sites include the loss of bare banks and tracks, excessive trampling (though a limited amount may be necessary), the removal of dead wood and too frequent cutting of bramble. All species are dependent to varying degrees on flowers for nectar or pollen, and the habitat requirements for nesting and for food gathering are often very different. Food resources are threatened by the mowing, over-grazing and spraying of herbage, and by the removal and cutting of flowering shrubs. Many species require a specific prey or host, and any threats to it pose an even more serious threat to the predator or parasite. Finally, the Hymenoptera appear to be more susceptible than most insects to the use of toxic sprays by gardeners and farmers.

An introduction and key to the families of Hymenoptera are included in the RESL's series of *Handbooks* (Richards, 1977). When the two titles under preparation (the spider wasps and the bees) are completed, all the aculeates will have been covered in this series. Unfortunately there is no general book on the group currently in print, though *Bees, ants and wasps. The British aculeates* (Willmer, 1985) in the Field Studies Council's AIDGAP series facilitates the identification of all genera occurring in Britain. Books by Spradbery on *Wasps* (1973), Brian on *Ants* (1977) and Alford on *Bumblebees* (1975) are also out of print. The Naturalists' Handbooks series includes an identification guide to *Solitary wasps* (Yeo & Corbet, 1983). NCC has published a booklet on *The conservation of bees and wasps* (Else, Felton & Stubbs, 1978).

259

There is an Aculeate Recording Scheme organised by one of the authors of these data sheets. Provisional distribution atlases have been published on the ants (Barrett, 1979) and the social wasps (Archer, 1979), and there is an *Atlas of the bumblebees of the British Isles* (Anon., 1980).

Omalus truncatus

A ruby-tailed wasp

ENDANGERED

Order **Hymenoptera**

Family **Chrysididae**

Omalus (Chrysellampus) truncatus (Dahlbom, 1831).

Identification	Morgan (1984), p.15.
Distribution	Only a few old records from Kent, Dorset, Gloucestershire (or Somerset?), Berkshire, Surrey, London and Essex.
Habitat and ecology	A specimen has been observed exploring the cavities in the stem of a rose *Rosa*; otherwise nothing is known about the life-history of this wasp. The host is apparently unknown. It flies in June.
Status	The most recent example was collected in 1910.
Authors	G. R. Else and G. M. Spooner, using information from Spooner (1954).

Chrysis fulgida

A ruby-tailed wasp

ENDANGERED

Order **Hymenoptera**

Family **Chrysididae**

Chrysis (Chrysis) fulgida L., 1761.

Identification	Morgan (1984), p.21.
Distribution	Very rare: there are no recent records. Kent to Devon, Hereford & Worcester, Berkshire, Surrey and Cambridgeshire (Wicken, June 1906, where it occurred in some numbers: over twenty collected by Nevinson (1916)).
Habitat and ecology	Little information is available. Has been reared from a nest of the wasp *Odynerus spinipes* (L.). Presumed hosts include the bee *Osmia leaiana* (Kirby) and possibly the wasp *Trypoxylon figulus* (L.). Flies in June and July.
Status	The last records were in 1929 at Portland, Dorset (G. M. Spooner), and in 1941 south of Bere Regis, Dorset (H. L. Andrewes).
Authors	G. R. Else and G. M. Spooner.

Chrysogona gracillima

A ruby-tailed wasp   **VULNERABLE**

Order **Hymenoptera**   Family **Chrysididae**

Chrysogona gracillima (Foerster, 1853), formerly known as
Chrysis gracillima.

Identification   Morgan (1984), p.20, figs 18, 23, 80 and 81.

Distribution   In Britain known only from four sites: Yalding, Kent, 1977,
G. W. Allen; Midhurst, West Sussex (two sites), 1982-84,
M. Edwards; Winchester, Hampshire, 1984, G. R. Else.

Habitat and ecology   The first British specimen was fished out of a dyke in Kent
in 1977. Five years later in 1982, and again in 1983, further
examples were collected in West Sussex from a wooden
post which contained nests of the sphecid wasps *Trypoxylon
clavicerum* Lepeletier and *Psenulus pallipes* (Panzer), both
possible hosts. In 1984 two specimens were collected from a
dead tree near Winchester, and two more in a Malaise trap
near Midhurst. In Europe the species has been reared from
a bramble *Rubus* stem. Small eumenid and sphecid wasps
and megachilid bees (e.g. *Osmia* species) are all possible
hosts in Britain. It flies in July and August.

Status   It seems reasonable to assume that the wasp is probably
more widely distributed in southern England.

Authors   G. R. Else and G. M. Spooner.

Chrysura hirsuta

A ruby-tailed wasp   **VULNERABLE**

Order **Hymenoptera**   Family **Chrysididae**

Chrysura hirsuta (Gerstaecker, 1869), formerly known as
Chrysis (Chrysogona) hirsuta.

Identification   Morgan (1984), p.19, figs 85 and 88.

Distribution   Restricted to Scotland, where it has been recorded from the
central Grampian Highlands (Speyside in Highland Region,
and one or two sites near Blair Atholl, Perth, Tayside
Region). Two specimens have also been collected
in Dumfries & Galloway (Whithorn, 16 May 1973,
A. B. Duncan).

Habitat and ecology   The special cleptoparasite of the mason bee *Osmia inermis*
(Zetterstedt) and possibly *O. parietina* Curtis. Very rare and
local, confined to a few sites on open upland base-rich soils
in Scotland. The wasp larva apparently attacks and devours
the host larva before spinning its own cocoon within that of
the bee (Morgan, 1984).

Threats	Destruction of habitat, especially by afforestation on upland sites between 350 and 400m.
Authors	G. R. Else and G. M. Spooner.

Formica pratensis

A wood ant   **ENDANGERED**

Order **Hymenoptera**   Family **Formicidae**

Formica pratensis Retzius *in* Degeer, 1783.

Identification	Bolton & Collingwood (1975), pp.7, 11 and 15.
Distribution	This species has always been a great rarity in Britain and is now almost extinct, being represented by perhaps less than half a dozen nests near Wareham, Dorset, e.g. on Morden and Gore Heaths. For map see Barrett (1979), map 39.
Habitat and ecology	Dry heathland. Nests are usually isolated, not occurring in groups, and have a single or very few queens. Winged queens and males are developed in the nests both in early summer and later in August-September.
Status	Last seen in 1975 on Gore Heath by G. M. Spooner.
Threats	The destruction of nests or nest habitat. In Britain this species is clearly on the very edge of its range and it is possible that adverse climatic changes may be the most significant threat.
Conservation	Morden Bog NNR lies between Morden and Gore Heaths. *F. pratensis* is among the *Formica* species listed as Vulnerable in the IUCN Red Data Book (Wells, Pyle & Collins, 1983).
Authors	G. R. Else and G. M. Spooner.

Formica transkaucasica

A wood ant   **ENDANGERED**

Order **Hymenoptera**   Family **Formicidae**

Formica transkaucasica Nasonov, 1889.

Identification	Bolton & Collingwood (1975), pp.6, 11 and 15.
Distribution	A very rare species found only in the New Forest, Hampshire (e.g. Matley and Ridley Bogs, Picket Plain), and near Wareham, Dorset (e.g. Morden Bog and Hartland Moor). There is an old record for the Isle of Wight. For map see Barrett (1979), map 48.

Habitat and ecology	A shining black ant confined to a few *Sphagnum* bogs. Colonies usually have a single queen and the nest, which is sometimes found in the very wettest parts of the bog, is built up in the form of a small, conical dome of fine grassy fragments in grass tussocks (e.g. purple moor-grass *Molinia caerulea*).
Threats	Drainage of wetland habitat. In dry years the species may not be seen.
Conservation	Morden Bog and Hartland Moor are NNRs.
Authors	G. R. Else and G. M. Spooner, using additional information from Collingwood (1954).

Arachnospila rufa

A spider wasp   **ENDANGERED**

Order **Hymenoptera**   Family **Pompilidae**

Arachnospila (*Arachnospila*) *rufa* (Haupt, 1927), formerly known as *Pompilus* or *Psammochares rufus.*

Identification	Wolf (1972), pp.91-108, figs 236, 240 and 278; Day (in preparation).
Distribution	South-east Dorset: Gore Heath, north of Wareham, a fresh male and female on a bank, 15 June 1934, G. M. Spooner (Spooner, 1937); Sherford Bridge (on the north-west boundary of Gore Heath), male at *Angelica* blossom, 15 September 1938, G. M. Spooner (unpublished; specimens housed in Spooner's collection). It is widely distributed and rather common on the Continent including the Channel Islands (Jersey).
Habitat and ecology	Heathland, from June to September. On the Continent the wasp is reported as occurring in sandy localities, frequenting banks and cuttings where there are suitable exposures of sand. A noteworthy peculiarity is its habit of reoccupying old burrows, the females apparently returning to those from which they have emerged. Prey consists mainly of spiders of the families Lycosidae and Drassidae, but also Attidae, Clubionidae and Salticidae (Richards & Hamm, 1939; Spooner, 1937). The nesting behaviour is described in some detail by Richards & Hamm (1939). A selection of photographs illustrating prey capture and nest provisioning is provided by Olberg (1959, pp.154-163).
Status	It is perhaps worth noting that the above specimens were collected close to a stretch of ground colonised by the eumenid wasp *Pseudepipona herrichii* (Saussure), a Vulnerable species which also has a southern range and which in Britain is confined to the heaths of south-east Dorset.

Threats	Much of Gore Heath has become a conifer plantation since Spooner's captures; only a small portion of the southern area remains open heathland.
Authors	G. R. Else and G. M. Spooner.

Evagetes pectinipes

A spider wasp   **ENDANGERED**

Order **Hymenoptera**   Family **Pompilidae**

Evagetes pectinipes (L., 1758), a name formerly used incorrectly in Britain for *E. crassicornis* (Shuckard).

Identification	Wolf (1972), pp.137-147, figs 372, 382 and 407; Day (in preparation).
Distribution	Occurs only in east Kent on the Deal-Sandwich dunes, where it was first collected by K. M. Guichard in 1966 (Day, 1979, p.14).
Habitat and ecology	Coastal sand dunes. Occasionally observed on umbellifer blossoms. A cleptoparasite, probably of the pompilid wasp *Episyron rufipes* (L.). Little is known about its biology, but no doubt it is very similar to that of *E. crassicornis* (Shuckard) (for details see Richards & Hamm, 1939, pp.88-89). Flies in July.
Status	Possibly a recent introduction, but apparently well-established. Several were recorded in 1975-81.
Threats	Destruction of the habitat (which includes the Royal Cinque Ports Golf Links).
Authors	G. R. Else and G. M. Spooner.

Homonotus sanguinolentus

A spider wasp   **ENDANGERED**

Order **Hymenoptera**   Family **Pompilidae**

Homonotus sanguinolentus (F., 1793), formerly known as *Pompilus* or *Wesmaelinius sanguinolentus*.

Identification	Wolf (1972), pp.87-89, figs 211-213; Day (in preparation).
Distribution	Rare, recorded from only a very few localities in Dorset, Hampshire and Surrey. The most recent record seems to be a male swept from roadside flowers at Tadnall Heath, Dorset, on 4 August 1962 by G. M. Spooner.

Habitat and ecology	Heathland and perhaps open woodland in southern England. On the Continent this pompilid attacks females of the spider *Cheiracanthium erraticum* (Walck) in their leaf-roll nests in grass (Richards & Hamm, 1939, pp.105-106). There have been no rearing records from Britain.
Status	If searched for in the right way and reared it might prove to be commoner than is generally supposed. For example, in France in early August 1934 and 1935, Maneval (1936) found that four-fifths of the spider nests contained early stages of *Homonotus*, but only one wasp was seen (Richards & Hamm, 1939).
Threats	The loss of heathland habitat.
Authors	G. R. Else and G. M. Spooner, using additional information from Champion, Champion & Morice (1914), Champion (1915), and Saunders (1900).

Ceropales variegata

A spider wasp   **ENDANGERED**

Order **Hymenoptera**   Family **Pompilidae**

Ceropales variegata (F., 1798).

Identification	Wolf (1972), pp.165-168, fig. 476; Day (in preparation).
Distribution	Rare. Recorded at irregular intervals from a few sites in Surrey, Hampshire and Dorset.
Habitat and ecology	Heathland in southern England. Specimens have been found flying round or under small pines (Richards & Hamm, 1939), visiting *Angelica* blossom, and have been swept from heather (*Calluna* and *Erica*) and bog myrtle *Myrica gale*. Nothing has been recorded of its life-history (Richards & Hamm, 1939), but it is probably another cleptoparasite like its relative *C. maculata* (F.). In this subfamily (Ceropalinae) the females oviposit in the lung books of spiders which have already been paralysed and are in the course of being dragged along the ground by females of other pompilid genera (Richards & Hamm, 1939, p.55). It flies in July-August.
Status	The most recent record appears to be a Dorset specimen collected in 1955.
Threats	The loss of vulnerable heathland habitat.
Authors	G. R. Else and G. M. Spooner.

Pseudepipona herrichii

A mason wasp

VULNERABLE

Order **Hymenoptera**

Family **Eumenidae**

Pseudepipona herrichii (Saussure, 1856), formerly known as *Odynerus* (*Lionotus*) *herrichii* or *O. basalis* Smith.

Identification

Richards (1980), p.23 and fig. 28.

Distribution

A very rare and attractive speciality of heathland in south-east Dorset – on the Isle of Purbeck between Wareham and Studland, and a little to the north of Wareham (Gore Heath). The first British example was collected on Stoborough Heath in 1868 and the species continues to survive on Purbeck, although it remains extremely local and elusive.

Habitat and ecology

Dry, open, sandy heathland. The life-history is described in detail by Mortimer (1908b) and Spooner (1934). The wasp is gregarious, occurring in rather compact colonies. Females excavate shallow nest burrows and provision the cells with green tortricid moth larvae extracted from webs in heather. G. R. Else and M. Edwards found the species nesting extensively on mounds of sand and clay spoil with a sparse covering of heather (*Erica* and *Calluna*). The nest burrows were flush with the surrounding soil, and one nest excavated consisted of vacated cells of the bee *Heliophila* (=*Anthophora*) *bimaculata* (Panzer), one cell being provisioned with 3-4 immobilised larvae. The flight period is a short one, lasting from mid or late June to late July (rarely early August).

Status

A few colonies have been discovered by G. M. Spooner and K. White in recent years. G. R. Else and M. Edwards found the species in profusion on Godlingston Heath on 24 June 1984, the season being an excellent one for eumenid wasps.

Threats

The east Dorset heathlands have been experiencing a variety of detrimental exploitation this century ranging from changes in land use (e.g. coniferous afforestation, building developments) to, in recent years, exploration for gas and oil and the extraction of ball clay. Pressures of this kind are bound adversely to affect the populations of such a rare insect. Heathland fires are an annual hazard (Hartland Moor NNR was almost entirely destroyed in 1976), particularly as the provisioned cells are constructed just beneath the surface of the soil. Recently one site on Stoborough Heath was destroyed, probably by the activities of motorcyclists "dirt-tracking" over the nesting site.

Conservation

Studland Heath and Godlingston Heath are NNRs.

Authors

G. R. Else and G. M. Spooner, using additional information from Haines (1934).

Odynerus reniformis

A mason wasp

ENDANGERED +

Order **Hymenoptera**

Family **Eumenidae**

Odynerus (Spinicoxa) reniformis (Gmelin *in* L., 1790).

Identification
Richards (1980), p.22 and fig. 35.

Distribution
Always a rarity since its discovery in Britain by Saunders in 1876 (Saunders, 1876). Surrey (Billups, 1884; Morice, 1906; Saunders, 1876, 1887); Hampshire (Arnold, 1905; Jones, 1925-26). Apart from Morice's colony – c. 50 nest entrance tubes in 1906 – specimens have been encountered in very small numbers. Jones (1925-26), however, reported that in the New Forest the species is local, but not very uncommon: the evidence for this statement is lacking.

Habitat and ecology
Small and very local colonies on heathland in southern England (also, once, on a railway embankment); usually on level ground, but once in the walls of a ruined cottage (Morice, 1906). Tends to be gregarious, each nest entrance characteristically surmounted by a vertical, slightly curved tubular chimney constructed from excavated spoil. The dimensions of these are about 20mm long x 4mm broad. Their purpose is not fully understood. The cells are provisioned with paralysed moth larvae (e.g. 33 small noctuid larvae in one cell (Billups, 1884)). Flies from late June (exceptionally late May) to mid July, rarely August.

Status
The reason for the abrupt decline is unknown. There have been no records since about 1915.

Authors
G. R. Else and G. M. Spooner.

Odynerus simillimus

A mason wasp

ENDANGERED +

Order **Hymenoptera**

Family **Eumenidae**

Odynerus (Spinicoxa) simillimus Morawitz, 1867.

Identification
Richards (1980), pp.22-23 and fig. 36.

Distribution
Essex: Colchester, 1901-1902, W. H. & B. S. Harwood (Saunders, 1903). Some specimens in museums were also collected in 1892, 1898 and 1905. The species was described from Russian material and is also rare on the Continent (Richards, 1980).

Habitat and ecology
Adults have been collected from flowers by a ditch on the marshes near Colchester (Saunders, 1903). Nothing seems to be known about its life history, but it almost certainly nests in the soil. Flies in July.

Status	There have been no records since about 1905.
Threats	Possibly loss of habitat.
Authors	G. R. Else and G. M. Spooner.

Miscophus ater — A digger wasp — VULNERABLE

Order **Hymenoptera** — Family **Sphecidae**

Miscophus ater Lepeletier, 1845, formerly known as *M. maritimus* Smith, 1858.

Identification	Richards (1980), p.38 and figs 167-168.
Distribution	F. Smith first discovered this species on the Deal dunes (east Kent) in early August 1856 (Smith, 1858, pp.91-92). The species remains firmly established on these dunes and north to Sandwich. It also occurs on the Camber dunes, East Sussex (M. Edwards and G. H. L. Dicker, pers. comm.), where O. W. Richards first collected it in 1945.
Habitat and ecology	Coastal sand dunes. The females nest in the soil and provision their cells with small spiders. A small, active, and easily overlooked wasp.
Status	Another Deal speciality (see *Evagetes pectinipes* (L.), Endangered).
Threats	Adverse development of the dunes and possible inundation by seawater during winter gales (as has happened recently).
Authors	G. R. Else and G. M. Spooner.

Crossocerus vagabundus — A digger wasp — ENDANGERED

Order **Hymenoptera** — Family **Sphecidae**

Crossocerus (*Acanthocrabro*) *vagabundus* (Panzer, 1798).

Identification	Richards (1980), p.47 and figs 95 and 97.
Distribution	Formerly widespread throughout much of southern England as far north as Leicestershire and Nottinghamshire.
Habitat and ecology	Nests are constructed in rotten wood, the wasp making use of old beetle galleries; galleries may be branched or straight. The prey normally consists of tipulid flies, which are stored after their legs have been amputated (Hamm & Richards, 1926, p.316; Lomholdt, 1975-76). The wasp flies from May to July.

Status	Within the zone described above the species has rarely been common. The absence of records for the past thirty years indicates a serious decline or possible extinction.
Authors	G. R. Else and G. M. Spooner.

Rhopalum gracile

A digger wasp

VULNERABLE

Order **Hymenoptera**

Family **Sphecidae**

Rhopalum (*Corynopus*) *gracile* Wesmael, 1852, formerly known as *Crabro kiesenwetteri* Morawitz.

Identification	Richards (1980), p.57 and figs 155-156.
Distribution	First recorded by C. G. Nurse at Ampton, Suffolk (two males, three females), June 1912, and at West Stow, Suffolk, June and August 1912 (Nurse, 1913). Other records include: Suffolk, Barton Mills, one female, 9 August 1901, A. H. Hamm Collection; Cambridgeshire, Wicken Fen, 1898 to 1973, and old records for Chippenham Fen (J. Field, pers. comm.).
Habitat and ecology	Restricted to two or three fenland localities in East Anglia where it remains very scarce. Females in Wicken Fen have been taken at *Angelica* blossom. The Ampton site was a swampy spot, on the bank of the River Lark, covered with reeds and rushes (*Phragmites* and *Juncus*), and studded with old sallows *Salix* and alders *Alnus*. The wasp nests in stems and (in Japan) preys on Psocoptera and Diptera (Richards, 1980).
Status	This species appears to belong to the 'Rhine-basin' element of our fauna, which also contains such aculeates as *Hylaeus pectoralis* Foerster and *Passaloecus clypealis* Faester (a Vulnerable species).
Threats	The drainage of wetland habitat.
Conservation	Wicken Fen is National Trust property, where current management of the carr vegetation appears to be benefiting the species. Countermeasures are necessary to safeguard the few remaining sites in the East Anglian fens where the species occurs or may occur.
Authors	G. R. Else and G. M. Spooner.

Psen atratinus

A digger wasp

VULNERABLE

Order **Hymenoptera**

Family **Sphecidae**

Psen (Mimumesa) atratinus (Morawitz, 1891).

Identification Richards (1980), p.62 and fig. 175.

Distribution At present known only from four sites on the southern coast of the Isle of Wight: Whale Chine, Blackgang Chine, Ventnor, and cliffs at Luccombe.

Habitat and ecology Confined to wet flushes at the base of clay cliffs or on landslips. The species associates in two sites with *P. unicolor* (Vander Linden) and in suitable weather both species frequently alight on the leaves of coltsfoot *Tussilago farfara* or fly amongst reeds *Phragmites*. Nests have not been found in Britain, but on the Continent the species has been described as nesting in dry, decayed wood, often in vacated insect burrows. This commodity is scarce in the Isle of Wight sites and it seems likely that females nest in dead *Phragmites* stems. Continental prey records involve nymphs of small cicadas (Issidae) (Lomholdt, 1975-76). The flight period extends from June-August.

Status The first British specimen was collected by O. W. Richards on 7 August 1950. In 1980-82 the species was locally common at two sites.

Threats Coastal subsidence probably destroys some nests, but otherwise the species does not appear to be at risk. Coastal defences could also jeopardise sites.

Conservation The Luccombe cliffs are owned by the National Trust.

Authors G. R. Else and G. M. Spooner.

Passaloecus clypealis

A digger wasp

VULNERABLE

Order **Hymenoptera**

Family **Sphecidae**

Passaloecus clypealis Faester, 1947.

Identification Richards (1980), p.72.

Distribution Very rare. Cambridgeshire: Wicken Fen (c. 1899, 1929, 1936) (Yarrow, 1970), Chippenham Fen, 1983 (J. Field, pers. comm.). Norfolk: Strumpshaw Reserve, 28 July 1980, A. Irwin. Essex: Benfleet, one female about *Phragmites* in ditch, 1 August 1971, P. J. Chandler. Kent: Higham (on the edge of the North Kent Marshes), three females reared from old *Lipara* galls, June 1978, G. H. L. Dicker; Burham (on the Medway), female reared from *Lipara* gall, June 1978,

G. H. L. Dicker (Dicker, 1979); Swanscombe, 1 July 1983, and Wouldham, 28 July 1983, G. H. L. Dicker.

Habitat and ecology   Fens and ditches. Has been reared from vacated galls of the fly *Lipara lucens* Meigen. Lomholdt (1975-76) reports that nests have been found in stems of honeysuckle *Lonicera* and reed *Phragmites*. Flies from June-August.

Status   Rare throughout Europe.

Threats   The drainage of suitable wetlands. The North Kent Marshes are currently threatened by drainage in order that parts at least can be developed for cultivation and building (e.g. oil refinery at Cliffe).

Conservation   Chippenham Fen is an NNR, and Wicken Fen is owned and managed by the National Trust.

Authors   G. R. Else and G. M. Spooner.

Mellinus crabroneus

A digger wasp   **ENDANGERED +**

Order **Hymenoptera**   Family **Sphecidae**

Mellinus crabroneus (Thunberg, 1791), formerly known as *M. sabulosa* (F.).

Identification   Richards (1980), pp.77-78 and fig. 217.

Distribution   Formerly widely distributed and locally common in good years. It has been recorded from Hampshire, the Isle of Wight, Dorset, Cornwall, Berkshire, Oxfordshire, Surrey, Suffolk, Norfolk, Lincolnshire, Nottinghamshire, Humberside, Tyne & Wear, Cumbria, West and Mid Glamorgan, Dyfed and Gwynedd. There has been no record for over thirty years.

Habitat and ecology   Nests in burrows in the ground and provisions its cells with paralysed Diptera (Hamm & Richards, 1930, p.101; Lomholdt, 1975-76). Specimens have been observed visiting *Angelica* and wild carrot *Daucus carota* blossom, and males have been seen in great numbers running on the leaves of coltsfoot *Tussilago farfara* (Smith, 1858, pp.114-116). The species flies from July to early September.

Status   Declined rapidly after the mid-1920s. The cause of the decline remains unknown and it is possible that it may now be extinct as a British species.

Authors   G. R. Else and G. M. Spooner.

Cerceris quadricincta	A digger wasp	**ENDANGERED**
	Order **Hymenoptera**	Family **Sphecidae**

Cerceris quadricincta (Panzer, 1799).

Identification Richards (1980), p.85 and figs 237, 240.

Distribution This has always been a very rare wasp; restricted to two sites in Kent, and formerly Colchester, Essex. G. H. L. Dicker (pers. comm.) found a colony in the training area of the Royal School of Military Engineering at Upnor, near Chatham, Kent, between 1977 and 1979. A female was found on a sandy area near the top of a chalk cliff at Ramsgate on 25 August 1979. In 1900 specimens were collected elsewhere in the county, from Tilmanstone and St Margaret's Bay (Sladen, 1900). There are no recent records from Essex, though it used to be found within the town of Colchester itself, but later died out (*teste* R. C. L. Perkins, manuscript).

Habitat and ecology Nests in clay or sand, provisioning its cells with weevils. It tends to be gregarious. The flight period extends from about mid-July to mid-September.

Status The Chatham colony was small, with probably less than twenty burrows, and was located in the vertical faces of bare, sandy terraces cut in a hillside. Shortly after 1979 the area was realigned, involving the removal of the nesting site. No specimens have been seen there since 1980.

Authors G. R. Else and G. M. Spooner.

Philanthus triangulum	The Bee Wolf	**VULNERABLE**
	Order **Hymenoptera**	Family **Sphecidae**

Philanthus triangulum (F., 1775).

Identification Richards (1980), pp.82-83 and figs 231, 232.

Distribution The British headquarters of this species has long been the Isle of Wight (St Helens, Shanklin, Totland Bay, and, since at least 1851, Sandown Bay where it used sometimes to occur in profusion). Since 1976 it has been found at three sites, in abundance at one in most seasons. It is very irregular elsewhere, although several were found on Nacton Heath, near Ipswich, Suffolk, by M. Archer on 5 August 1976 (flying over heather *Calluna*), and one on a thistle flower on a heath in south Norfolk by J. P. Field in July 1983. There are also ancient records from Hampshire, Surrey, Kent, Essex and south Wales. For map of European distribution see Heath & Leclercq (1981), map 17.

Habitat and ecology	Coastal sand dunes and cliffs on the Isle of Wight, and heathlands in East Anglia. The nest burrows are excavated in both vertical and level sandy soil. The cells are provisioned with paralysed bees, most frequently honeybees *Apis mellifera*, but if these are scarce then with various suitably-sized mining-bees (*Andrena* and *Lasioglossum* species). This habit has earned the wasp the colloquial name of 'Bee Wolf'. The species flies from early July to mid or late August, and visits bramble *Rubus*, thrift *Armeria maritima* and thistle *Cirsium* flowers. The life-history and ecology has been studied in depth by Tinbergen (1951).
Threats	The destruction of existing sites. It seems to benefit from trampled sandy soil with sparse vegetation on the St Helens dunes.
Conservation	One Isle of Wight site is on National Trust property, another is on an SSSI.
Authors	G. R. Else and G. M. Spooner, using additional information from Smith (1851a), Saunders (1896), Blair (1948) and Wakely (1955).

Andrena ferox

A mining bee   **ENDANGERED**

Order **Hymenoptera**   Family **Andrenidae**

Andrena (*Hoplandrena*) *ferox* Smith, 1847.

Identification	Else (in preparation).
Distribution	It has apparently always been a rarity and, on account of its unusual nesting behaviour, extremely local. There are records from Kent, Berkshire, Hampshire, East Sussex, Cornwall and Avon. The most recent is a small collection of females from Pluckley, Kent, 15 May 1966, K. M. Guichard.
Habitat and ecology	Meadowland and probably open woodland. In common with the related *A. bucephala* Stephens and *A. scotica* Perkins, the nesting behaviour is remarkable among British bees. The females of an entire colony use a single entrance hole in the ground to gain access to their underground cells (Yarrow & Guichard, 1941; Leys, 1978). Each shared nest is inhabited by up to eighty females, and (in a Dutch example) consisted of one vertical shaft with side passages radiating from it in all directions, each of the side passages terminating in a cell. A continuous flow of females passes through the entrance in fine weather. In a Hampshire locality about four such colonies have been discovered in close proximity to one another. The species is also unusual in that provisioning females visit oak *Quercus* flowers. A spring species, flying in April-May.

Threats	A rare species with such unusual nesting behaviour is clearly at risk, as it would obviously be very easy to destroy an entire colony.
Authors	G. R. Else and G. M. Spooner, using additional information from Perkins (1919b).

Andrena floricola

A mining bee   **ENDANGERED**

Order **Hymenoptera**   Family **Andrenidae**

Andrena (Micrandrena) floricola Eversmann, 1852.

Identification	Else (in preparation).
Distribution	The sole British specimen was a female taken at Princes Risborough, Buckinghamshire, on 11 May 1939 by E. Ernest.
Habitat and ecology	The British specimen was probably taken at late sallow *Salix*. On the Continent this species is double-brooded, the first visiting shepherd's purse *Capsella bursa-pastoris* and mustards *Brassica*, while the second visits only *Berteroa incana* (a cruciferous plant not indigenous to this country). The species nests in the soil.
Authors	G. R. Else and G. M. Spooner, using additional information from Stoeckhert (1933, p.125) and Yarrow & Guichard (1941).

Andrena gravida

A mining bee   **ENDANGERED**

Order **Hymenoptera**   Family **Andrenidae**

Andrena (Zonandrena) gravida Imhoff, 1832, formerly misidentified as *A. fasciata*.

Identification	Else (in preparation).
Distribution	Kent has always been the British headquarters for this bee, with records from numerous localities including Maidstone, East Malling, St Leonards (possibly the one near Malling), Canterbury, Gravesend, and Chatham. It has also been collected in Essex (Colchester, Dovercourt), and East Sussex (Hastings and south of Tunbridge Wells). The record for Perth, Tayside (cited in Saunders, 1896 and Perkins, 1919b) can safely be dismissed. Most records were made in the latter half of the last century and the early years (up to 1931) of the present one. The latest is from East Malling, Kent, a female on apple flowers, 25 April 1961, J. R. Chiswell.
Habitat and ecology	The typical habitat in Britain is not known. Flower visits include sallow *Salix*, mallows *Malvus* and dandelions

Taraxacum. The bee flies from late March to May, but there are three records of a second brood in July and August. (Its sibling *A. flavipes* Panzer is regularly double-brooded.)

Status

The above history certainly suggests a marked decline which cannot easily be explained. However, it is most unlikely that this species is extinct in Kent. No one has especially searched for it in recent years and unless one happened to chance upon a nesting aggregation the chances of success are probably remote (Felton, pers. comm.).

Authors

G. R. Else and G. M. Spooner, using additional information from Jones (1932).

Andrena hattorfiana

A mining bee   **VULNERABLE**

Order **Hymenoptera**   Family **Andrenidae**

Andrena (*Charitandrena*) *hattorfiana* (F., 1775).

Identification

Else (in preparation). This, our largest and perhaps most attractive *Andrena*, is usually black-brown, but forms of the female with red-banded abdomens are occasionally encountered.

Distribution

Rare and declining. Formerly widely distributed, but local and not always common where it did occur, over much of southern England and parts of south Wales – Norfolk, Essex, Kent to Cornwall (including the Isle of Wight), Wiltshire, Oxfordshire, Surrey and Glamorgan. In Devon it was even found high up on Dartmoor. In recent years there have only been a few, scattered records (usually of odd specimens) from Kent, East Sussex, Wiltshire, Cornwall and Devon. Its special nest parasite, *Nomada armata* Herrich-Schaeffer, is even rarer (an Endangered species).

Habitat and ecology

Dry grassland (particularly on calcareous soils) and even roadside verges with field scabious *Knautia arvensis.* Females provision their cells only with field scabious pollen. Males have been observed visiting nipplewort *Lapsana.* The bee also visits white clover *Trifolium repens* and smooth hawk's-beard *Crepis capillaris*, probably for nectar. The flight period extends from July to August.

Threats

The decline is almost certainly the result of loss of habitat, especially the ploughing-up of downland for cultivation; indeed one East Sussex colony manages to exist on the edge of a cereal field. Field scabious is becoming more a plant of roadside verges and railway cuttings and embankments.

Conservation

The purchase (or agreement on land use) of the remaining sites should be considered.

Authors

G. R. Else and G. M. Spooner, using information from Hamm (1901) and Perkins (1919b).

Andrena lathyri

A mining bee   **ENDANGERED**

Order **Hymenoptera**   Family **Andrenidae**

Andrena (Taeniandrena) lathyri Alfken, 1899.

Identification
Else (in preparation).

Distribution
Wiltshire: near Burbage, 16 and 19 May 1970, K. M. Guichard and S. Thewes (Guichard, 1971) and 15 May and 4 July 1971 (a worn female), K. M. Guichard. Somerset: Moorlinch, a female, 22 May 1950, J. Cowley (unpublished). It is widespread on the Continent.

Habitat and ecology
The Wiltshire colony was located along the banks of a disused railway line where the bees were visiting the flowers of common vetch *Vicia sativa* and less frequently bush vetch *V. sepium*. In France males have been taken at the pink flowers of a vetchling (*Lathyrus* species). The species nests in the soil.

Status
The above are the only known British records. None were observed on two visits in 1984 to the Burbage site by G. R. Else and M. Edwards.

Threats
The destruction of habitat.

Conservation
No measures proposed, though clearly steps to protect the habitat should be taken.

Authors
G. R. Else and G. M. Spooner.

Andrena lepida

A mining bee   **ENDANGERED**

Order **Hymenoptera**   Family **Andrenidae**

Andrena lepida Schenck, 1859. Misidentified as *A. combinata* Christ by Yarrow (1955).

Identification
Else (in preparation).

Distribution
Extremely rare, recorded only from one site in Berkshire and two in Dorset. A male was collected at Aldworth, on the Berkshire Downs, on 9 May 1931, by E. Burtt (BM(NH)); a female at Witchampton, Dorset on 11 July 1951, by P. Harwood; and a female at Badbury Rings, near Wimborne, Dorset, 2 August 1952, by G. M. Spooner (a second possible specimen in poor condition was observed but not retained). (See Yarrow, 1955 and 1968.)

Habitat and ecology	Chalk grassland. The Badbury Rings specimen was visiting hogweed *Heracleum sphondylium*. In Britain the species is clearly double-brooded, as on the Continent (where the spring brood flies in April and May, the summer one in July and August).
Status	Searches at Badbury Rings in 1953 and 1954 by G. M. Spooner and in 1984 by G. R. Else and M. Edwards have failed to produce further specimens.
Threats	Loss of habitat.
Authors	G. R. Else and G. M. Spooner.

Andrena nana

A mining bee **ENDANGERED**

Order **Hymenoptera** Family **Andrenidae**

Andrena (Micrandrena) nana (Kirby, 1802).

Identification	Else (in preparation). In the past other distinct species in the *A. minutula* (Kirby) complex were sometimes misidentified as *A. nana*.
Distribution	There are only four British specimens. The first was collected at Barham, Suffolk, by W. Kirby (Kirby, 1802, pp. 161–162) and this is the type specimen; it is in the Kirby Collection, BM(NH). The second specimen was a female collected near Luddesdown, Kent, on 27 August 1899 by H. Elgar, and is in the Maidstone Museum (Felton, 1963, p.185). A male was collected at Oxshott, Surrey in July 1915, collector unknown (specimen in the University Museum, Oxford). Finally, a female was obtained at Sudbury, Suffolk, in 1923 by Harwood (BM(NH)).
Habitat and ecology	There is nothing on record for Britain, but it is almost certainly double-brooded (as in Europe).
Authors	G. R. Else and G. M. Spooner.

Andrena polita

A mining bee **ENDANGERED +**

Order **Hymenoptera** Family **Andrenidae**

Andrena polita Smith, 1847.

Identification	Else (in preparation).

Distribution	In Britain the bee has been recorded from only two sites, both in north Kent. Northfleet: at least two examples prior to 1855 by F. Smith (Smith, 1855, p.88). Halling: one female, 6 July 1901, H. Elgar (Maidstone Museum Collection); one female, 6 July 1902, H. Lamb (BM(NH)); one male, 2 July 1933, G. E. Frisby (Frisby, 1934, p. 136); and one male, 1 July 1934, J. F. Perkins (Oxford University Museum). (See also Elgar, 1901b; Frisby, 1928, p. 98; Felton, 1963, p. 184.)
Habitat and ecology	The Northfleet specimens were collected in chalk pits, and those from Halling were taken on chalk grassland at Upper Halling. In West Germany the bee has been observed nesting gregariously in a rock wall (Stoeckhert, 1933). The Elgar specimen was reported as visiting a flower of field rose *Rosa arvensis*; the Frisby male was visiting a yellow composite. On the Continent the following are said to be visited: bindweed *Convolvulus arvensis*, chicory *Cichorium intybus* and mouse-ear hawkweed *Hieracium pilosella*. In Europe the species is widespread, but uncommon in the north. The flight period extends from early June to mid August.
Status	The last British record was more than fifty years ago and it must be feared that the species may now be extinct here.
Threats	Loss of chalk downland habitat.
Authors	G. R. Else and G. M. Spooner.

Andrena tridentata

A mining bee **ENDANGERED**

Order **Hymenoptera** Family **Andrenidae**

Andrena (*Cnemidandrena*) *tridentata* (Kirby, 1802).

Identification	Else (in preparation).
Distribution	Very rare with only a few scattered records from East Anglia (Suffolk, Norfolk and Essex) and Dorset. The majority of the few British records were made in the last century. Since 1901 only five females from four localities have been recorded from Britain, and only one since 1920 – Norden, Corfe, Dorset, a female at smooth hawk's-beard *Crepis capillaris* on a railway bank, 30 July 1944, C. D. Day.
Habitat and ecology	Little information. Specimens have been collected from ragwort *Senecio*, purple loosestrife *Lythrum salicaria*, and smooth hawk's-beard. The bee flies in July-August.
Authors	G. R. Else and G. M. Spooner, using additional information from Perkins (1919b).

Andrena vaga

A mining bee   **ENDANGERED**

Order **Hymenoptera**   Family **Andrenidae**

Andrena (*Melandrena*) *vaga* Panzer, 1799.

Identification   Else (in preparation).

Distribution   There are just four British records: an ancient (pre-1850) male, without locality in Walcott's collection (Perkins, 1917); Deal, Kent: a male on 12 April 1939, K. M. Guichard (Yarrow & Guichard, 1941); Bignor, West Sussex: a female on 16 April 1945, C. H. Andrewes (Andrewes, 1946); and Folkestone, Kent: a female on 12 April 1946 (Collins, 1946).

Habitat and ecology   Of the two British females, one was investigating a garden bank (in which was a large colony of *Andrena flavipes* Panzer) and the other was flying above a roadside bank and bore a load of pollen. A soil-nester.

Status   Yarrow (in Yarrow & Guichard, 1941) reports that this species is not uncommon on the Continent and individuals may well be blown across the Channel to this country, where they may survive and breed for a few seasons. However, the possibility of the species being indigenous but extremely local must not be overlooked, since a collector would never find it unless he chanced to be in the right place at the right time.

Authors   C. R. Else and G. M. Spooner, using additional information from Perkins (1919b).

Halictus eurygnathus

A mining bee   **ENDANGERED +**

Order **Hymenoptera**   Family **Halictidae**

Halictus (*Halictus*) *eurygnathus* Bluethgen, 1931, formerly misidentified as *H. quadricinctus* (Kirby).

Identification   Else (in preparation).

Distribution   In Britain this bee has always been a very rare species with a few very old sporadic records from the London district, Dorset (Portland), and Suffolk. Its headquarters, however, in the first half of the present century, have been Kent (Rochester, Dover, St Margaret's Bay, Upper Halling) and East Sussex (Brighton, Eastbourne, Ovingdean, Seaford, Littlington).

Habitat and ecology	Chalk downland, usually near the coast. In the south-east it was sometimes reported as being abundant, but forming extremely local colonies. Both sexes visit *Centaurea* flowers, including greater knapweed *C. scabiosa* and lesser knapweed *C. nigra*. Females have been collected from early June to late September, males from early August to early September.
Status	The most recent record was about forty years ago. It may well be extinct in Britain.
Threats	The loss of suitable habitat (e.g. chalk grassland on the cliff top at St Margaret's Bay has been ploughed up), and doubtless too by pressure from the holiday trade (chalets and similar developments).
Authors	G. R. Else and G. M. Spooner, using information from Saunders (1881), Sladen (1897), Elgar (1901a), and Malloch (1904).

Halictus maculatus

A mining bee   **ENDANGERED +**

Order **Hymenoptera**   Family **Halictidae**

Halictus (Halictus) maculatus Smith, 1848.

Identification	Else (in preparation).
Distribution	Although widely distributed in western Europe this is another bee which has always been very rare in Britain, with only a few records (nearly all of single examples). It has been collected in Kent (Upper Halling), East Sussex (Hastings), Hampshire (Blackwater), Isle of Wight (Sandown Bay), south Devon (Chudleigh and possibly Exeter) and Surrey (Weybridge).
Habitat and ecology	The only detailed information available is provided by Perkins (1919a). In a Devon colony the bees nested in burrows scattered singly over three or four square metres of level ground in a pasture field. There are no flower records for Britain. Females fly from May to September, males from early July to September.
Status	Perkins (1919a) discovered a thriving colony at Chudleigh which persisted from 1919 to 1930. His son, J. F. Perkins, informed G. M. Spooner that it was a prolific colony in the bank of an old gravel pit (in valley alluvium) by the River Teign opposite Chudleigh Knighton; it also occurred down the river valley at Gooseham. Shortly after 1930 the pit was filled with rubbish and levelled off, and the colony wiped out. The species has not been seen in Britain since.
Authors	G. R. Else and G. M. Spooner, using additional information from Elgar (1901a).

Lasioglossum laticeps	A mining bee	**VULNERABLE**
	Order **Hymenoptera**	Family **Halictidae**

Lasioglossum (*Evylaeus*) *laticeps* (Schenck, 1870), formerly misidentified as *Halictus semipunctulatus* Schenck.

Identification Else (in preparation).

Distribution In Britain it is confined to the coast of Dorset and extreme east Devon, from Kimmeridge in the east to the Devon side of Lyme Regis in the west. However, since its discovery in Britain in 1903 (Saunders, 1904) the species has been reported from only about five or six sites. Colonies appear to be few and far between and the attendant females are extremely localised and elusive. When colonies are found both sexes can be locally common.

Habitat and ecology Coastal undercliffs and landslips, nesting, usually gregariously, in the clay soil (some have also been noted nesting in the joints of a stone wall). Females have been collected from wild carrot *Daucus carota* flowers and the males, which appear in late summer, have been swept from fleabane *Pulicaria dysenterica*, ragwort *Senecio* and *Daucus*. This bee is one of many *Lasioglossum* species which are semisocial, i.e. a worker caste is produced in the early summer. L. Packer has recently studied the life-history of this species in Dorset (Packer, 1983). The flight period of the females is April-August, and the males July-August.

Status Probably not declining, but the extreme localisation of colonies and the difficult terrain make this a difficult species to monitor.

Threats Sections of the Dorset coast are extremely unstable and it is thus probable that some colonies are occasionally eliminated by landslips or cliff falls.

Conservation Two sites are on National Trust property, one is a reserve of the Dorset Naturalists' Trust, one is probably on the Axmouth-Lyme Regis Undercliffs NNR, and one is on Ministry of Defence property.

Authors G. R. Else and G. M. Spooner, using additional information from Nevinson (1904).

Dufourea minuta

A mining bee   **ENDANGERED**

Order **Hymenoptera**   Family **Halictidae**

Dufourea minuta Lepeletier, 1841, formerly known as
D. halictula (Nylander).

Identification

Else (in preparation).

Distribution

Extremely rare with very few British records, which are
summarised as follows. Surrey: Byfleet, many specimens
1913–20, C. H. Mortimer and E. Nevinson (specimens in
BM(NH)); Woking, a female from a large sand-pit on
Woking Heath, O. C. Silverlock (Saunders, 1910, p. 11).
Dorset: Ferndown, four males, 14 July 1948, P. Harwood;
Parley, one female, 30 July 1953, P. Harwood (Harwood
specimens also in BM(NH)).

Habitat and ecology

Confined to sandy soils. Mortimer (1913) described a
populous nesting aggregation at Byfleet. Here the males
were usually found at rest on stones or low-growing plants
and within a week the females appeared in equal
abundance. These constructed their burrows between
stones, chiefly on a hard sandy pathway, less frequently in
an adjoining sandy, moss-covered bank. The cells were
provisioned with sheep's-bit *Jasione montana* pollen. The
species has been found on the wing from late June to late
July.

Threats

Loss of heathland habitat.

Authors

G. R. Else and G. M. Spooner.

Dufourea vulgaris

A mining bee   **ENDANGERED**

Order **Hymenoptera**   Family **Halictidae**

Dufourea vulgaris Schenck, 1859.

Identification

Else (in preparation).

Distribution

Recorded only from Surrey, the south Hampshire-Dorset
boundary, and Dorset. The records are as follows: Surrey:
Woking, 1 August 1881, a number observed by banks of the
canal, visiting ragwort *Senecio*, a few caught (Billups, 1881).
Hampshire-Dorset boundary: Chewton, coastal undercliff, by
sweeping chamomile *Matricaria* flowers and low herbage,
12 August 1879, one male (S. S. Saunders, 1880). Dorset:
Holt, 14 August 1956, fresh female, P. Harwood
(unpublished).

Habitat and ecology	Sandy soils. Specimens have been collected from dandelion *Taraxacum* and ragwort flowers: E. Saunders (1896) describes the male as wriggling into the flower in a highly characteristic manner. The flight period extends from early to mid August.
Status	A small active species, readily overlooked or not recognised.
Authors	G. R. Else and G. M. Spooner

Melitta dimidiata

A mining bee   ENDANGERED

Order **Hymenoptera**   Family **Melittidae**

Melitta dimidiata Morawitz, 1876, formerly known as *Pseudocilissa dimidiata*.

Identification	Else (in preparation).
Distribution	Very rare, known in Britain from only two or three sites near Tilshead, Salisbury Plain, Wiltshire, and from another on chalk downland in the Vale of Pewsey, near Easton Royal, Wiltshire. It is also rare in Europe.
Habitat and ecology	The largest of the four British *Melitta* species, occurring on chalk grassland. The species exclusively provisions its cells with sainfoin *Onobrychis viciifolia* pollen and nectar. During dull, cold spells males have been observed sheltering in the racemes of the host plant (Baker, 1965). A typical 'mining-bee', the nest burrows being excavated in soil. Flies from June to late July.
Status	The small, vulnerable colony near Easton Royal was observed as recently as 30 June 1984 (G. R. Else).
Threats	The loss of habitat. A major colony on White Barrow, near Tilshead, was destroyed a few years ago when the ancient monument was surrounded by fencing and sheep introduced. The grazing has favoured the chalk grassland flora generally, but the stock virtually eliminated the sainfoin. Although the plant is still found outside the fencing, the bee has not been seen since despite special searches made during the flight season and in favourable weather conditions.
Conservation	White Barrow is a property of the National Trust.
Authors	G. R. Else and G. M. Spooner, using additional information from Yarrow (1968) and Guichard (1973).

Stelis breviuscula

A cuckoo bee

ENDANGERED

Order **Hymenoptera**   Family **Megachilidae**

Stelis breviuscula (Nylander, 1848).

Identification   Else (in preparation).

Distribution   A very recent addition to the British list. A fresh male was collected from a flower of ragwort *Senecio jacobaea* at Iping Common, near Midhurst, West Sussex, on 8 August 1984 by G. R. Else.

Habitat and ecology   In Western Europe the bee *Heriades truncorum* (L.) is reported as the host of *S. breviuscula* (Bischoff, 1927, p. 397; Schmiedeknecht, 1930, p. 836; Stoeckhert, 1933, p. 230). The host nests in burrows in dead wood and occasionally crumbling masonry. The British specimen of *S. breviuscula* was collected on the edge of heathland, close to felled, stacked trees where *H. truncorum* also occurred. Stoeckhert (1933) records the following flowers visited by *S. breviuscula*: bramble *Rubus*, sheep's-bit *Jasione montana*, yarrow *Achillea millefolium*, mouse-ear hawkweed *Hieracium pilosella*, and dandelion *Taraxacum*.
On the Continent the flight period extends from early June to the beginning of September.

Status   All four British *Stelis* species are rare bees, but although there is only a single record of *S. breviuscula* it is considered to be an indigenous species in view of its obligate association with *H. truncorum*.

Threats   Probably in no immediate danger; although its host is nationally a very scarce species, it seems to be well-established in the Midhurst area.

Authors   G. R. Else and G. M. Spooner.

Osmia inermis

A mason bee

VULNERABLE

Order **Hymenoptera**   Family **Megachilidae**

Osmia (*Melanosmia*) *inermis* (Zetterstedt, 1838), formerly misidentified as *O. parietina* Curtis.

Identification   Else (in preparation).

Distribution   An arctic-alpine mason bee which is one of the rarest and, until recently, least known of British bees. It is confined to the central Grampian Highlands in both Highland and Tayside Regions (Speyside in Inverness District, several sites between Blair Atholl and Rannoch, and Glen Almond, north-west of Perth).

Habitat and ecology	Exposed upland sites between about 350 and 400m on floristically diverse base-rich soils. The female constructs from leaf mastic tight clusters of naked oval cells attached to the underside of a flat rock overlying a slight depression in the ground. The number of cells per rock varies between one and about sixty, but up to 230 have been found. Very large totals are probably the product of more than one female, or more than a single generation. Adults resulting from these cells usually emerge after two or more winters, the first spent as a prepupa, the second as a diapausing bee. One south-facing site near Blair Atholl consisted of heavily-grazed sheep pasture on well-drained hillocky ground dominated by a short sward of heather *Calluna vulgaris* interspersed with various herbs (e.g. violets *Viola*, bilberry *Vaccinium myrtillus*, primrose *Primula vulgaris*, bugle *Ajuga reptans*, and birdsfoot-trefoil *Lotus corniculatus*). A further important feature was numerous loose rocks of suitable size. Forage plants have not been recorded from Britain, but probably include birdsfoot-trefoil, sallows *Salix* and bilberry, as quoted in the literature for Europe and North America. The bees fly from late May to July.
Threats	The destruction of habitat by afforestation of upland sites. According to the recent Perthshire Structure Plan there is at present an area of 11% forestation, but this is likely to be increased.
Authors	G. R. Else and G. M. Spooner, using additional information from Smith (1851b).

Osmia uncinata · A mason bee · VULNERABLE

Order **Hymenoptera** Family **Megachilidae**

Osmia (*Melanosmia*) *uncinata* Gerstaecker, 1869, formerly misidentified as *O. inermis* (Zetterstedt), another Vulnerable species.

Identification	Else (in preparation).
Distribution	A very rare boreo-alpine mason bee, recorded only from a few sites in Speyside (Inverness, Highland), between Kincraig and Nethy Bridge (c. 250-300m). A very recent addition to the British list.
Habitat and ecology	Open sites in relict Caledonian Forest, at lower altitudes than *O. inermis*. British nests have not been found, but in Europe they occur in borings in the trunks and stumps of pine *Pinus*, including pieces of loose bark lying on the ground. Both sexes visit birdsfoot-trefoil *Lotus corniculatus*, occasionally broom *Cytisus scoparius* and bilberry *Vaccinium myrtillus*, and fly from late April to late June (sometimes early July).

Threats	Reduction and destruction of the surviving remnants of its forest habitat.
Authors	G. R. Else and G. M. Spooner, using additional information from Stoeckhert (1933), pp. 205-206.

Osmia xanthomelana

A mason bee **ENDANGERED**

Order **Hymenoptera** Family **Megachilidae**

Osmia (*Melanosmia*) *xanthomelana* (Kirby, 1802), formerly known as *Osmia atricapilla* Curtis.

Identification	Else (in preparation).
Distribution	Now only on the south coast of the Isle of Wight. Formerly as two apparently discontinuous populations, one in southern England (Suffolk, Essex, Kent, Sussex, Hampshire, Isle of Wight, Devon, Cornwall, Gloucestershire and Avon), the other in north-west England and north Wales (Cumbria, Durham, Lancashire, Merseyside and north Gwynedd – especially the north and south coastline of the Lleyn Peninsula).
Habitat and ecology	On the Isle of Wight coastal landslips and cliffs. The females forage on birdsfoot-trefoil *Lotus corniculatus* and horse-shoe vetch *Hippocrepis comosa* and probably nest at the roots of vegetation on the less steep gradients of cliff faces. The nest consists of several 'pot-like' cells constructed from mud (see Waterhouse, 1844). Females visit seepages at the base of the cliffs to collect the mud. The flight period extends from April to July, both sexes overwintering in their cells as freshly emerged adults.
Status	The species always appears to have been uncommon and very local. After an interval of twenty-six years, when no specimens were recorded in Britain, C. H. Andrewes took a female at Chale, Isle of Wight, on 18 May 1954. No more were found until G. R. Else and D. M. Appleton discovered two sites in 1977 and 1978, but only one of these seems to have a small but permanent population.
Threats	The cause of decline (which began during the last century) of this handsome bee is not known, but may be related to climatic changes. The females are perhaps vulnerable to collectors as they congregate at wet mud. Also, the sites are threatened by cliff falls, which occasionally occur along the Isle of Wight coastline.
Conservation	Former sites need to be visited to establish if the species has survived to the present day.
Authors	G. R. Else and G. M. Spooner, using additional information from Kirby (1802, pp.246-247), Smith (1876, pp.155-156), Saunders (1896; 1909), Perkins (1923, p.217; 1924, p.147), and Jones (1932).

287

Nomada armata

A cuckoo bee   **ENDANGERED**

Order **Hymenoptera**   Family **Anthophoridae**

Nomada armata Herrich-Schaeffer, 1839.

Identification Else (in preparation).

Distribution To Perkins (1919b) this species seemed generally to occur more or less freely in all the districts recorded for its host (with the exception of the eastern counties where it appeared unexpectedly rare), though not with every host colony. Its distribution within Britain includes Kent, Isle of Wight, Dorset, Devon, Cornwall, Berkshire, Oxfordshire, Surrey, Essex, Norfolk and West Glamorgan.

Habitat and ecology The special cleptoparasite or cuckoo-bee of *Andrena hattorfiana* (F.). Both sexes, in common with the host, visit field scabious *Knautia arvensis* flowers. Flies from June to August.

Status Today it is an extremely rare species, the most recent record being a specimen taken in a malaise trap in an Oxford garden in 1974 (C. O'Toole).

Threats The present scarcity of this bee can be at least partially explained by the decline of its host, which is itself a Vulnerable species.

Authors G. R. Else and G. M. Spooner, using additional information from Hamm (1901).

Nomada errans

A cuckoo bee   **ENDANGERED**

Order **Hymenoptera**   Family **Anthophoridae**

Nomada errans Lepeletier, 1841.

Identification Else (in preparation).

Distribution Only known from a short stretch of coast in the Isle of Purbeck, south-east Dorset. First discovered in Britain by C. D. Day on 6 August 1944 (Spooner, 1946). Subsequently it was found in very small numbers in July and August 1945-46, Spooner & Day; 21 July 1974, K. M. Guichard; and 26 July 1982, G. R. Else. The first British specimen, however, was a male collected in 1878 by C. W. Dale, but was misidentified until correctly determined by G. M. Spooner in 1971 (unpublished).

Habitat and ecology Rough grassland and landslip. Specimens have been observed visiting yarrow *Achillea millefolium*, wild carrot *Daucus carota* and ragwort *Senecio* flowers. On the

Continent the species is a nest parasite of the bees *Andrena nitidiusculus* Schenck and *A. pallitarsis* Perez (a species not found in Britain) (Stoeckhert, 1933, pp. 157-158). In Purbeck the presumed host is *A. nitidiusculus*, which in this site is usually uncommon and, nationally, occurs sporadically in about half a dozen southern counties.

Status   Other colonies of *A. nitidiusculus* in Dorset and Hampshire have been investigated for *N. errans*, but none have so far been found.

Threats   The small, permanent population is perhaps at risk from over-collecting. The host too seems to be scarce in this locality (in contrast to one or two other sites along the Dorset coast), only rarely becoming abundant.

Conservation   The locality is a Country Park, administered by the Dorset County Council, from whom a permit is necessary for collecting.

Authors   G. R. Else and G. M. Spooner.

Nomada guttulata

A cuckoo bee   **ENDANGERED**

Order **Hymenoptera**   Family **Anthophoridae**

Nomada guttulata Schenck, 1859.

Identification   Else (in preparation).

Distribution   Formerly widely distributed in the south, but has always been considered a rarity since its discovery in Britain in 1897. Dorset (Swanage, Mortimer, 1908a), Suffolk (Morley, 1897), Kent (Chitty, 1903), Cornwall (G. M. Spooner), Devon (Hamm, 1903, etc.), and East Sussex (Ditchling, 8 May 1943). Also reported from the London area, Essex and Buckinghamshire.

Habitat and ecology   The special nest parasite of *Andrena labiata* F. The species has been collected on coastal cliffs and in woodland, and flies in May and June. Both sexes have been taken at the flowers of germander speedwell *Veronica chamaedrys*, which is also the host's main forage plant, and at tormentil *Potentilla*.

Status   The most recent record known to the authors is a female collected at Wembury, south Devon, on 11 May 1967 by G. M. Spooner. The host bee is by no means a common species and may be decreasing.

Authors   G. R. Else and G. M. Spooner, using additional information from Perkins (1919b).

Nomada sexfasciata

A cuckoo bee   **ENDANGERED**

Order **Hymenoptera**   Family **Anthophoridae**

Nomada sexfasciata Panzer, 1799.

Identification   Else (in preparation). The largest British *Nomada* species.

Distribution   A rare and declining species known today only from one coastal site in south Devon which supports a thriving extended colony of *Eucera longicornis* (L.). In the past it was widely distributed but local and recorded from localities in Hampshire (New Forest), Surrey, East Sussex, Gloucestershire and south Devon.

Habitat and ecology   The special nest parasite of *E. longicornis* (and perhaps the Endangered *E. tuberculata* (F.)?). Flies in May and June.

Status   The Devon colony was discovered by G. M. Spooner in the mid-1970s and seems to be stable, as specimens have been seen several times in subsequent years.

Threats   The cause of decline is not known; doubtless the host bee is not as widespread as in earlier decades, but still remains quite common, especially along the south coast (e.g. Isle of Wight and Dorset).

Conservation   The site is in need of protection.

Authors   G. R. Else and G. M. Spooner, using additional information from Perkins (1919b)

Nomada xanthosticta

A cuckoo bee   **ENDANGERED**

Order **Hymenoptera**   Family **Anthophoridae**

Nomada xanthosticta (Kirby, 1802).

Identification   Else (in preparation).

Distribution   Very rare, recorded from Hampshire, Dorset, Buckinghamshire, the London area, Bedfordshire, Hertfordshire, Cambridgeshire, Leicestershire, Suffolk and Norfolk. Old literature records (e.g. Smith, 1876, pp.121-122) quote Yorkshire, Northumberland and other northern records, but these really refer to *N. obtusifrons* Nylander. In common with other cleptoparasites, it is usually scarcer than its host, though on one or two occasions it has been reported as locally abundant in the vicinity of its host's colonies. There has been no record since specimens were collected at Leckford, Hampshire on 17 April 1947 (J. Lewis Collection).

Habitat and ecology   The special cleptoparasite of the mining-bee *Andrena praecox* (Scopoli). It is mainly associated with open broad-leaved woodland, visiting sallow *Salix* catkins.

Individuals have also been observed flying low over dead leaf litter in partial shade (presumably searching for the host's nesting burrows). It flies from April to May.

Status   The reason for its rather dramatic decline to the point of extinction within Britain remains a mystery. However, two other *Nomada* species (*N. sexfasciata* Panzer and *N. signata* Jurine) have similarly declined sharply, in contrast to their hosts which remain locally common in many areas. *Andrena praecox* similarly remains a common early spring bee pre-eminently associated with *Salix* blossom over much of southern England.

Authors   G. R. Else and G. M. Spooner, using additional information from Perkins (1919b) and Chambers (1949, p. 246).

Eucera tuberculata

A mining bee   **ENDANGERED +**

Order **Hymenoptera**   Family **Anthophoridae**

Eucera tuberculata (F., 1793).

Identification   Else (in preparation).

Distribution   Formerly rather widely distributed but rare in southern England, recorded from Kent, East Sussex, Isle of Wight, Gloucestershire, Berkshire, and Suffolk. Some of these records are very old. It has not been found in Britain for over forty years.

Habitat and ecology   Virtually unknown for Britain, but it has occurred in open deciduous woodland, and at least one site (since built over) was open grassland. Its flower preferences and nesting habits are probably similar to *E. longicornis* (L.), i.e. various vetches *Vicia*, and nesting burrows excavated in soil.

Status   Much less common than the widespread *E. longicornis*, except in Kent. Occasionally the two species fly together, as at Hothfield (Felton, 1963), but *E. tuberculata* seems to be more confined to sheltered or wooded situations. The reason for its apparent decline remains unknown. It has not been recorded in Britain since 1941.

Authors   G. R. Else and G. M. Spooner, using additional information from Yarrow (1968).

Melecta luctuosa	A cuckoo bee	**ENDANGERED**
	Order **Hymenoptera**	Family **Anthophoridae**

Melecta luctuosa (Scopoli, 1770).

Identification   Else (in preparation).

Distribution   Rare, with no recent British records. Dorset (several localities), Surrey, Hampshire (New Forest), Essex, and London (Hampstead Heath). The host bee is also decreasing: there are recent records only from a site in Essex and one on the Isle of Wight.

Habitat and ecology   A nest parasite of the bee *Anthophora retusa* (L.) (e.g. Morice, 1901). It flies in April and May. It may be expected flying about banks, sandy cliffs and cuttings where the host nests.

Threats   Not known. However, a favoured locality many years ago was the New Forest (near Lyndhurst). As a result of very heavy grazing by ponies flowering plants are generally scarce and are invariably at their best on the roadside verges, protected for the most part by the enclosure fences. Most bees have declined in this once famous locality. *A. retusa* was once abundant there, but is now perhaps extinct.

Authors   G. R. Else and G. M. Spooner.

Bombus cullumanus	A bumblebee	**ENDANGERED +**
	Order **Hymenoptera**	Family **Apidae**

Bombus (Cullumanobombus) cullumanus (Kirby, 1802).

Identification   Else (in preparation).

Distribution   Formerly widespread but always very rare and local. It has been recorded from Kent, East Sussex, Hampshire, Dorset, Berkshire (several localities on downland in the Thames Basin, 1916-1926), the border of Bedfordshire and Hertfordshire (the Chilterns between Tring and Dunstable), Hertfordshire, Essex, Bedfordshire and Suffolk. There has been no record in Britain since May 1926. For map of former distribution see Anon. (1980), map 6.

Habitat and ecology   Chalk or limestone grassland.

Status   In spite of searches by different observers, especially in Dorset and Berkshire, no specimens have been found. It is feared that the species may be extinct in Britain.

Threats   If the species has survived it is threatened by the loss of habitat and by modern agricultural practices which are destroying natural downland ecology.

Authors   G. R. Else and G. M. Spooner, using additional information from Yarrow (1954) and Alford (1975).

DIPTERA

The Flies

With about 6000 species in Britain, the Diptera are the largest order covered in the Red Data Book. The majority are small, rather poorly-known and often difficult to identify. Three sections, however, are quite well-known – the Tipulidae (craneflies), the larger Brachycera (horseflies, robber-flies, soldier-flies, etc.), and the Syrphidae (hoverflies). Because of the large size of the order and the relatively poor knowledge of many of the groups, species accounts have been prepared for only 82 of the Endangered and Vulnerable species – about 17% of the species listed in those categories.

The Red Data Book includes 270 Endangered, 226 Vulnerable and 328 Rare species. With a further three species included in the Appendix (extinct before 1900), a total of 827 species are listed. This represents approximately 14% of the British fly fauna – the same proportion as for the Coleoptera.

Of the selection of Endangered and Vulnerable species described in these accounts, 45% are aquatic. Their larvae occur in more or less still water (ponds, ditches, bogs, marshes, etc.) or in wet habitats adjacent to water (e.g. wet moss by streams). The adults may be seen in flight around waterside vegetation. A quarter of the aquatic species are associated with the brackish conditions found in coastal ditches and pools. As has been seen in the previous orders, aquatic habitats of all types are greatly threatened by land drainage and other aspects of agricultural improvement. 37% of the species described occur in broad-leaved woodland, many of them associated with rot-holes in old trees. As in the Coleoptera, ancient woodlands such as Windsor Forest are frequently the only known sites for such species. Their future depends upon the retention of over-mature, dead and fallen timber, and less zeal in the 'tidying-up' of forests. The remaining 18% of described species occur in other terrestrial habitats such as pine forest, heathland, sand dunes and grassland.

A general introduction to the Diptera is provided by Colyer & Hammond's *Flies of the British Isles* (1968), though this is now out of print. An introduction and key to the families of Diptera are included in the RESL's series of *Handbooks* (Oldroyd, 1970), and many families are covered in this series. *A key to the families of British Diptera* (Unwin, 1981) is a title in the Field Studies Council's AIDGAP series. A good recent guide to a single popular family is *British hoverflies* (Stubbs & Falk, 1983). The AES has published *A dipterist's handbook* (Stubbs & Chandler, 1978).

There are several Diptera recording schemes, coordinated by A. E. Stubbs. A bulletin is issued, and there are regular meetings. A preliminary distribution atlas of the hoverflies has been produced (Entwistle & Stubbs, 1983).

Ctenophora flaveolata

A cranefly	ENDANGERED
Order **Diptera**	Family **Tipulidae**

Ctenophora flaveolata (F., 1794).

Identification R. L. Coe *in* Coe *et al* (1950), p.8. A large ichneumon wasp-mimic with yellow and black banded abdomen and large feathery antennae in the male.

Distribution Formerly widespread in central southern England though with few localities; also in North Wales and Yorkshire. There are recent records only from the New Forest, Windsor Forest, the south Chilterns and the Sussex downs.

Habitat and ecology Woodland with ancient trees, especially beech *Fagus*. Breeds in dead wood, probably on an annual life cycle. The adults fly in May and June. It is believed to breed in large over-mature beech trees.

Status Of fifteen historic 10km squares for this large spectacular species, only five apply to the post-1960 period. The New Forest is possibly the best area, with two sites (in different 10km squares). In Windsor Forest it is exceedingly rare, and there are possible problems of habitat continuity affecting the other two sites.

Threats The reduction and loss of dead wood habitat.

Conservation In Windsor Forest there is a conservation management agreement and a less precise one concerning the New Forest.

Author A. E. Stubbs.

Nephrotoma sullingtonensis

A cranefly	ENDANGERED
Order **Diptera**	Family **Tipulidae**

Nephrotoma sullingtonensis Edwards, 1938.

Identification R. L. Coe *in* Coe *et al* (1950), p.8.

Distribution Confined in Britain to Sullington near Worthing in West Sussex. It has been recorded on the Continent so it is not endemic.

Habitat and ecology Heathland with pine woods. It was recently taken beside a sandy path across a patch of heather *Calluna* with lichens. This patch of heather is in a glade only 100m across, surrounded by pine *Pinus*. It is not known whether the insect is strictly confined to this type of habitat on the site.

Status	Only known from the type locality at Sullington Warren, where it was taken on two occasions in June 1938 (Edwards, 1938b). The Warren was subject to several unsuccessful searches in the 1970s, but two males and a female were found (by M. Edwards) on 4 June 1983. The area of available habitat is extremely small since pine now covers much of the site, open areas now being mostly grassland. Southern heathland and pine woods have been well worked for craneflies, especially in the adjacent county of Surrey, so this is considered to be a genuinely very rare insect.
Author	A. E. Stubbs.

Limonia aperta — A cranefly — ENDANGERED

Order **Diptera**　　　　　　　　　　　　　Family **Tipulidae**

Limonia (*Dicranomyia*) *aperta* (Wahlgren, 1904).

Identification	Edwards (1938a), p.41; R. L. Coe *in* Coe *et al* (1950), p.28.
Distribution	Only known from Craven District (North Yorkshire) and Moray (Grampian).
Habitat and ecology	Adults have been found sitting on the flowers of grass of Parnassus *Parnassia palustris* at a bog locality. The details are otherwise unknown.
Status	Although said to be 'common locally', it is only known from Austwick Bog, where it was taken on 3 September 1930, and it is said to have been found in Moray (Coe, 1950).
Conservation	Austwick Bog is now an SSSI, though somewhat changed since the record was made.
Author	A. E. Stubbs.

Limonia bezzii — A cranefly — VULNERABLE

Order **Diptera**　　　　　　　　　　　　　Family **Tipulidae**

Limonia (*Geranomyia*) *bezzii* (Alexander & Leonard, 1912).

Identification	R. L. Coe *in* Coe *et al* (1950), p.30.
Distribution	Originally found at Chesil Beach, Dorset, in 1891 and again in 1939, but not confirmed there recently. In recent years it has been found at Arne in Poole Harbour (Dorset), Pagham Harbour (West Sussex), and Stiffkey (Norfolk).

Habitat and ecology	Coastal lagoons where the upper tidal shore has gravel with the alga *Enteromorpha*. Its life history is unknown but the larvae probably live in intertidal gravel in brackish lagoons, possibly feeding on *Enteromorpha*. The adults fly between June and September.
Status	Of interest as one of the few marine craneflies independent of saltmarsh. Its potential habitat is of limited occurrence. Though the sites are in amenity areas, they are sensitive to many pressures. Shores with gravel would not attract the same conservation concern as muddy shores of high ornithological value.
Threats	Sailing and other amenity facilities could affect shores directly or indirectly by disrupting the sedimentary regime; mineral workings may upset the shore at Arne, and oilfield development in Poole Harbour may have a direct or indirect impact; a proposed nuclear power station in the Fleet could affect water temperatures on the Chesil Beach saltmarsh; potential gravel extraction.
Conservation	All sites are of some conservation status – an LNR at Pagham, an RSPB reserve at Arne (though the lease does not cover mineral workings), and an SSSI.
Author	A. E. Stubbs.

Limonia omissinervis

A cranefly   **VULNERABLE**

Order **Diptera**   Family **Tipulidae**

	Limonia (Dicranomyia) omissinervis (de Meijere, 1918), formerly misidentified as *L. patens* (Lundstroem).
Identification	R. L. Coe *in* Coe *et al* (1950), p.28 (as *L. patens*); Hutson & Stubbs (1974).
Distribution	Very sporadic occurrence. At one site on the River Tay (Tayside), two nearby sites on the River Spey (Highland), a site on the River Usk (Gwent), and another on the River Wye (Hereford & Worcester). It is only found commonly on the Spey.
Habitat and ecology	Alluvial, usually sandy river banks within the shade of alders *Alnus*, willows *Salix* or other trees. Its life cycle is unknown but the larvae probably occur in alluvial river banks. The adults may be found in July and August.
Status	Apart from a previously misidentified specimen taken in 1911, all records date from 1972. Though it may yet prove more widespread, it does seem to be highly localised even on its chosen rivers.

Threats	River improvement, including the removal of trees on the Usk and the Wye. Amenity management could affect a critical section of the Spey.
Author	A. E. Stubbs.

Limnophila fasciata

A cranefly	**ENDANGERED**
Order **Diptera**	Family **Tipulidae**

Limnophila (Idioptera) fasciata (L., 1767).

Identification	R. L. Coe *in* Coe *et al* (1950), p.40. A medium-sized species with banded wings.
Distribution	Between 1920 and 1938 it was found in five localities in north-west England, comprising one in Cumbria, two in Yorkshire and two in north Cheshire. In 1964 it was found at one site in Cheshire, which was probably an additional site though this cannot be certain.
Habitat and ecology	Mosses and marshes beside lakes. Its life history is unknown but it is assumed to be univoltine, with the larvae occurring in marsh soil. The adults fly May to July.
Status	A very attractive species, yet there have been no records in the last fifteen years despite an unprecedented level of recording.
Threats	The 1964 site was very vulnerable to damage by trampling from amenity use. Austwick Moss (North Yorkshire) has become drier and scrubbed over in part, and Cliburn Moss (Cumbria) has been partially drained. The exact location of the other old sites is unknown.
Conservation	Austwick Moss and the more recent Cheshire site are SSSIs. All localities need further checking.
Author	A. E. Stubbs.

Gonomyia punctata

A cranefly	**VULNERABLE**
Order **Diptera**	Family **Tipulidae**

Gonomyia (Idiocera) punctata Edwards, 1938.

Identification	Edwards (1938a), pp.107-108; R. L. Coe *in* Coe *et al* (1950), p.50.
Distribution	Northern and western England: Hereford & Worcester, North Yorkshire and Cumbria.
Habitat and ecology	Unknown.

Status	Very rare, with no recent records. The type locality is Mulgrave Woods in North Yorkshire, where it was taken in the period 23 August-1 September 1937 (Edwards, 1938a). The other localities are the Monnow Valley on 3 July 1906 and the Wyre Forest in 1938 (Hereford & Worcester), and Melkinthorpe in Cumbria on 27 June 1922.
Author	A. E. Stubbs.

Gonomyia sexguttata

A cranefly   **ENDANGERED**

Order **Diptera**   Family **Tipulidae**

Gonomyia (Idiocera) sexguttata (Dale, 1842).

Identification	Edwards (1938a), p.107; R. L. Coe *in* Coe *et al* (1950), p.49.
Distribution	Confined to Cornwall and Dorset.
Habitat and ecology	Unknown.
Status	Only known from the type locality, Glanvilles Wootton, Dorset, in about 1860, and from St Merryn, Cornwall, in June 1912.
Author	A. E. Stubbs.

Erioptera bivittata

A cranefly   **VULNERABLE**

Order **Diptera**   Family **Tipulidae**

Erioptera (Mesocyphona) bivittata (Loew, 1873).

Identification	Hutson & Vane-Wright (1969), p.249 and figs 7-10. A small dark brown species only recently added to the British list.
Distribution	Originally discovered on the North Kent Marshes, and subsequently found at Romney Marsh (Kent), Walberswick (Suffolk), and Stiffkey and Catfield Fen (Norfolk). Common in restricted areas.
Habitat and ecology	Coastal ditches with mildly brackish water, in one case an inland fen where other brackish species also occur. Its life history is unknown but the larvae are assumed to breed in wet, slightly brackish mud. The adults have been found between June and August.
Status	Not quite as endangered as recently feared because some new sites have been found. However, the total area of potential habitat is becoming very reduced because of agricultural improvement, and on the safer sites it remains to be seen whether the right brackish conditions and management can be maintained.

Threats	Agricultural improvement of coastal levels could largely eliminate the Kent populations. The East Anglian sites are relatively safe even though problems remain.
Conservation	Occurs on one NNR (Walberswick), and all other populations are on SSSIs. Firmer habitat protection measures on certain Kent sites are proposed.
Author	A. E. Stubbs.

Erioptera limbata

A cranefly	**VULNERABLE**
Order **Diptera**	Family **Tipulidae**

Erioptera (Erioptera) limbata Loew, 1873.

Identification	Edwards (1938a), p.123 and fig. 24i; R. L. Coe *in* Coe *et al* (1950), p.55 and fig. 25i.
Distribution	Dorset, Gwent and east Kent.
Habitat and ecology	By a small, wooded stream with tufa (in Kent), and under willows *Salix* on the banks of a river (in Gwent).
Status	Only known from three specimens in Great Britain. The Dorset record is from Glanvilles Wootton, taken in 1864. The Gwent record is for a specimen taken by the River Usk at Newbridge-on-Usk on 7 August 1972, and the Kent record was from Asholt Wood in August 1974 (Stubbs, 1976).
Conservation	Asholt Wood is an SSSI.
Author	A. E. Stubbs.

Erioptera pusilla

A cranefly	**ENDANGERED**
Order **Diptera**	Family **Tipulidae**

Erioptera (Psiloconopa) pusilla (Schiner, 1865).

Identification	Edwards (1938a), p.130 and fig. 23e; R. L. Coe *in* Coe *et al* (1950), p.57 and fig. 24e.
Distribution	Hereford & Worcester.
Habitat and ecology	Unknown, though assumed to be associated with sandy river banks.
Status	Only known from the River Monnow, where it was taken on 17 July 1907, 31 July 1908 and 30 May 1911. There are no recent records.

| Threats | The Monnow has already been modified by the water authorities along some stretches. |
| Author | A. E. Stubbs. |

Dasyhelea lithotelmatica

A biting midge	**VULNERABLE**
Order **Diptera**	Family **Ceratopogonidae**

Dasyhelea lithotelmatica Strenzke, 1951.

Identification	Strenzke (1950).
Distribution	Limestone pavement karst of the Yorkshire Dales and about Morecambe Bay, occurring from near sea level to about 350m. Suitable breeding sites are sparse, though individual solution cups can have about 100 larvae. The majority of limestone pavement is unsuitable.
Habitat and ecology	Small solution cups on exposed limestone pavement clints. The larvae are aquatic, able to withstand drying-out of the sediment in and on which they live.
Status	A prime example of an insect with a highly specialised habitat of exceedingly localised occurrence. It is in danger through illicit limestone pavement removal, though the problem is now reduced and some localities have effective protection.
Threats	The destruction of limestone pavement by removal as rockery stone. Quarrying is a more local threat. The development of vegetation cover is a potential threat on some sites.
Conservation	The Wildlife and Countryside Act 1981 has strengthened legislation for the conservation of limestone pavements. Present on one, possibly two, NNRs. Also occurs on several SSSIs, including those situated in the Yorkshire Dales National Park. It will be necessary to locate breeding cups on pavements where scrub encroachment is a potential threat, so that management can take the species' needs into account.
Author	A. E. Stubbs, using additional information from Disney (1975).

Asindulum nigrum

A fungus gnat   **VULNERABLE**

Order **Diptera**   Family **Mycetophilidae**

Asindulum nigrum Latreille, 1805.

Identification	Hutson *et al* (1980), p.34, figs 15 and 131.
Distribution	Only known from East Anglia (the Norfolk Broads south to Thorndon Fen and Mildenhall in Suffolk), Oxfordshire (Longwall Street, Oxford), and Somerset (Shapwick Heath).
Habitat and ecology	Fenland. The adults feed at umbel flowers. The biology is not known. The larvae of related species are predatory, spinning webs in which they catch their prey.
Status	It was found relatively frequently in the earlier years of this century but appears to have become scarcer and has not been found in recent years.
Threats	The drainage of fenland.
Conservation	Shapwick Heath is an NNR.
Author	P. J. Chandler, using additional information from Edwards (1913), Morley (1920), and Hamm (1926).

Neoempheria lineola

A fungus gnat   **ENDANGERED**

Order **Diptera**   Family **Mycetophilidae**

Neoempheria lineola (Meigen, 1818), formerly known as *Empheria lineola*.

Identification	Hutson *et al* (1980), p.45 and fig. 184.
Distribution	Only known from the New Forest in Hampshire, where it has been found at Brockenhurst and in Denny Wood.
Habitat and ecology	Old deciduous forest. It develops in decaying wood, according to continental records.
Status	It has been found in the New Forest area on several occasions but most recently in 1939 at Denny Wood, and confirmation is required of its survival there.
Threats	The removal of old trees and dead wood.
Author	P. J. Chandler, using additional information from Jenkinson (1908), p. 154.

Sciophila ochracea

A fungus gnat   **ENDANGERED**

Order **Diptera**   Family **Mycetophilidae**

Sciophila ochracea Walker, 1856.

Identification   Hutson *et al* (1980), p.52 and fig. 207.

Distribution   Very local but evidently widespread in southern England. There are records from a Cambridge garden in 1915, of larvae on fungus on an old plum tree at Woodwalton Fen before 1925, and of larval webs on a cherry branch near Oxford in 1956.

Habitat and ecology   Deciduous woodland. Probably in old orchards, etc., where its host fungus occurs. The larvae spin webs on the surface of hard bracket fungi (probably tawny fomes *Phellinus pomaceus*) on plum and cherry trees (*Prunus* species), feeding on the spores.

Status   No records are more recent than 1956, and the species should be sought in suitable habitats where the presence of larvae is probably easier to establish than that of adults.

Threats   The destruction of old and dying trees.

Conservation   Woodwalton Fen is an NNR.

Author   P. J. Chandler, using additional information from Edwards (1925) and Smith (1957).

Oxycera dives

A soldier fly   **VULNERABLE**

Order **Diptera**   Family **Stratiomyidae**

Oxycera dives Loew, 1845.

Identification   Oldroyd (1969), p.26.

Distribution   The Highland, Tayside, Central and Strathclyde Regions of Scotland, and Co. Durham and North Yorkshire in northern England.

Habitat and ecology   At mossy springs, wet rock faces and small streams in partially shaded situations. A calcareous influence is usually apparent. Larvae are assumed to live in wet moss kept moist by seepages in woodland. The adults are found on foliage in the vicinity of probable breeding sites.

Status   Historically a rare species. Verrall (1909) was only aware of a few specimens: one was taken at Rannoch on 8 June 1896 ("Rannoch" was used as a very general label at that time), and three were found near Rob Roy's Leap waterfall at Aberfoyle (Central) between 6 and 9 July 1903. Another was found in Lanark (Strathclyde). Recently it has been found at four localities, all associated with exceedingly small breeding sites. It was taken in forest beside Loch Ness (Highland) at Port Clair in June 1965, at the Pass of Killiecrankie (Tayside), at Cotherstone Wood near Barnard Castle (Co. Durham) on 23 June 1981, and recently at Ashbury Pastures (North Yorkshire). The species is also rare in Europe, with the majority of records from the Alps.

Conservation Whilst the three most recent sites are all within SSSIs, the habitat is so small and fragile that Vulnerable status is justified. Ashbury Pastures is a reserve of the Yorkshire Wildlife Trust.

Author A. E. Stubbs.

Oxycera pardalina

A soldier fly **VULNERABLE**

Order **Diptera** Family **Stratiomyidae**

Oxycera pardalina Meigen, 1822.

Identification Oldroyd (1969), p.26.

Distribution England, South Wales, and the Scottish Highlands.

Habitat and ecology Verrall (1909) cites an observation that the species is associated with the margins of small overgrown streams in hilly districts. Oldroyd (1969) reports that the males hover 6-10m up near trees by a stream and that females have been swept from vegetation. Recent experience indicates that calcareous flushes are a favoured habitat. Rozkosny (1983, pp.138-144), in commenting on the European position, says that limestone water is preferred and that the larvae are on wet rocks and stones and in wet moss by streams and torrents. In Britain it has been bred from moss on a wet limestone rock face in woodland. The adults can occur at flowers, including hogweed *Heracleum sphondylium*.

Status Verrall (1909, pp.104-106) comments that this was a rare species, even at that time. It was recorded in Dorset in about 1830 (though Verrall did not examine specimens to confirm identification). A specimen was taken in 1901, it is believed near Abergavenny in Gwent. A few years later it was found at Tarrington, Woolhope, Pembridge and Cusop in south Hereford & Worcester (the last locality being on the Welsh border). Audcent noted it at Wells, Somerset and Rozkosny (*loc. cit.*) gives a record for Failand, Somerset (the dates of these records are not stated). Oldroyd (1969) refers to a record for Dovedale, Derbyshire, which was in fact taken on 4 July 1950. Recent records are as follows: 1 June 1970, Guiting Power reserve (Gloucestershire); 5 July 1979, Petits Tor Point, Torbay (Devon); 1 July 1980, Luccombe

Chine (Isle of Wight); and 23 June 1981, Cotherstone Wood (Co. Durham). It was also found in June 1982 near Tomintoul in the Scottish Highlands.

Conservation	Dovedale is a property of the National Trust and Cotherstone Wood is part of an SSSI.
Author	A. E. Stubbs.

Oxycera terminata

A soldier fly   **VULNERABLE**

Order **Diptera**   Family **Stratiomyidae**

Oxycera terminata Meigen, 1822.

Identification	Oldroyd (1969), p.26.
Distribution	South-west England (Dorset, Avon, Gloucestershire, Hereford & Worcester), Bedfordshire, and the Welsh Borders. This is a rare species in Europe, indeed most records are from eastern Europe. The map in Rozkosny (1983, pp.153-154) indicates one record for the Pyrenees and one off southern Sweden; the next nearest record is inside Czechoslovakia. (His map wrongly places a spot near the west coast of Wales; the text lists all records and makes no reference to a record in this district.)
Habitat and ecology	Oldroyd (1969) mentions that the species was once found in great numbers where a woodland stream had been diverted. Rozkosny (*loc. cit.*) simply says that adults have been collected along streams. The larva is unknown, though it is probable that it lives in streamside moss.
Status	Verrall (1909, pp.102-104) regarded this as a very rare species. He notes reports for Dorset dating from the period 1830-40. The other records that he cites are from Hereford & Worcester: Stoke Wood (in and after 1897), one at West Malvern on 8 June 1901, and it was not uncommon in the Monnow Valley on 3 July 1906. The Monnow River runs along the Hereford/Wales border for some miles and it is believed that the most frequently collected stretch was a little north of Pontrilas. The only more recent records are for Bridge Fall, Sundon (Bedfordshire), on 13 July 1947 and for Blaise Woods, near Bristol, Avon, in July 1947 and 1948.
Author	A. E. Stubbs.

Odontomyia angulata

A soldier fly

ENDANGERED

Order **Diptera**   Family **Stratiomyidae**

Odontomyia angulata (Panzer, 1798).

Identification	Oldroyd (1969), p.31 and fig. 67.
Distribution	Norfolk, Somerset and Suffolk.
Habitat and ecology	The larvae are aquatic and the only breeding record (from Denmark) was of a larva found in a lake, and adults have been found on waterside vegetation and flowers beside standing water.
Status	No recent records are available for this very rare species. Verrall (1909, pp.137-140) found it at Tuddenham, Suffolk, on 20 July 1880 and later saw it at Chippenham Fen, Cambridgeshire (but it has not been confirmed from the latter locality), and noted that H. W. Andrews found it at Sutton Broad, Norfolk, on 14 July 1905. Subsequently J. Cowley found it in Somerset, at Edington on 27 June 1947, Chilton Polden on 3 July 1951, and Street Heath on 7 July 1951.
Threats	The drainage of pools and the lowering of water levels in ditches, pollution of standing water bodies, and extensive machine clearance of ponds and ditches.
Author	I. F. G. McLean.

Odontomyia argentata

A soldier fly

VULNERABLE

Order **Diptera**   Family **Stratiomyidae**

Odontomyia argentata (F., 1794).

Identification	Oldroyd (1969), p.31, figs 68 and 70.
Distribution	Somerset, Dorset, Hampshire, Suffolk, East Sussex, Cambridgeshire, Bedfordshire, Surrey, London, Essex, and Kent.
Habitat and ecology	Larvae have been found in marshes and probably also occur at ditch margins. The adults are found early in the year, April-May in Britain.
Status	A rare species in Britain and Europe. Verrall (1909, pp.131-134) implies that it was more frequent in the early 19th century than in his time, and records it from Fordingbridge, Hampshire (1897), Mildenhall, Suffolk (c. 1901), Seaford, East Sussex (before 1860), Dorset, and Cambridgeshire (1832). Since then it has been found in Somerset (Street Heath, 1949), Dorset (Witchampton, 1947),

Hampshire (Leckford, 1940s and 1970s), Surrey (Bookham Common, 1948, and Staines Moor, 1955), Greater London (Uxbridge, 1926), Kent (Erith, 1948), Essex (Henny, 1911), Suffolk (Timworth, 1913), Bedfordshire (Fancott, 1944), and Cambridgeshire (Milton, 1924, Wicken Fen, 1929 and 1957, Woodwalton Fen, 1949, and Chippenham Fen, currently). There are therefore only two post-1960 localities.

Threats

Drainage of wetlands, pollution of standing water bodies, and extensive machine clearance of ponds and ditches.

Conservation

Chippenham and Woodwalton Fens are NNRs, and Wicken Fen is owned by the National Trust.

Author

I. F. G. McLean.

Odontomyia ornata

A soldier fly   **VULNERABLE**

Order **Diptera**   Family **Stratiomyidae**

Odontomyia ornata (Meigen, 1822).

Identification

Oldroyd (1969), p.31 and fig. 66.

Distribution

Somerset, East Sussex, Norfolk, Kent, London, Surrey and Wiltshire.

Habitat and ecology

The larvae are found in shallow standing water in pools and dykes, mainly in levels marshes. The adults can be found in May and June on vegetation near the breeding sites and also feeding at flowers (especially on umbels).

Status

This rare species is now almost confined to the Somerset Levels, where a detailed NCC entomological survey in 1983 revealed its presence in ten 10km squares, and one 10km square in Avon, showing a preference for sites on peat. Other available records are mostly old, suggesting that this species has undergone a considerable recent decline: Wiltshire (South Marston, 1922), East Sussex (Bexhill, 1872, Lewes Levels, 1885, Pevensey Levels, 1973, Pett Level, 1986), Surrey (Byfleet, 1939), Kent (Cliffe, 1897), Greater London (Acton, 1894, Mitcham, 1900, and Stanmore, 1953), and Norfolk (Barton Broad, 1937).

Threats

The drainage of wetlands, pollution of standing water bodies, and extensive machine clearance of ponds and ditches.

Author

I. F. G. McLean.

Stratiomys chamaeleon	A soldier fly	**ENDANGERED**
	Order **Diptera**	Family **Stratiomyidae**

Stratiomys chamaeleon (L., 1758).

Identification
Oldroyd (1969), p.27, figs 79, 80 and 82; Rozkosny (1973), pp. 69-72.

Distribution
Has been recorded from Cambridgeshire, Leicestershire, Norfolk and Oxfordshire. Currently known from only one site (Oxfordshire).

Habitat and ecology
In pools and ponds at least partially fringed with emergent vegetation. There may be a requirement for areas of shallow water overlying a fine muddy substrate, and a generally shallow profile at the water margin. The larvae are aquatic, floating on the water-surface among vegetation, and often hibernate in mud. The adults fly from July to September and visit flowers.

Status
Adults have been found in the late 1970s and early 1980s at one site in Britain (Dry Sandford Pit, Oxfordshire) but at no other site in Britain since at least before 1940. It has not been found recently at Chippenham Fen NNR, Cambridgeshire, (recorded 1892) but has not been looked for at the former Leicestershire or Norfolk sites. The continuing loss of its already scarce habitat makes it increasingly unlikely that new sites will be discovered.

Threats
The drainage and robust clearance of small water bodies, resulting in the loss of larval habitat by its modification to deep, steep-sided ponds which lack marginal emergent vegetation.

Conservation
Believed to be breeding on one local Trust reserve (Berks, Bucks & Oxon Naturalists' Trust), and possibly on a nearby NNR (Cothill). It is necessary to investigate probable breeding sites (in the vicinity of the location of adult sightings) to determine the distribution of larvae in relation to available habitat, in order to assess what management may be required.

Author
I. F. G. McLean, using additional information from J. W. Ismay and A. G. Irwin (pers. comms).

Stratiomys longicornis

A soldier fly   **VULNERABLE**

Order **Diptera**   Family **Stratiomyidae**

Stratiomys longicornis (Scopoli, 1763).

Identification   Oldroyd (1969), p.27; Colyer & Hammond (1968), pl. 8:2.

Distribution   Coast from East Anglia to Hampshire.

Habitat and ecology   The larvae develop in standing water among aquatic vegetation in saline coastal marshes and saltmarsh pools. The adults occur on low vegetation and flowers, usually near the larval habitats.

Status   This rare species has been principally known from the Thames Marshes of Essex and Kent (Shoeburyness, Benfleet and Belvedere, Isle of Grain, Northfleet, and Gravesend), and also Walland Marsh, Kent (1954), Salisbury, Wiltshire (1950: likely to be a stray), Wicken Fen, Cambridgeshire (likely to be a stray), Yarmouth, Isle of Wight (1922), Felixstowe, Suffolk, and Lymington, Hampshire, but there are very few recent records.

Threats   Agricultural 'improvement' of saltmarshes and coastal levels marshes, coastal defence works, and the associated destruction of larval habitat.

Author   I. F. G. McLean.

Xylomyia maculata

A soldier fly   **VULNERABLE**

Order **Diptera**   Family **Xylomyiidae**

Xylomyia maculata (Meigen, 1820).

Identification   Oldroyd (1969), p.33, figs 89 and 99. A medium-sized black and yellow fly, mimicking a wasp in pattern and behaviour.

Distribution   The three major southern ancient forests – New Forest, Windsor Forest (including Silwood Park), and Epping Forest. Also Finchley in London. Rarely found, even in apparently suitable trees.

Habitat and ecology   Ancient forest or remnants with large over-mature trees with rot holes. The life cycle takes one or possibly more years to complete. The adults fly in May and June. The larvae and pupae have been found in dead wood, including rot holes above ground, being occasionally numerous in small pockets of breeding material. Beech *Fagus* has been recorded as a host tree.

Status   This has always been an infrequent species to find. There are long series in collections because larvae and pupae have been found on a few occasions. The adult is rarely seen, despite its striking appearance. Today it is rarely found even in apparently suitable trees, so there must be concern at the progressive decline in suitable habitat.

Threats	Large numbers of ancient trees have been cleared for modern afforestation, for firewood, or for safety or amenity tidiness in public areas. Age-gap problems in the supply of suitable over-mature trees may arise, and with a smaller population of ancient trees there is less chance of ideal breeding sites being available.
Conservation	Conservation management for over-mature timber is in hand in Windsor Forest. Strengthening of the conservation measures in the New Forest and Epping Forest is required.
Authors	A. G. Irwin and A. E. Stubbs.

Xylophagus junki

A soldier fly   **ENDANGERED**

Order **Diptera**   Family **Xylophagidae**

Xylophagus junki Szilady, 1932.

Identification	Oldroyd (1969), p.34; the male is unknown.
Distribution	Strathspey, Highland Region.
Habitat and ecology	The larvae of members of this genus are found in dead wood, and it is probable that *X. junki* breeds in over-mature pine trees *Pinus*, because the only British example was found in an ancient Caledonian pine forest. The adults are elusive in this genus, but may be found resting on tree trunks.
Status	A very rare species in Britain, still only known from a single female found by J. E. Collin in Glenmore Forest, Aviemore, on 5 June 1913 (see Collin, 1962). The subsequent extraction of mature pine trees from this forest makes the continued survival of this species at its only known site very doubtful, but possibly it may yet be re-found in one of the Caledonian pine woods of the Spey or Dee valleys. For any site to support this species it is essential that continuity in the presence of ancient trees and dead wood is maintained. It is considered most improbable that it could survive in commercially managed pine woods.
Threats	This species would be threatened by the felling of mature and over-mature trees or the clearance of dead wood. In commercially managed forests trees are not allowed to reach an age or condition suitable for the larvae to develop successfully.
Author	I. F. G. McLean.

Chrysopilus erythrophthalmus	A snipe fly	**VULNERABLE**
	Order **Diptera**	Family **Rhagionidae**

Chrysopilus erythrophthalmus Loew, 1840.

Identification Cole (1981).

Distribution Hereford & Worcester, and North Yorkshire.

Habitat and ecology Larvae are found in cool water streams running at 30-70cm per second, under stones and among aquatic bryophytes (Cole, 1981, quoting data obtained by Thomas in France). Upland streams in western and northern Britain are most likely to support this species, and, as adults are seldom captured even within the known range of the species in continental Europe, it is possible that further sites may be found only by searching for larvae.

Status Known in Britain from one female found by J. H. Wood at Stoke Plantation, Hereford & Worcester (thought to be the site now called Haugh Wood which has one quite large stream), on 1 July 1896. A second female was found by J. H. Cole on 3 July 1979 at Rake Beck, North Yorkshire, along the banks of a stream within a clearing in a wooded gully at about 250m above sea level (Cole, 1981).

Author I. F. G. McLean.

Chrysopilus laetus	A snipe fly	**ENDANGERED**
	Order **Diptera**	Family **Rhagionidae**

Chrysopilus laetus (Zetterstedt, 1842).

Identification Oldroyd (1969), p.46 and fig. 102. A medium-sized yellow fly.

Distribution The original rearing record is from Windsor Great Park. All subsequent records are from a nearby area of Windsor Forest. The larvae are of fairly regular occurrence in wet wood mould, though only one or two occur in any one piece of medium.

Habitat and ecology Open-structured beech woodland with ancient beech trees *Fagus*. Probably univoltine. Adults probably fly in May and June. Bred in 1939 from a pupa said to have been found in mud, but this information is probably erroneous or the circumstances misleading. In the 1960s and 1970s larvae have been found in wet wood mould in rotten stumps, rot holes and aerial logs up to 3m above ground, nearly always in beech. All British specimens have been bred except for one recent capture of an adult. The larvae are very active as if predatory, but such habits have not been confirmed.

Status	It is of interest that this species has never been found in other major areas of ancient forest such as the New Forest or Epping Forest. It is one of the special elements of the dead-wood fauna of Windsor Forest.
Threats	Windsor Forest has a much reduced area of ancient trees following widespread introduction of modern forestry. Fallen ancient trees have been cut up for firewood on many occasions.
Conservation	A conservation management agreement for ancient trees provides reasonable safeguards for the future.
Author	A. E. Stubbs.

Chrysops sepulcralis

A horse fly   **VULNERABLE**

Order **Diptera**   Family **Tabanidae**

Chrysops sepulcralis (F., 1794).

Identification	Oldroyd (1969), pp.52-54; see also Colyer & Hammond (1968), pl. 9:5.
Distribution	Confined to Dorset, apart from a recent record from the New Forest (Hampshire).
Habitat and ecology	Adults have been found in the vicinity of ponds and boggy areas on heaths and do not fly far from their breeding sites. It is probable that this species is breeding in damp ground within its known heathland localities. Unlike other tabanids, the larvae of *Chrysops* are probably saprophagous rather than predatory. Adults have been taken in late July and August.
Status	Apparently confined to a few localities in the Dorset Heaths: Wareham, 1915 and 1919; Wareham Common, 1916; Studland, 1906, 1909 and 1933; Studland Heath, 1895; Morden Heath, 1916; Verwood, 1922; Rempstone Heath, 1931; near Agglestone (Godlingston Heath), 1933; and Stoborough Heath, 1953. Verrall (1909) gives additionally Parley Heath and Bloxworth and mentions old records from Scotland which are very doubtful (these may be referable to the black form of *C. caecutiens* (L.)). Goffe (1931) refers to a record from Hengistbury Head (Dorset) but he gave no records for the New Forest. However, a specimen has now been taken in the New Forest, at Holmhill on 11 July 1983 (by D. Sheppard), though this could be a stray from Dorset.
Threats	The drainage of wet heath resulting in loss of suitable habitat for larvae is believed to be the most significant threat to the survival of this species in Britain. Other threats are ball clay extraction, oil-related developments, and building development.
Authors	I. F. G. McLean and A. E. Stubbs.

Atylotus plebeius

A horse fly   **ENDANGERED**

Order **Diptera**   Family **Tabanidae**

Atylotus plebeius (Fallen, 1817).

Identification	Chvala *et al* (1972), pp.260-262 and 264-266.
Distribution	Cheshire.
Habitat and ecology	The larvae occur in "marshy places near peat bogs" (Chvala *et al*, 1972) where they are predators of other insect larvae. The females have not yet been observed as blood-sucking.
Status	A very rare species in Britain with no recent records, it is known only from Abbots Moss (22 July 1911 and 6 June 1922) and Delamere (15 July 1911) and so is apparently confined to bogs in Cheshire. It is also a rare species in Europe (Chvala *et al*, 1972).
Threats	Drainage of mosses and their invasion by pine trees, and possibly recreational pressure round Delamere.
Conservation	Abbots Moss is an SSSI.
Author	I. F. G. McLean.

Atylotus rusticus

A horse fly   **ENDANGERED**

Order **Diptera**   Family **Tabanidae**

Atylotus rusticus (L., 1758).

Identification	Oldroyd (1969), p.64 and fig. 126.
Distribution	The only records are from Cambridgeshire (Monks Wood, 1828) (presumed to have originated from nearby fenland) and East Sussex (two records from near Lewes in the early 1880s, one record from near Eastbourne in 1900, one record from near Lewes in the 1960s, and one record from the Pevensey Levels in 1981).
Habitat and ecology	Cattle-grazed levels marshes, with ditches managed on a medium length (probably about five years) clearance regime. The larvae probably live in mud at the margins of ditches on levels marshes. The adults fly from July to September.
Status	The few records available suggest that this species is likely to be confined to the remaining grazing levels marshes in East Sussex, as this habitat type no longer occurs in Cambridgeshire, with the exception of the similar fen habitat at Woodwalton Fen NNR where this species is unlikely to have been overlooked.

Threats	Drainage and agricultural improvement of the Lewes and Pevensey Levels, resulting in lower water tables and aquatic pollution from run-off from arable fields.
Conservation	The most recent record is within an SSSI. A clearer definition of status and requirements is necessary.
Author	I. F. G. McLean.

Hybomitra expollicata

A horse fly **ENDANGERED**

Order **Diptera** Family **Tabanidae**

Hybomitra expollicata (Pandelle, 1883).

Identification	Chvala *et al* (1972), pp.170-177 and 243-245.
Distribution	Dorset and Essex.
Habitat and ecology	A marsh species usually associated with brackish biotopes in Europe and recorded from two coastal localities in Britain. The larvae of Tabanidae are typically found in damp soil where they are predators of other insect larvae, and it is probable that this species is breeding beside saline pools and dykes in its known localities.
Status	Only recorded from Studland, Dorset, on 1 and 3 August 1909, from Hadleigh, Essex, on 27 July 1969, and from Langenhoe, Essex, on 20 July 1983. This is a very rare species not recorded from coastal marshes during detailed recent surveys in Norfolk, Suffolk, Kent, Sussex, Somerset and Gwent.
Threats	Drainage and agricultural improvement of coastal marshes.
Author	I. F. G. McLean.

Epitriptus arthriticus

A robber fly **ENDANGERED**

Order **Diptera** Family **Asilidae**

Epitriptus arthriticus (Zeller, 1840).

Identification	Oldroyd (1969), p.93.
Distribution	Norfolk and Somerset.
Habitat and ecology	A dune locality in Somerset and the edge of the Breck (which has sandy heaths) in Norfolk. The adults prey upon other insects. The larvae may be predicted to be soil-dwelling.

Status	The only known British records are those given in Oldroyd (1969): a female on 14 July 1907 at Merton, Norfolk, and a male on 16 July 1955 on Berrow sand dunes, Somerset.
Author	A. E. Stubbs.

Epitriptus cowini

A robber fly   **VULNERABLE**

Order **Diptera**   Family **Asilidae**

Epitriptus cowini Hobby, 1946.

Identification	Oldroyd (1969), p.93.
Distribution	Confined to north-west Wales.
Habitat and ecology	Recorded from sand-dunes.
Status	Only known recently from Morfa Harlech, where it was taken on 23 August 1968 and 17 August 1969 by P. Crow. There remains a possibility that Newborough Warren NNR and Morfa Dyfryn NNR may support this species. It has an interesting distribution in that, as far as the British Isles are concerned, it is confined to the coast of the Irish Sea; apart from north-west Wales, it is also known from eastern Ireland and the Isle of Man.
Conservation	Morfa Harlech is an NNR.
Author	A. E. Stubbs.

Eutolmus rufibarbis

A robber fly   **VULNERABLE**

Order **Diptera**   Family **Asilidae**

Eutolmus rufibarbis (Meigen, 1820).

Identification	Oldroyd (1969), p.92 and fig. 223. A large yellowish-grey fly.
Distribution	The New Forest and eastern England up to Lincolnshire, but always regarded as rare and local. However, most records are old. Records from Surrey and Sussex are recent.
Habitat and ecology	Open dry heathland. Possibly univoltine. The adults fly in late June to late August. It is probable that the larvae are predatory on beetle larvae such as those of chafers or dung beetles. The adults are predatory.
Status	Since this species is confined to large blocks of open dry heathland, it is in an especially vulnerable habitat and it is on relatively few sites.

Threats	The destruction of heathland, natural tree invasion of heathland (especially pines), and frequent fires reducing the age class of heath.
Conservation	Occurs on Chobham Common LNR, Surrey, and on several SSSIs. Clarification of its status on other historic sites is required.
Authors	A. G. Irwin and A. E. Stubbs.

Neoitamus cothurnatus

A robber fly **ENDANGERED**

Order **Diptera** Family **Asilidae**

Neoitamus cothurnatus (Meigen, 1820).

Identification	Oldroyd (1969), p.90.
Distribution	Two sites in Oxfordshire.
Habitat and ecology	Woodland, though its exact requirements are unknown. The related species *N. cyanurus* (Loew) occurs in woodland rides and along wood edges, often on tree foliage. It is assumed that *N. cothurnatus* occurs in a similar situation. Adult robber flies catch other insects as prey. The larvae are likely to be soil-dwelling (rather than living in dead wood).
Status	Verrall (1909) summarises the records of his time: a male was taken at Stow Wood, Oxford, on 10 June 1895 and one of each sex at Tubney Wood (then placed in Berkshire) on 2 June 1901. Subsequent searches were unsuccessful. These remain the only British records. Tubney Wood has been extensively converted to conifers so it is questionable whether a very rare asilid would have survived.
Author	A. E. Stubbs.

Laphria gilva

A robber fly **ENDANGERED**

Order **Diptera** Family **Asilidae**

Laphria gilva (L., 1758).

Identification	Oldroyd (1969), p.87. A large black fly with golden reflections formed by hairs on parts of the abdomen.
Distribution	Only reputed to be British before 1938, but in that year several specimens were taken in Windsor Forest. A pair was taken *in cop.* at Oxshott, Surrey, in 1946, and a pupa was found at Silchester (about the Berkshire/Hampshire border). None have been found since.

Habitat and ecology	Pine *Pinus* woodland. Assumed to be univoltine. The adults fly mostly in July, also June. Pupae have been recorded from pine stumps. It is possible that the larvae are predatory on xylophagous beetle larvae. The adults are predatory on other insects.
Status	Pine was introduced into southern England in the 1800s, so mature pine and the related dead wood was not really available until this century. It is not surprising that this species should be among the many pine species to have colonised the large areas of pine habitat now available; rather it is less easy to explain why, having bred here, the species should die out. It could be that there was a temporary period of favourable climate. It is quite likely that it has remained in elusive small numbers or that the species will attempt to re-establish.
Author	A. E. Stubbs.

Psilocephala melaleuca

A stiletto fly   **ENDANGERED**

Order **Diptera**   Family **Therevidae**

Psilocephala melaleuca (Loew, 1847).

Identification	Oldroyd (1969), p.100, figs 244 and 246. The male is covered in silver hairs, and the female is a drab brown.
Distribution	All records but one are from Windsor Forest or nearby (Ascot and Egham). First found (as a larva) in 1929. The most recent records are of a larva in 1980 from Greenwich Park, Greater London, and an adult which emerged in 1981 from a pupa collected in Windsor Forest. Overall there are very few records.
Habitat and ecology	Ancient woodland with over-mature oaks *Quercus*. Presumed to be univoltine. The adults fly in June and early July. Larvae have been found in decayed oak in the autumn, becoming adult the following summer.
Status	One of the rarest and least known of our spectacular flies. It has not been found in other ancient forest areas.
Threats	Reduction in the population of ancient oaks, either through direct destruction following modern afforestation or through shading out. A major age-class gap in suitable oaks could arise.
Conservation	A conservation management agreement for Windsor Forest gives some hope for the future.
Author	A. E. Stubbs.

Villa cingulata

A bee fly   **VULNERABLE**

Order **Diptera**   Family **Bombyliidae**

Villa cingulata (Meigen, 1804).

Identification	Oldroyd (1969), p.118, figs 328 and 330.
Distribution	Oxfordshire, Buckinghamshire and Kent.
Habitat and ecology	A species found in southern dry grassland or woodland localities; the larvae are parasitoids of other insects (no British breeding records). Adults have been found in July and August.
Status	A rare species known from Stokenchurch (1898) in Buckinghamshire, Wormsley (1907) and Hell Coppice (Bernwood Forest) (1935) in Oxfordshire, and Soakham Down, Kent (1937, 1938).
Author	I. F. G. McLean.

Villa circumdata

A bee fly   **VULNERABLE**

Order **Diptera**   Family **Bombyliidae**

Villa circumdata (Meigen, 1820).

Identification	Oldroyd (1969), p.118, figs 327 and 331.
Distribution	Dorset, Surrey, Hampshire and the Isle of Wight.
Habitat and ecology	A species of southern heaths; the larvae are parasitoids of other insects (no British breeding records). Adults may be found sunning themselves on bare patches of sandy ground in July and August.
Status	A rare species known only from Arne (1901), Bloxworth (1906), Tadnoll Winfrith (1909), Wareham Heath (1918), Corfe Castle (1944), and Morden (1956) in Dorset; Chobham, Surrey (1904); Lyndhurst, Hampshire (1894); and St Helens, Isle of Wight (1950).
Author	I. F. G. McLean.

Syneches muscarius

A dance fly   **ENDANGERED**

Order **Diptera**   Family **Empididae**

Syneches muscarius (F., 1794).

Identification	Collin (1961).
Distribution	Known only from two sites in Dorset.

Habitat and ecology	Beside or close to ditches in unimproved wet meadows. Adults occur low down on vegetation or can be taken by sweeping. The larval biology is unknown (may be predatory in soil). The adults are predatory on other insects among grass stems and have been recorded during July.
Status	Recorded from The Moors, Wool, Dorset, in 1953 and 1954, but it is unlikely that the habitat remains suitable. It was refound a few miles away near Turners Puddle on 4 July 1984 during an NCC survey of Dorset meadows. The rapid and continuing loss of agriculturally-unimproved damp meadows makes it increasingly unlikely that any further sites will be discovered. This species must be at the edge of its range in southern Britain, as it is regarded as a species of south-west Europe.
Threats	Modification of habitat by changed agricultural methods.
Conservation	Assessment of the current status of the only known site and the population size of the single colony of this species is required.
Authors	I. F. G. McLean and A. E. Stubbs, using additional information from E. C. M. d'A. Fonseca (pers. comm.).

Poecilobothrus ducalis

VULNERABLE

Order **Diptera**   Family **Dolichopodidae**

Poecilobothrus ducalis (Loew, 1857).

Identification	Fonseca (1978), p.37.
Distribution	Recorded from Essex, Kent, Sussex and Somerset.
Habitat and ecology	Saltmarsh pools and also brackish ditches in levels marshes. The larval biology is unknown: they may be predatory in mud beside saline pools and ditches. The adults fly from July to September and are found on patches of mud beside these pools and ditches where they are predators of small insects.
Status	Known from eight sites recently in Britain.
Threats	The destruction of saltmarsh, and the intensive management of ditches on levels marshes, resulting in the loss of associated mud banks of low gradient, so that only steep-sided ditches remain.
Conservation	Occurs at Chetney Marshes, Kent, within an SSSI.
Author	I. F. G. McLean.

Callomyia elegans

A flat-footed fly   **VULNERABLE**

Order **Diptera**   Family **Platypezidae**

Callomyia elegans Meigen, 1804.

Identification	Chandler (1974).
Distribution	Very local in south-west England (Dorset and the New Forest), South Wales (Glamorgan and Powys), Hereford & Worcester, and one record from south-west Scotland (Dumfries). All localities except those in Powys and Hereford & Worcester are near the coast. (It is scarce but widespread in Ireland.)
Habitat and ecology	Mixed deciduous woodland. Its biology is not known but is probably similar to related species, i.e. the larva is a surface feeder on encrusting fungi on dead wood.
Status	Most records are from the period 1861 to 1913, only the Dumfries (Gretna) record being more recent (1940). It has, however, been found in two Irish localities in recent years. Confirmation is necessary of its survival in its range in Great Britain.
Threats	The loss of old-established woodland.
Author	P. J. Chandler.

Nephrocerus scutellatus

A big-headed fly   **ENDANGERED**

Order **Diptera**   Family **Pipunculidae**

Nephrocerus scutellatus Macquart, 1834.

Identification	Coe (1966), p.36.
Distribution	A single specimen was taken in 1979 at Kings Park Wood, West Sussex (Stubbs, 1980).
Habitat and ecology	Deciduous woodland (with partial coniferisation; taken along a ride). Its life history is unknown but it is assumed to be an internal parasite of a large leaf-hopper (Homoptera, Auchenorhyncha). The adult was taken in mid-June.
Status	Being an inch across, very much larger than the previously known British species of this family, this is an interesting addition to the British fauna. It seems highly unlikely that the specimen was a single stray blown across from Europe. Unless it is a recent colonist, the species must be very localised in occurrence to have escaped notice for so long.

Threats	It is not clear whether the growth of conifers, which will swamp out much of the deciduous woodland, will have an effect. Sufficient deciduous trees may remain.
Conservation	Kings Park Wood is a Forestry Commission conservation area.
Author	A. E. Stubbs.

Cephalops perspicuus

A big-headed fly	**VULNERABLE**
Order **Diptera**	Family **Pipunculidae**

Cephalops perspicuus (de Meijere, 1907).

Identification	Coe (1966), p.58.
Distribution	Only recorded from Norfolk (two localities).
Habitat and ecology	The margin of fenland with a rich fen plant community. The larvae of Pipunculidae are internal parasites of plant bugs (Homoptera); the genus *Cephalops* has only been reared from bugs of the family Delphacidae. The adults of this species have only definitely been recorded in September (Irwin) but there may be an earlier brood in June-July (see Coe, 1966).
Status	The only British records known are Horning Ferry (by J. E. Collin) and Catfield Fen (1977, by A. C. Irwin). Any further loss of fen habitat through agricultural reclamation will make a decline in the population of this species likely.
Threats	The proposed Yare barrage would result in the loss of fen habitat which could have serious repercussions for this species.
Conservation	Horning Ferry is within Bure Marshes NNR, and Catfield Fen is a Norfolk Naturalists' Trust reserve.
Author	A. G. Irwin.

Parasyrphus nigritarsis

A hoverfly	**ENDANGERED**
Order **Diptera**	Family **Syrphidae**

Parasyrphus nigritarsis (Zetterstedt, 1843).

Identification	Stubbs & Falk (1983), pp. 69 and 150.
Distribution	The Scottish Highlands.
Habitat and ecology	The larvae are recorded (on the Continent) as feeding on the eggs and larvae of chrysomelid beetles. The habitat details in Britain are unknown.

Status	There are only a few British specimens, all old. This is one of four British hoverflies which have not been confirmed as occurring in Britain in the post-1970 period.
Author	A. E. Stubbs.

Doros conopseus

A hoverfly **VULNERABLE**

Order **Diptera** Family **Syrphidae**

Doros conopseus (F., 1776).

Identification	Stubbs & Falk (1983), pp. 61 and 135, pl. 4:14.
Distribution	The western Weald, also south Essex, Wiltshire, Hampshire, and a few other records including north Cumbria.
Habitat and ecology	Mainly chalk grassland, at the edge of scrub or woodland, often in association with bramble *Rubus*. The ecology of the larva is unknown but it will be of the predatory type.
Status	Always very rare, recent records being confined to a few chalkland sites in the western Weald, Wiltshire and south Essex. Two were taken by D.A. Sheppard on Martin Down, Hampshire, in June 1982.
Conservation	Martin Down is an NNR.
Author	A. E. Stubbs.

Didea alneti

A hoverfly **ENDANGERED**

Order **Diptera** Family **Syrphidae**

Didea alneti (Fallen, 1817).

Identification	Stubbs & Falk (1983), pp. 61 and 134, pl. 3:17.
Distribution	The West Midlands, also Essex, Kent and north Scotland.
Habitat and ecology	Unknown. The larvae will be of the aphid-feeding type.
Status	Always a great rarity, last taken in 1948 in Kent. This is one of four British hoverflies which have not been confirmed as occurring in Britain in the post-1970 period.
Author	A. E. Stubbs.

Sphaerophoria loewi

A hoverfly   **VULNERABLE**

Order **Diptera**   Family **Syrphidae**

Sphaerophoria loewi Zetterstedt, 1843.

Identification	Stubbs & Falk (1983), pp. 70 and 153, pl. A:17,18.
Distribution	Scattered coastal localities in southern counties and also north Lancashire. One inland locality in the Scottish Highlands.
Habitat and ecology	Mainly a species of brackish marsh, usually in association with sea club-rush *Scirpus maritimus* or reed *Phragmites*. The larvae will be of the aphid-feeding type.
Status	Very rare and in very few localities.
Author	A. E. Stubbs.

Chrysotoxum octomaculatum

A hoverfly   **VULNERABLE**

Order **Diptera**   Family **Syrphidae**

Chrysotoxum octomaculatum Curtis, 1837.

Identification	Stubbs & Falk (1983), pp. 60 and 131, pl. 4:12.
Distribution	Confined to heaths in east Dorset, the New Forest and the western Weald. For map see Entwistle & Stubbs (1983), map 11.
Habitat and ecology	Confined to dry heathland. The ecology is virtually unknown, but the larvae will be of the aphid-feeding type, probably subterranean.
Status	Very rare.
Author	A. E. Stubbs.

Chrysotoxum vernale

A hoverfly   **ENDANGERED**

Order **Diptera**   Family **Syrphidae**

Chrysotoxum vernale Loew, 1841.

Identification	Stubbs & Falk (1983), pp. 59 and 131, pl. 4:8.
Distribution	The southern coastal belt of south-west England, from south-west Hampshire to east Cornwall. For map see Entwistle & Stubbs (1983), map 12.

Habitat and ecology	Unknown. The larvae will be of the aphid-feeding type, probably subterranean.
Status	Historically seemingly very rare; only one recent record, in Dorset.
Author	A. E. Stubbs.

Rhingia rostrata

A hoverfly **VULNERABLE**

Order **Diptera** Family **Syrphidae**

Rhingia rostrata (L., 1758).

Identification	Stubbs & Falk (1983), pp. 88 and 178, pl. 5:5.
Distribution	Scattered records for southern England, also north-west Wales.
Habitat and ecology	Woodland. The larval habitat is unknown; *R. campestris* feeds in cattle dung so *R. rostrata* could use dung or perhaps carrion.
Status	Recorded very infrequently but it can suddenly appear in numbers at a site for a few weeks and then vanish. No permanent populations are known. It was last reported in Britain in 1976.
Author	A. E. Stubbs.

Ferdinandea ruficornis

A hoverfly **VULNERABLE**

Order **Diptera** Family **Syrphidae**

Ferdinandea ruficornis (F., 1775).

Identification	Stubbs & Falk (1983), pp. 87 and 177, pl. 5:2.
Distribution	Only currently known from a few places in the New Forest. Otherwise there are only a few old records for southern England, and one specimen from Derbyshire.
Habitat and ecology	Woodland with sufficient goat moth trees. Adults occur in mid-summer sitting on tree trunks with sap runs caused by caterpillars of the goat moth *Cossus cossus*. The larvae have also been found in such situations, seemingly the essential breeding conditions.
Status	This species has always been rare, but it is in danger of extinction if the goat moth declines for any reason at the only known sites. The population is estimated to be very small.

Threats	The major decline in the status of the goat moth in the last thirty years has severely reduced the potential habitat. The hoverfly clearly requires continuity of habitat in viable quantity. The reason for the decline of the moth is not entirely clear, though reduction in the abundance of old trees and the removal of unsound infested trees must have contributed to the problem.
Conservation	The priority is to ensure that the habitat is not destroyed. It is very difficult to devise positive measures: a survey of any new major sites for goat moth will be required.
Author	A. E. Stubbs, using additional information from Coe (1953) and I. Perry (pers. comm.).

Chamaesyrphus caledonicus

A hoverfly   ENDANGERED

Order **Diptera**   Family **Syrphidae**

Chamaesyrphus caledonicus Collin, 1940.

Identification	Stubbs & Falk (1983), pp. 102 and 204, pl. 5:20.
Distribution	Moray (Grampian).
Habitat and ecology	Unknown.
Status	One female was taken in August 1938 at Culbin Sands, a locality now largely covered in conifer plantations. This is the only reliable specimen (M. C. D. Speight, pers. comm.) though a very few other specimens from the Scottish Highlands have been attributed to this species. If these other specimens are in future regarded as a different species, such a species will itself be a Red Data Book candidate.
Author	A. E. Stubbs.

Myolepta potens

A hoverfly   ENDANGERED

Order **Diptera**   Family **Syrphidae**

Myolepta potens (Harris, 1780).

Identification	Stubbs & Falk (1983), pp. 92 and 184, pl. 7:2.
Distribution	Only recorded from a small area near Bristol and the Shapwick/Edington area of Somerset. For map see Entwistle & Stubbs (1983), map 22.
Habitat and ecology	Unknown. It is assumed to be a woodland species, breeding in dead wood (in common with *M. luteola*, whose larvae are adapted to live in wet rot-holes).

Status	Only a few specimens are known, all found in the 1940s. At least one of its former woods has been coniferised. This is one of four British hoverflies which have not been confirmed as occurring in Britain in the post-1970 period.
Author	A. E. Stubbs.

Brachyopa bicolor

	A hoverfly	**VULNERABLE**
	Order **Diptera**	Family **Syrphidae**

Brachyopa bicolor (Fallen, 1817).

Identification	Stubbs & Falk (1983), pp. 89 and 180.
Distribution	The New Forest and Windsor Forest; also Hertfordshire and Sussex.
Habitat and ecology	Dead wood (or possibly sap runs), associated with large standing live trees, especially beech *Fagus*.
Status	The only known regular site is in the New Forest. It is certainly very rare in Windsor Forest/Great Park. The other records are old.
Author	A. E. Stubbs.

Hammerschmidtia ferruginea

	A hoverfly	**ENDANGERED**
	Order **Diptera**	Family **Syrphidae**

Hammerschmidtia ferruginea (Fallen, 1871), formerly known as *Brachyopa ferruginea*.

Identification	Stubbs & Falk (1983), pp. 91 and 183, pl. 7:12.
Distribution	Only positively known from Strathspey (Highland) but there is another probable sighting from Torboll, south-east Sutherland. The population is believed to be small.
Habitat and ecology	Open structured woodland with birch *Betula* and aspen *Populus tremula*. Its ecology is unknown but the related genus *Brachyopa* breeds in dead wood and sap runs. The adult has been reported from the stumps and trunks of aspen and birch, and also at flowers including rose *Rosa*. Recently three females were found at a large rot-hole in the side of a mature aspen, suggesting that this is the real breeding site.

Status	It has always been a great rarity; there are very few recent sightings and it is in danger of extinction. It was found at an aspen stand in Sutherland in 1984. Suitable breeding sites are few and large aspens with rot-holes are particularly rare. Its ecological requirements are poorly understood.
Threats	The removal and coniferisation of native deciduous woodland. Also the felling of aspens before maturity, when rot-holes and sap runs develop.
Conservation	Recorded in one SSSI, but whether there is breeding here is unknown. There is a need for another SSSI in the Spey Valley to include the best historic locality where it still occurs.
Author	A. E. Stubbs, using additional information from Coe (1953) and I. Perry (pers. comm.).

Callicera aenea

A hoverfly **VULNERABLE**

Order **Diptera** Family **Syrphidae**

Callicera aenea (F., 1777).

Identification	Stubbs & Falk (1983), pp. 73 and 159, pl. 9:2.
Distribution	Scattered records, mainly in southern England but extending northwards to Yorkshire. For map see Entwistle & Stubbs (1983), map 3.
Habitat and ecology	Unknown. The larvae almost certainly live in dead wood (an adult has been seen about birch logs). There is no obvious habitat association, perhaps open structured woods being the most plausible.
Status	Unpredictable in occurrence and seemingly extremely rare.
Author	A. E. Stubbs.

Callicera rufa

A hoverfly **ENDANGERED**

Order **Diptera** Family **Syrphidae**

Callicera rufa Schummel, 1841.

Identification	Stubbs & Falk (1983), pp. 73 and 159, pl. 9:3.
Distribution	Ancient Caledonian pine forests on the eastern side of the Scottish Highlands. For map see Entwistle & Stubbs (1983), map 3. The population is believed to be small.

Habitat and ecology	The larvae live in partially water-filled rot-holes in large ancient pine trees *Pinus sylvestris*. The needs of the adults are unknown, but they are normally seen on the trunks of live trees and on stumps.
Status	It has always been rare, but is now in danger of extinction. A large area of over-mature trees is required to ensure that some are in the right condition. It has a chance on two NNRs, but otherwise the outlook is bleak.
Threats	Suitable ancient pines with the right type of rot-hole would seem to be very rare nowadays. Modern commercial forestry practice is changing the structure of native forests so that over-mature trees with rot-holes will not be represented in the future.
Conservation	Present on two NNRs, but only one has long-term provision for the right habitat. There is a need to ensure that other sites have suitable forestry plans.
Author	A. E. Stubbs, using additional information from Coe (1953).

Callicera spinolae

A hoverfly   **ENDANGERED**

Order **Diptera**   Family **Syrphidae**

Callicera spinolae Rondani, 1844.

Identification	Stubbs & Falk (1983), pp. 73 and 159, pl. 9:1.
Distribution	A few localities in East Anglia. For map see Entwistle & Stubbs (1983), map 3.
Habitat and ecology	Adults occur at ivy blossom *Hedera helix* in the autumn. The larvae are unknown, but almost certainly live in rot-holes in trees.
Status	Always a rarity but was reasonably strong at one site in the 1970s. However, it has rapidly declined and has seemingly disappeared in the last few years. There is strong reason to believe that it bred in elm trees (*Ulmus* species) which have now died and been removed after Dutch elm disease. It was rediscovered at its former strongest site in 1984, but is scarce, apparently dependent now on beech *Fagus*.
Author	A. E. Stubbs, using additional information from I. Perry (pers. comm.).

Microdon devius	A hoverfly	VULNERABLE
	Order **Diptera**	Family **Syrphidae**

Microdon devius (L., 1761).

Identification
Stubbs & Falk (1983), pp. 112 and 228 (genus, pl. 9:4,5).

Distribution
Mainly the North Downs of Surrey and the Chilterns, but also the South Downs, Oxfordshire and perhaps Wyre Forest, and more doubtfully north-west Wales. However, records are few and mostly old. Only known in recent years from the North Downs. The population is believed to be small.

Habitat and ecology
Chalk grassland is the normal habitat. Some localities would equate with other calcareous grassland and possibly other habitats. Scrub edge may or may not be required. The larvae live in ants' nests, feeding on buccal pellets. The literature is confused and probably unreliable as to the ant hosts, but the best candidates are in the genera *Lasius* and *Formica*, probably also *Myrmica*. The adults are normally swept from long grass or found sitting beside paths.

Status
The absence of knowledge about its ecological requirements makes the future very uncertain. Only the two North Downs sites are good prospects and one of these is extremely small. It is possible that further sites may be located on the North Downs, the Chilterns or elsewhere though the species is always very localised and elusive.

Threats
Changes in the character of chalk grassland and its ant fauna; scrub encroachment; ploughing, afforestation and other forms of land improvement. Close grazing is also probably damaging.

Conservation
Present on two National Trust properties in Surrey, of which one is an SSSI. The management plan for the main site is probably satisfactory for this species. There is a need to survey the distribution and status more accurately, and in particular the biology.

Author
A. E. Stubbs, using additional information from Donisthorpe (1927, pp. 125-126) and Coe (1953).

Chalcosyrphus eunotus

A hoverfly — **VULNERABLE**

Order **Diptera** Family **Syrphidae**

Chalcosyrphus eunotus (Loew, 1873), formerly known as *Brachypalpus eunotus*.

Identification	Stubbs & Falk (1983), pp. 110 and 221, pl. 10:7.
Distribution	Hereford & Worcester, and Oxfordshire (that part formerly in Berkshire).
Habitat and ecology	Undoubtedly breeds in dead wood but nothing is known of the early stages. Since the adult has been found on a log resting in a stream, and flying over a shaded pool, it is possible that it breeds in semi-submerged logs, but this remains far from proven.
Status	Has only been found on four occasions, two of them in 1899 near Ledbury (Hereford & Worcester). In 1953 one was found at Cothill (Oxfordshire) and another in the Wyre Forest in 1977. There is thus only one recent record of this very rare species and nothing is known of management needs; possibly this species should be classified as Endangered, but the Welsh Borders are poorly recorded at present.
Conservation	Cothill and Wyre Forest are NNRs.
Author	A. E. Stubbs.

Caliprobola speciosa

A hoverfly — **ENDANGERED**

Order **Diptera** Family **Syrphidae**

Caliprobola speciosa (Rossi, 1790).

Identification	Stubbs & Falk (1983), pp. 110 and 219, pl. 10:9.
Distribution	Currently only in Windsor Forest and the New Forest. There are very old records for Yorkshire and Derbyshire.
Habitat and ecology	A puparium was found in wet wood pulp in the base of a hollow beech stump *Fagus*. The adults seem to favour tall stumps in small sunny glades, mainly of beech but rarely also of oak *Quercus*.
Status	A great rarity. It is now almost certainly confined to the New Forest, where it is only frequent at one site, and to Windsor Forest, where it has become much rarer over the last twenty years. This is one of our most handsome hoverflies, so the restriction and decline at its best sites in the last forty years as a consequence of reduction in habitat is of concern.
Author	A. E. Stubbs.

Pocota personata	A hoverfly	VULNERABLE
	Order **Diptera**	Family **Syrphidae**

Pocota personata (Harris, 1780).

Identification Stubbs & Falk (1983), pp. 110 and 222, pl. 10:11.

Distribution Mainly southern England, but sparse records extend to Devon and Nottinghamshire.

Habitat and ecology Breeds in rot-holes in trees, usually high above ground. It occurs in ancient forests but there are a few records in other places.

Status This has always been a rarity though on a few occasions it has been reared in numbers from a concentration of larvae in rot-holes. Currently it is rare even in major ancient forests such as Windsor Forest and the New Forest, and modern records outside these are very infrequent.

Author A. E. Stubbs.

Blera fallax	A hoverfly	ENDANGERED
	Order **Diptera**	Family **Syrphidae**

Blera fallax (L., 1758).

Identification Stubbs & Falk (1983), pp. 109 and 218, pl. 10:5.

Distribution Historically in the main Caledonian pine forests of eastern Scotland, but currently only known at one site in the Spey Valley. The population is believed to be small.

Habitat and ecology Mature or over-mature native pines *Pinus sylvestris*, and possibly deciduous trees, in Caledonian forests. An old observation of unknown source or reliability is of a female laying eggs in sap exuding from beech *Fagus* and oak *Quercus* trees. Recent observations have been of adults sitting on live pine trunks and flying about the bases of such trunks where a thick mass of flakes of bark is exposed end-on at soil level. The hoverfly is related to genera which breed in dead wood, so it is possible that the larvae live between such pine-bark flakes and perhaps under similar circumstances about deciduous trees.

Status It was formerly local but widespread in the pine-woods of the eastern Highlands, but is now in danger of extinction. Its ecological requirements are unknown so it is difficult to cater for.

Threats The loss of ancient trees through forest clearance and modern forestry practice in Scotland.

Conservation	The one remaining known site is an RSPB reserve. Further survey is required to check on its biology and to find further populations.
Author	A. E. Stubbs, using additional information from Coe (1953), G. Else and I. Perry (pers. comms).

Psilota anthracina

A hoverfly **VULNERABLE**

Order **Diptera**   Family **Syrphidae**

Psilota anthracina Meigen, 1822.

Identification	Stubbs & Falk (1983), pp. 101 and 203, pl. 5:3.
Distribution	Southern England, principally the New Forest (Hampshire) and Windsor Forest (Berkshire).
Habitat and ecology	The larval ecology is unknown. Sites usually contain ancient trees so dead wood could be the breeding site (though apparently related genera feed in bulbs and herbaceous roots). The adults are normally found on hawthorn blossom *Crataegus*.
Status	A great rarity, only regularly seen at Windsor Forest. It is difficult, in the absence of meaningful ecological information, to assess the stability of its status on sites.
Author	A. E. Stubbs.

Anasimyia interpuncta

A hoverfly **VULNERABLE**

Order **Diptera**   Family **Syrphidae**

Anasimyia interpuncta (Harris, 1776) (no longer regarded as synonymous with *A. transfuga*).

Identification	Stubbs & Falk (1983), pp. 96, 97 and 191, pl. 12:8.
Distribution	Greater London, and in the fens and marshes of East Anglia and the East Midlands. A total of four sites.
Habitat and ecology	The larvae are of the rat-tailed maggot type, living an aquatic existence (details are unknown). The margins of ditches and ponds provide breeding sites.
Status	A very little-known species. Its London site has been destroyed (by industrial infilling). It occurs on Wicken Fen and has been recorded from Woodwalton Fen, but it is scarce and its management requirements are not known. In Norfolk it has been taken on one site which is grazing marsh.

Lejops vittata

A hoverfly — **VULNERABLE**

Order **Diptera** — Family **Syrphidae**

Lejops vittata (Meigen, 1822).

Identification	Stubbs & Falk (1983), pp. 99 and 197, pl. 12:5.
Distribution	Mainly coastal: the Thames estuary (Kent and Essex), the south-eastern Channel coast (East Sussex and Kent), and in Norfolk and Somerset.
Habitat and ecology	Mainly coastal grazing marshes, associated with mildly brackish ditches (especially those with sea club-rush *Scirpus maritimus* intermixed with freshwater plants). Some sites are several miles from the coast where sea club-rush survives from earlier times of more saline conditions. The larvae are unknown but are predictably of the rat-tailed maggot type adapted to aquatic conditions.
Status	In the past it was regarded as a rarity, apart from in the "Thames Marshes" where it was locally frequent. It is now much more localised and rare in the Thames estuary, but it has recently been found in small areas in some additional counties. At only one site, in Somerset, has it been seen in reasonable numbers, and then only along one short length of dyke (1983, A. P. Foster).
Threats	The extensive conversion of coastal grazing marshes to intensive cereal farming has destroyed a great deal of habitat and threatens most of the known sites. Major deepening and clearance of ditches, often with pump drainage, is associated with the eutrophication of ditches from fertiliser run-off. The Thames Barrage has resulted in extensive modification of flood embankments and ditches for many miles of coast. Saline influence is likely to weaken on most remaining sites. Nearly all sites are in areas suffering conservation problems, such as the Somerset Levels.
Conservation	Present on at least two SSSIs.
Author	A. E. Stubbs.

Parhelophilus consimilis

A hoverfly	**VULNERABLE**
Order **Diptera**	Family **Syrphidae**

Parhelophilus consimilis (Malm, 1863).

Identification
Stubbs & Falk (1983), pp. 100 and 199.

Distribution
Scattered records in England, South Wales and south-west Scotland.

Habitat and ecology
The transition between bog and fen, with pools and great reedmace *Typha latifolia*, is apparently preferred. However, the habitat does not always agree with this description. The larvae are aquatic.

Status
There are few records, either old or recent, often concerning small and vulnerable sites.

Conservation
Only one record applies to a nature reserve, run by the Herefordshire and Radnorshire Nature Trust.

Author
A. E. Stubbs.

Eristalis cryptarum

A hoverfly	**VULNERABLE**
Order **Diptera**	Family **Syrphidae**

Eristalis (Eoseristalis) cryptarum (F., 1794).

Identification
Stubbs & Falk (1983), pp. 97 and 194, pl. 11:8.

Distribution
South-west England to the New Forest and Gloucestershire.

Habitat and ecology
The larvae are of the rat-tailed maggot type adapted to aquatic conditions. Little is known of the ecology but it is believed that there may be a preference for stream sides and pond margins with a rich marsh soil and plants such as yellow flag *Iris pseudacorus*.

Status
Records are sparse and mostly old. Brown & Searle (1974) in a survey of east Dorset cited 1938 as the last known record. Recent surveys in the New Forest have not revealed the species. There has been recording effort in south-west England in recent years which, though not exhaustive, has only revealed a single specimen, in Devon.

Author
A. E. Stubbs.

Rainieria calceata	A stilt-legged fly	**ENDANGERED**
	Order **Diptera**	Family **Micropezidae**

Rainieria calceata (Fallen, 1820).

Identification
Collin (1945); see also Colyer & Hammond (1968), pl. 50:5.

Distribution
Only known from a limited part of Windsor Forest. The population fluctuates; some years few are seen but it can be frequent on a few trees on occasion.

Habitat and ecology
Forest with large, old beech trees *Fagus*. The biology is unknown, but the larvae are assumed to live in dead wood. The adults walk over the standing and fallen trunks of dead beech trees.

Status
A large and rather peculiar fly which would readily gain attention if it had been seen elsewhere, so Windsor Forest is almost certainly the only site in Britain.

Threats
A partial age-class gap in beech trees may occur in the future, reducing the quantity of dead beech to a level which may not be viable for this species, since only a small percentage of trees seem to reach the required state.

Conservation
The site is an SSSI subject to a management agreement with the Crown Estate. There is a need to clarify its life cycle and ecological requirements.

Author
A. E. Stubbs, using additional information from P. J. Chandler (pers. comm.).

Acrometopia wahlbergi	A silverfly	**VULNERABLE**
	Order **Diptera**	Family **Chamaemyiidae**

Acrometopia wahlbergi (Zetterstedt, 1846).

Identification
Cogan (1978), pp. 228-229; Seguy (1934), pp.354 and 356.

Distribution
Recorded from Lancashire (one site), and Anglesey and Gwynedd (four sites). The population size is not known, but it is highly localised within the available area of fen habitat.

Habitat and ecology
Fens with sedges (*Carex* species) and a rich botanical community. The known larvae of Chamaemyiidae are predators of homopteran bugs, but there is no information on the biology of the early stages of *Acrometopia*.

Status
This species can be frequent, but only on small areas within each fen. The single Lancashire site where it was first discovered in Britain by Sir C. H. Andrewes (Cliburn Moss) may no longer support the species, because of habitat changes associated with forestry operations.

Threats	The drainage of fens for agriculture (Wales) or forestry planting (Lancashire) would severely modify or destroy the required habitat.
Conservation	The Welsh sites are all either NNRs (Cors Erddreiniog and Cors Geirch) or SSSIs (Cors Bodeilio and Cors Goch); the last is also a North Wales Naturalists' Trust reserve.
Author	I. F. G. McLean, using additional information from A. E. Stubbs (pers. comm.).

Salticella fasciata

A snail-killing fly **VULNERABLE**

Order **Diptera** Family **Sciomyzidae**

Salticella fasciata (Meigen, 1830), p.68.

Identification	Knutson & Lyneborg (1965), p.68.
Distribution	Recorded from nine coastal dunes in southern Britain. The population size is not known, but it is very restricted in distribution within the localities where it occurs. Adults may be found at any one time in areas of a few square metres only, and not nearby in apparently identical habitat.
Habitat and ecology	In Britain confined to coastal dunes, and recorded from fixed dune grassland at Tenby, Dyfed, by Knutson *et al* (1970). The larvae have been recorded feeding on living or dead snails of the family Helicidae, and pupariate externally. There are two or three generations per year.
Status	With some records over seventy years old (localities not recently searched), this is a species with few known current localities and it is believed to be vulnerable to any loss of habitat for the reason given below.
Threats	The erosion of dune habitat by recreational pressure, and construction or modification of golf courses and other developments affecting dunes. It is likely to be particularly vulnerable because of the highly localised nature of its colonies.
Conservation	Occurs on Gibraltar Point NNR and Tenby SSSI.
Author	I. F. G. McLean.

Sciomyza dryomyzina

A snail-killing fly   **VULNERABLE**

Order **Diptera**   Family **Sciomyzidae**

Sciomyza dryomyzina Zetterstedt, 1846.

Identification   Knutson & Lyneborg (1965), p.76.

Distribution   Recorded from Conwy, Gwynedd (one locality), Oxfordshire (one locality), Suffolk (two localities) and Yorkshire (one locality), with only one example recorded from each locality. All records date from the 1920s except Port Meadow, Oxford, 3 June 1962 (K. G. V. Smith) and Dolgarrog Marsh, Conwy, 2 August 1969 (P. Skidmore).

Habitat and ecology   Marshes and water meadows. The larvae have been recorded as parasitoids of the snail *Oxyloma* in North America. (*Oxyloma pfeifferi* is a frequent species in fens and marshes in Britain but *S. dryomyzina* has not yet been reared here.) The adults fly in May and June and again in August.

Status   A rare species which must have declined owing to the drainage and agricultural improvement of its marsh and wet meadow habitats.

Threats   The drainage of wetlands.

Conservation   Port Meadow and Dolgarrog Marsh are SSSIs.

Author   I. F. G McLean.

Centrophlebomyia furcata

The Bone Skipper   **ENDANGERED +**

Order **Diptera**   Family **Piophilidae**

Centrophlebomyia furcata (F., 1794).

Identification   McAlpine (1977), p.53.

Distribution   The only known sites are Porthcawl (Mid Glamorgan) and Mount Edgecumbe Park (Cornwall).

Habitat and ecology   The habitat preferences in Britain are unknown. The adults are attracted to large carcasses (of horses, cattle, dogs, etc), especially around wounds and the skull. Adults have been recorded in spring and autumn. The larvae develop in the bone marrow and are able to leap distances of several centimetres on leaving the bone tissue, as do related *Piophila* species (hence the English name coined by Friedberg, 1981).

Status   As this species has not been recorded in Britain since 1906 there is a strong possibility that it may now be extinct.

Threats	The more hygienic practices associated with the disposal of large carcasses in Britain have resulted in the virtual disappearance of potential breeding sites.
Author	I. F. G. McLean, using additional information from Cogan & Dear (1975).

Paraclusia tigrina

VULNERABLE

Order **Diptera**   Family **Clusiidae**

Paraclusia tigrina (Fallen, 1820).

Identification	Seguy (1934), pp.351 and 353. An attractively marked species with spotted wings, the largest member of the family.
Distribution	About ten British records; scattered sites in southern England and one in South Wales. The population size is not known, but is apparently always small.
Habitat and ecology	Old trees in copses, shelter belts, hedgerows or ancient parkland, more rarely within larger woods. Believed to be univoltine, the adults flying mainly in August. The life cycle is unknown but it almost certainly breeds in dead wood. The adults are usually found on the surface of dead wood on live tree trunks, mainly beech *Fagus* but also elm *Ulmus.*
Status	It is noteworthy that this species has not been found in the large ancient forests noted for their dead-wood faunas. This is one of the few dead-wood Diptera known to prefer parkland or otherwise isolated large trees.
Threats	By inhabiting isolated or small groups of over-mature trees, this species is very vulnerable to losing its habitat through the felling or natural death of those trees. Dutch elm disease has reduced the chances of finding breeding sites, an aspect of the wider problem of the decline of large trees in the agricultural landscape. The future will be precarious in some districts.
Conservation	Occurs in three SSSIs (in only one of which are trees a reason for notification), but most sites are too small for such status. Recorded from National Trust properties in Kent and Cornwall. There is a need to consider replacement generations of trees on SSSIs.
Author	A. E. Stubbs.

Anthomyza bifasciata

VULNERABLE

Order **Diptera**
Family **Anthomyzidae**

Anthomyza bifasciata Wood, 1911.

Identification	Collin (1944).
Distribution	Formerly only known by old specimens from Hereford & Worcester. It has been recorded recently from single sites in Oxfordshire, East Sussex and Essex, and at two coastal sites in Kent. The population is usually small, more rarely abundant in a small area.
Habitat and ecology	Ditches and pondsides with the foodplant. It breeds in the seed heads of reedmace *Typha*, probably only lesser reedmace *T. angustifolia*. The adults may be swept from the seed heads.
Status	Though small, the fly is very distinctive because of its banded wings. It does appear to be genuinely rare.
Threats	Clearance of the foodplant, especially during mechanical ditch clearance; drainage.
Conservation	Within an RSPB reserve which is also an SSSI. The best recent site will be within an SSSI extension, with an NNR under negotiation.
Author	A. E. Stubbs, using additional information from Ismay (1981).

Ochthera schembrii

A shore fly

ENDANGERED

Order **Diptera**
Family **Ephydridae**

Ochthera schembrii Rondani, 1847, formerly known as *O. mantispa* Loew.

Identification	Claussen (1977), pp.516-518; Seguy (1934), p.420.
Distribution	Recorded from only one site in Cornwall (St Merryn) by G. C. Lamb in 1908, and not found since. The population size is not known, but is likely to be very small.
Habitat and ecology	Its known habitat in Britain is the edge of a freshwater stream entering the sea over a sandy substrate, but the species may not be confined to coastal situations and could occur beside streams or ponds inland. Its larval biology is unknown. Adults were found by G. C. Lamb over sand and plants at the margin of a stream entering the sea, where they would be predators of other small insects (including related Ephydridae).

Status	This species is believed to have a mainly southern European distribution and must be on the edge of its range in south-west England. The known habitat is very vulnerable to damage as a result of its limited size and distribution. One recent visit failed to locate the fly but apparently suitable habitat is still present.
Threats	Recreational activities on beaches, and the modification of stream channels for any purpose.
Author	I. F. G. McLean.

Ernoneura argus

VULNERABLE

Order **Diptera**　　　　　　　　　　Family **Scathophagidae**

Ernoneura argus (Zetterstedt, 1838).

Identification	Collin (1958), p.54.
Distribution	Known from Loch Garten and Loch Einich, Speyside (Highland); Loch Etchachan, Aberdeen (Grampian); and a lochan north of Lochavat, Lewis (Western Isles). The population size is not known, but it is locally frequent where it occurs.
Habitat and ecology	Adults have been recorded on stony lake shores, or 'hydroplaning' on the water surface, in June and July. The larval biology is unknown.
Status	This is a rare northern element in the Scottish fauna, which on present information is highly restricted in its distribution.
Threats	Loss of the shingle shore zone following any change in water level, or disturbance associated with recreational activity.
Conservation	Loch Garten is an RSPB reserve. Loch Einich is an SSSI.
Author	I. F. G. McLean, using additional information from A. C. Pont and E. C. M. d'A. Fonseca (pers. comms).

Parallelomma paridis

VULNERABLE

Order **Diptera**　　　　　　　　　　Family **Scathophagidae**

Parallelomma paridis Hering, 1923, formerly known as *Americina paridis.*

Identification	Collin (1958), p.40.
Distribution	Known from Chapel le Dale, North Yorkshire (1921), and Woodditton Wood, Cambridgeshire (1908) (Collin, 1958). The population size is not known: only two British specimens have been recorded.

Habitat and ecology	Woods where the larval foodplant occurs. The larvae mine the leaves of herb paris *Paris quadrifolia*. The adults fly in May.
Status	Woodditton Wood has been converted to a conifer plantation by the Forestry Commission. The status of the site at Chapel le Dale is unknown.
Threats	Loss of ancient woodland where the foodplant occurs, through clearance or coniferisation.
Conservation	Investigation of its current status is needed, preferably by searching for the leaf mines.
Author	I. F. G. McLean.

Chirosia montana

ENDANGERED

Order **Diptera**   Family **Anthomyiidae**

Chirosia montana Pokorny, 1893.

Identification	Collin (1955).
Distribution	Only recorded from Perth (Tayside).
Habitat and ecology	Probably open-structured woodland. Its biology is unknown, but the larvae probably live in bracken *Pteridium aquilinum* or some other fern. The adults are found in June.
Status	Originally collected in 1932, but not found in recent surveys.
Threats	The destruction of forests and of the foodplant.
Author	A. C. Pont.

Pseudomyopina moriens

VULNERABLE

Order **Diptera**   Family **Anthomyiidae**

Pseudomyopina moriens (Zetterstedt, 1845).

Identification	Hennig (1969), p.323.
Distribution	Probably confined to the high peaks of the Cairngorms (Grampian), and perhaps other parts of Scotland.
Habitat and ecology	Mountain tundra. Its biology and larvae are unknown. The adults are found in early July.
Status	Originally collected in 1951, and may be locally frequent in high mountain tundra habitats.

Threats	Habitat loss, or damage from recreational activities such as ski development leading to the loss of vegetation and soil erosion.
Conservation	Occurs within the Cairngorms NNR.
Author	A. C. Pont.

Lispocephala rubricornis

VULNERABLE

Order **Diptera**   Family **Muscidae**

Lispocephala rubricornis (Zetterstedt, 1849).

Identification	Fonseca (1968), p.68.
Distribution	Coastal, and now restricted to a few areas of unspoiled dunes: Bettyhill, Caithness (Highland); Culbin Sands, Moray (Grampian); Aberffraw, Anglesey; Oxwich, West Glamorgan; and Braunton Burrows, Devon.
Habitat and ecology	Dunes, dune slacks and dune copses, in the vicinity of water. Univoltine, the adults flying from June to early August. Its biology is unknown, but the larvae probably live in mosses and soggy vegetation in or near slow-flowing water.
Status	Genuinely rare and, like many other species in the coastal environment, under threat from the pressures of recreation requirements.
Threats	The draining of dune slacks; recreational activities and developments; afforestation.
Conservation	Oxwich and Braunton Burrows are NNRs.
Author	A. C. Pont.

BIBLIOGRAPHY

AGUESSE, P. 1968. Les Odonates. *Faune de l'Europe et du Bassin Mediterraneen, 4.* 258pp.

AIRY SHAW, H.K. 1944. *Dictyopterus (Platycis) cosnardi* Chevr. (Col., Cantharidae, Lycinae) new to Britain. *Entomologist's Monthly Magazine, 80:* 204-205.

AIRY SHAW, H.K. 1961. *Phosphaenus hemipterus* (Goeze) (Col., Lampyridae) in Ashdown Forest. *Entomologist's Monthly Magazine, 97:* 182.

ALFORD, D.V. 1975. *Bumblebees.* London: Davis-Poynter. xii + 352pp.

ALLEN, A.A. 1936. *Adelocera quercea* Herbst (Col., Elateridae) established as British. *Entomologist's Monthly Magazine, 72:* 267-269.

ALLEN, A.A. 1937a. Two species of Coleoptera new to science. *Entomologist's Monthly Magazine, 73:* 51-54.

ALLEN, A.A. 1937b. *Limoniscus violaceus,* Mull. (Elateridae), a genus and species of Coleoptera new to Britain. *Entomologist's Record & Journal of Variation, 49:* 110.

ALLEN, A.A. 1938. *Elater ruficeps* Muls.: a beetle new to Britain. *Entomologist's Monthly Magazine, 74:* 172.

ALLEN, A.A. 1942. Some records of *Aleochara* and *Anthicus* spp. (Col.). *Entomologist's Monthly Magazine, 78:* 117-118.

ALLEN, A.A. 1945. *Globicornis nigripes* F. (Col., Dermestidae) rediscovered in Windsor Forest and reinstated as British. *Entomologist's Monthly Magazine, 81:* 84-85.

ALLEN, A.A. 1947a. *Hypulus quercinus* Quens. (Col., Melandryidae) not extinct in Britain. *Entomologist's Monthly Magazine, 83:* 9.

ALLEN, A.A. 1947b. *Globicornis nigripes* F. (Col., Dermestidae) in Britain: corrections and additions. *Entomologist's Monthly Magazine, 83:* 171.

ALLEN, A.A. 1950. *Laemophloeus monilis* F. (Col., Cucujidae) recaptured in Sussex. *Entomologist's Monthly Magazine, 86:* 70.

ALLEN, A.A. 1953. Two remarkable discoveries in the British Coleoptera. *Entomologist's Monthly Magazine, 89:* 148-149.

ALLEN, A.A. 1954. *Gastrallus immarginatus* Mull., not *laevigatus* Oliv. (Col., Anobiidae), a British species. *Entomologist's Monthly Magazine, 90:* 16.

ALLEN, A.A. 1955a. *Rhizophagus simplex* Reit. (Col., Rhizophagidae) in Oxfordshire. *Entomologist's Monthly Magazine, 91:* 129.

ALLEN, A.A. 1955b. *Procraerus tibialis* Lac. (Col., Elateridae), *Hylotrupes bajulus* L. and *Obrium brunneum* F. (Cerambycidae), etc., in Hants. *Entomologist's Monthly Magazine, 91:* 140.

ALLEN, A.A. 1956a. Maple confirmed as the host-tree of *Gastrallus immarginatus* Mull. (Col., Anobiidae) at Windsor. *Entomologist's Monthly Magazine, 92:* 42.

ALLEN, A.A. 1956b. *Copris lunaris* L. (Col., Scarabaeidae) in the Box Hill area of Surrey. *Entomologist's Monthly Magazine, 92:* 382.

ALLEN, A.A. 1958. A comment on the recurrence in Britain of *Platydema violaceum* F. (Col., Tenebrionidae). *Entomologist's Monthly Magazine, 94:* 235.

ALLEN, A.A. 1960a. The history and present-day status of *Gnorimus variabilis* L. (Col., Scarabaeidae) in Britain. *Entomologist's Record & Journal of Variation, 72:* 129-132.

ALLEN, A.A. 1960b. A new capture of *Cryptocephalus 10-maculatus* L. (Col., Chrysomelidae) in Scotland. *Entomologist's Monthly Magazine, 96:* 271.

ALLEN, A.A. 1962. A short account of *Emus hirtus* L. in Britain. *Entomologist's Record & Journal of Variation, 74:* 219-221.

ALLEN, A.A. 1963. The occurrence of *Teretrius picipes* F. (Col., Histeridae) at Oxshott, Surrey: with short notes on the other British records. *Entomologist's Monthly Magazine, 99:* xix.

ALLEN, A.A. 1964a. *Megapenthes lugens* Redt. (Col., Elateridae) in Hants., Gloucs., etc., with additional notes. *Entomologist's Monthly Magazine, 100:* 95-96.

ALLEN, A.A. 1964b. A postcript on *Emus hirtus* L. *Entomologist's Record & Journal of Variation, 76:* 145-146.

ALLEN, A.A. 1964c. *Harpalus honestus* Duft. (Col., Carabidae) confirmed as British. *Entomologist's Monthly Magazine, 100:* 155-157.

ALLEN, A.A. 1966. The rarer Sternoxia (Col.) of Windsor Forest. *Entomologist's Record & Journal of Variation, 78:* 14-23.

ALLEN, A.A. 1967. A review of the status of certain Scarabaeoidea (Col.) in the British fauna: with the addition to our list of *Onthophagus similis* Scriba. *Entomologist's Record & Journal of Variation, 79:* 201-206.

ALLEN, A.A. 1968. Two additions to the British species of *Atomaria* Steph. (Col., Cryptophagidae), with notes on others of the genus in Britain. *Entomologist's Record & Journal of Variation, 80:* 318-326.

ALLEN, A.A. 1969a. Notes on some British Staphylinidae (Col.). 1. – The genus *Scopaeus* Er., with the addition of *S. laevigatus* Gyll. to our list. *Entomologist's Monthly Magazine, 104* (1968): 198-207.

ALLEN, A.A. 1969b. Notes on some British serricorn Coleoptera, with adjustments to the list. 1.- Sternoxia. *Entomologist's Monthly Magazine, 104* (1968): 208-216.

ALLEN, A.A. 1969c. Notes on some British Scydmaenidae (Col.), with corrections to the List. *Entomologist's Record & Journal of Variation, 81:* 239-246.

ALLEN, A.A. 1970a. *Scopaeus minutus* Er. (Col., Staphylinidae) in Devon. *Entomologist's Monthly Magazine, 105* (1969): 162.

ALLEN, A.A. 1970b. Notes on various little-known, doubtful, or misidentified British Staphylinidae (Col.). *Entomologist's Monthly Magazine, 105* (1969): 193-196.

ALLEN, A.A. 1970c. *Emoporus caucasicus* Lind. and *Leperisinus orni* Fuchs (Col., Scolytidae) in Britain. *Entomologist's Monthly Magazine, 105* (1969): 245-249.

ALLEN, A.A. 1970d. An overlooked Sussex record of *Cryptocephalus 10-maculatus* L. (Col., Chrysomelidae), and *C. biguttatus* Scop. in Surrey. *Entomologist's Monthly Magazine, 106:* 120.

ALLEN, A.A. 1971a. Notes on *Omophron limbatum* F. (Col., Carabidae) in Britain. *Entomologist's Monthly Magazine, 106* (1970): 221-223.

ALLEN, A.A. 1971b. *Procraerus tibialis* Lac. (Col., Elateridae) in Wilts. and Herts. *Entomologist's Monthly Magazine, 107:* 12.

ALLEN, A.A. 1971c. *Microlomalus parallelepipedus* Hbst. (Col., Histeridae) in Kent. *Entomologist's Monthly Magazine, 107:* 80.

ALLEN, A.A. 1971d. British Coleoptera: corrections and supplementary notes, including the addition of *Axinotarsus marginalis* Lap. (Melyridae) to our list. *Entomologist's Record & Journal of Variation, 83:* 46-51.

ALLEN, A.A. 1973. *Melandrya barbata* F. (Col., Serropalpidae) in Surrey, with further notes. *Entomologist's Monthly Magazine, 108* (1972): 239.

ALLEN, A.A. 1974a. *Rhinoncus albicinctus* Gyll. (Col., Curculionidae) new to Britain. *Entomologist's Monthly Magazine, 109* (1973): 188-190.

ALLEN, A.A. 1974b. *Bledius crassicollis* Bsd. & Lac. (Col., Staphylinidae) reinstated in the British list. *Entomologist's Monthly Magazine, 109* (1973): 234-235.

ALLEN, A.A. 1975. Two species of *Anaspis* (Col.: Mordellidae) new to Britain: with a consideration of the status of *A. hudsoni* Donis., etc. *Entomologist's Record & Journal of Variation, 87:* 269-274.

ALLEN, A.A. 1977. *Microglotta picipennis* (Gyll.) (Col., Staphylinidae): another Devonshire locality. *Entomologist's Monthly Magazine, 112* (1976): 154.

ALLEN, A.A. 1979. *Longitarsus rutilus* (Ill.) (Col., Chrysomelidae) in East Cornwall. *Entomologist's Monthly Magazine, 114* (1978): 62.

ALLEN, A.A. 1980. *Peritrechus gracilicornis* Puton (Hem., Lygaeidae) well established in the Studland area, Dorset. *Entomologist's Monthly Magazine, 116:* 65-66.

ALLEN, A.A. & LLOYD, R.W. 1951. *Pyrrhidium sanguineum* L. (Col., Cerambycidae) as a British species. *Entomologist's Monthly Magazine, 87:* 157-158.

ANDREWES, C.H. 1946. *Andrena vaga* Panz. (Hym., Apidae) in Sussex. *Entomologist's Monthly Magazine, 82:* 39.

ANGUS, R.B. 1964. Some Coleoptera from Cumberland, Westmorland and the nothern part of Lancashire. *Entomologist's Monthly Magazine, 100:* 61-69.

ANGUS, R.B. 1971. Revisional notes on *Helophorus* F. (Col., Hydrophilidae). 3: Species resembling *H. strigifrons* Thoms. and some further notes on species resembling *H. minutus* F. *Entomologist's Monthly Magazine, 106* (1970): 238-256.

ANGUS, R.B. 1976. A preliminary note on the British species of *Graphoderus* Sturm, with the additions of *G. bilineatus* Degeer and *G. zonatus* Hoppe to the British list. *Balfour-Browne Club Newsletter* No. 1: 1-3.

ANGUS, R.B. 1978. The British species of *Helophorus. Balfour-Browne Club Newsletter,* No. 11: 2-15.

ANON., 1980. *Atlas of the bumblebees of the British Isles.* Cambridge: Institute of Terrestrial Ecology. 32pp.

ANON., 1981. *The conservation of butterflies.* London: Nature Conservancy Council. 28pp.

APPLETON, D. 1970. *Pterostichus aterrimus* (Herbst) (Col., Carabidae) in the New Forest. *Entomologist's Monthly Magazine, 105* (1969): 179.

APPLETON, D. 1972. *Eucnemis capucina* Ahr. (Col., Eucnemidae) in the New Forest. *Entomologist's Monthly Magazine, 108:* 2.

APPLETON, D. 1974. *Corymbites castaneus* (L.) (Col., Elateridae) in the Isle of Wight. *Entomologist's Monthly Magazine, 109* (1973): 202.

APPLETON, D. 1975. Two interesting rediscoveries in the Isle of Wight Coleoptera during 1973. *Entomologist's Monthly Magazine, 110* (1974): 122.

ARCHER, M.E. (ed.) 1979. *Provisional atlas of the insects of the British Isles: Part 9, Hymenoptera: Vespidae, Social wasps.* 2nd edition. Huntingdon: Biological Records Centre.

ARNOLD, G. 1905. Aculeate Hymenoptera in the New Forest. *Entomologist's Monthly Magazine, 41:* 261-262.

ASHE, G.H. 1944. Devonshire and Sussex Coleoptera in 1942-43. *Entomologist's Monthly Magazine, 80:* 70.

ASHE, G,H, 1952. Coleoptera at Nethy Bridge, Inverness-shire. *Entomologist's Monthly Magazine, 88:* 165-168.

ATTY, D.B. 1970. Gloucestershire beetles: a few records and an appeal. *Entomologist's Monthly Magazine, 105:* 199.

ATTY, D.B. 1983. *Coleoptera of Gloucestershire.* Cheltenham: privately published. 136pp.

BADCOCK, R.M. 1978. The *Hydropsyche fulvipes – instabilis – saxonica* (Trichoptera) complex in Britain and the recognition of *H. siltalai* Dohler. *Entomologist's Monthly Magazine, 113* (1977): 23-29.

BAKER, D.B. 1965. Two bees new to Britain (Hym., Apoidea). *Entomologist's Monthly Magazine, 100* (1964): 279-286.

BALACHOWSKY, A.S. (ed.) 1963. *Entomologie appliquee a l'agriculture. Tome 1: Coleopteres.* Part 2. Paris: Masson & Cie. 1391pp.

BALFOUR-BROWNE, F. 1940. *British water beetles.* Vol. 1. London: Ray Society. 375pp.

BALFOUR-BROWNE, F. 1950. *British water beetles.* Vol. 2. London, Ray Society. xx + 394pp.

BALFOUR-BROWNE, F. 1953. Coleoptera: Hydradephaga. *Handbooks for the identification of British insects, 4* (3).

BALFOUR-BROWNE, F. 1958. *British water beetles.* Vol. 3. London: Ray Society. liii + 210pp.

BANNISTER, R.T. 1969. *Halticus macrocephalus* Fieber (Hem., Miridae) in Cornwall. *Entomologist's Monthly Magazine, 104* (1968): 284.

BARNARD, P.C. 1985. An annotated check-list of the Trichoptera of Britain and Ireland. *Entomologist's Gazette, 36:* 31-45.

BARRETT, C.G. 1891. *Coleophora leucanipennella*, Hb.: an addition to the British fauna. *Entomologist's Monthly Magazine, 27:* 302.

BARRETT, K.E.J. (ed.) 1979. *Provisional atlas of the insects of the British Isles: Part 5, Hymenoptera: Formicidae, Ants.* 2nd edition. Huntingdon: Biological Records Centre.

BEDWELL, E.C. 1909. Coleoptera captured in various localities in 1908. *Entomologist's Monthly Magazine, 55:* 163-165.

BEDWELL, E.C. 1923. *Prionychus* (*Eryx*) *fairmairei* Reiche: a southern record. *Entomologist's Monthly Magazine, 59:* 236-237.

BEDWELL, E.C. 1926. *Lymexylon navale* L. at Windsor. *Entomologist's Monthly Magazine, 62:* 240.

BEIRNE, B.P. 1952. *British pyralid and plume moths.* London: Warne. 208pp.

BENICK, L. 1952. Pilzkafer und Kaferpilze. *Acta Zoologica Fennica, 70.*

BILLUPS, T.R. 1881. *Dufourea vulgaris*, Schk., at Woking. *Entomologist's Monthly Magazine, 18:* 161.

BILLUPS, T.R. 1884. *Odynerus reniformis*, Gmel., at Chertsey. *Entomologist's Monthly Magazine, 21:* 68-69.

BILTON, D.T. 1984. Four water beetles (Col., Dytiscidae) new to Cumberland, including *Hydroporus scalesianus* Stephens. *Entomologist's Monthly Magazine, 120:* 251.

BISCHOFF, H. 1927. *Biologie der Hymenopteren eine Naturgeschichte der Hautfluegler.* Berlin: Springer Verlag. vii + 598pp.

BLAIR, K.G. 1930. *Aglyptinus agathidioides* sp. n. (Fam. Silphidae), a new British beetle. *Entomologist's Monthly Magazine, 66:* 7-8.

BLAIR, K.G. 1935. *Bagous frit* Herbst in Britain, with notes on some other species of the genus. *Entomologist's Monthly Magazine, 71:* 249-253.

BLAIR, K.G. 1933. *Aleochara inconspicua* Aube reinstated in the British list of Coleoptera. *Entomologist's Monthly Magazine, 69:* 250.

BLAIR, K.G. 1934. A new species of *Cathormiocerus* from Britain (Col.). *Entomologist's Monthly Magazine, 70:* 26-28.

BLAIR, K.G. 1948. *Philanthus triangulum* F. (Hym., Sphecidae) in the Isle of Wight. *Entomologist's Monthly Magazine, 84:* 240.

BLAIR, K.G. & DONISTHORPE, H. St J. 1943. *Hypebaeus flavipes* F. (not *Ebaeus abietinus* Abeille) (Col., Malachiidae) in Britain: a correction. *Entomologist's Monthly Magazine, 79:* 16.

BOLTON, B. & COLLINGWOOD, C.A. 1975. Hymenoptera: Formicidae. *Handbooks for the identification of British insects, 6* (3c).

BRADLEY, J.D. & FLETCHER, D.S. 1979. *A recorder's log book or label list of British butterflies and moths.* London: Curwen Books. 136pp.

BRADLEY, J.D., TREMEWAN, W.G. & SMITH, A. 1973. *British tortricoid moths, Cochylidae and Tortricidae: Tortricinae.* London: Ray Society. viii + 251pp.

BRADLEY, J.D., TREMEWAN, W.G. & SMITH A. 1979. *British tortricoid moths, Tortricidae: Olethreutinae.* London: Ray Society. viii + 336pp.

BRAY, R.P. 1967. The taxonomy of the larvae and pupae of the British Phryganeidae (Trichoptera). *Journal of Zoology, London, 153:* 223-244.

BRENDELL, M.J.D. 1975. Coleoptera: Tenebrionidae. *Handbooks for the identification of British insects, 5* (10).

BRIAN, M.V. 1977. *Ants.* London: Collins. 223pp.

BRINDLE, A. 1964. Notes on *Anabolia* (*Phacopteryx*) *brevipennis* (Curtis), and *Ironoquia* (*Caborius*) *dubia* (Stephens), (Trichoptera, Limnephilidae). *Entomologist's Record & Journal of Variation, 76:* 289-292.

BRITTON, E.B. 1956. Coleoptera: Scarabaeoidea. *Handbooks for the identification of British insects, 5* (11).

BROMLEY, P.J. 1947. Biological observations on *Chrysomela tremula* F. (Col., Chrysomelidae) at Oxford. *Entomologist's Monthly Magazine, 83:* 57-58.

BROOKS, M. & KNIGHT, C. 1982. *A complete guide to British butterflies.* London: Jonathan Cape. 157pp.

BROWN, A.J. & SEARLE, C.A. 1974. Syrphidae (Diptera) in Dorset. *Entomologist's Gazette, 25:* 111-123.

BROWN, C. & CROWSON, R.A. 1980. Observations on scydmaenid (Col.) larvae with a tentative key to the main British genera. *Entomologist's Monthly Magazine, 115* (1979): 49-59.

BROWN, E.S. 1965. Notes on the migration and direction of flight of *Eurygaster* and *Aelia* species (Hemiptera, Pentatomoidea) and their possible bearing on invasions of cereal crops. *Journal of Animal Ecology, 34:* 93-107.

BROWN, S.C.S. 1954. The Britsh Lyonetiidae. *Proceedings & Transactions of the South London Entomological & Natural History Society, 1952-53:* 110-116, pl. 9.

BROWN, S.C.S. 1963. The early history of *Emus hirtus* (L.) in Britain. *Entomologist's Record & Journal of Variation, 75:* 87-88.

BROWN, S.C.S. 1982. *Pyrrhocoris apterus* L. (Hem.: Pyrrhocoridae) in Dorset. *Entomologist's Record & Journal of Variation, 94:* 96.

BROWN, V.K. 1983. *Grasshoppers. Naturalists' Handbooks* No. 2. Cambridge: University Press. 65pp.

BUCK, F.D. 1952. *Melandrya dubia* Schall. (Col., Serropalpidae) not a British insect. *Entomologist's Monthly Magazine, 88:* 189.

BUCK, F.D. 1954. Coleoptera: Lagriidae to Meloidae. *Handbooks for the identification of British insects, 5* (9).

BUCK, F.D. 1955. A provisional list of the Coleoptera of Epping Forest. *Entomologist's Monthly Magazine, 91:* 174-192.

BUCKLAND, P.C. & JOHNSON, C. 1983. *Curimopsis nigrita* (Palm) (Coleoptera: Byrrhidae) from Thorne Moors, South Yorkshire. *Naturalist, Hull, 108:* 153-154.

BUNTING, W. 1955. Water beetles at Thorne, Yorkshire. *Entomologist's Monthly Magazine, 91:* 85.

BURTON, J.A. 1984. Bibliography of Red Data Books (Part 1. Animal Species). *Oryx, 18:* 61-64.

BUTLER, E.A. 1923. *A biology of the British Hemiptera-Heteroptera.* London: Witherby. 682pp.

BUTTERFLIES UNDER THREAT TEAM. 1986. The management of chalk grassland for butterflies. *Focus on Nature Conservation,* No. 17. Peterborough: Nature Conservancy Council. 80pp.

CAMERON, M. 1917. On the occurrence of *Trogophloeus schneideri* Ganglb. in Britain. *Entomologist's Monthly Magazine, 53:* 156-157.

CAREY RIGGALL, E. 1944. Additions to the list of Lincolnshire Coleoptera. *Entomologist's Monthly Magazine, 80:* 74-75.

CARR, J.W. 1916. *The invertebrate fauna of Nottinghamshire.* Nottingham: Bell. 618pp.

CARTER, I.S., OWEN, J.A. & TAYLOR, S. 1980. *Haploglossa picipennis* (Gyll.) (Col., Staphylinidae) and other beetles from an osprey's nest in Speyside. *Entomologist's Monthly Magazine, 116:* 70.

CHAMBERS, V.H. 1949. The Hymenoptera Aculeata of Bedfordshire. *Transactions of the Society for British Entomology, 9:* 197-252.

CHAMPION, G.C. 1908. *Aleochara crassiuscula* Sahlb., a British insect. *Entomologist's Monthly Magazine, 44:* 194-195.

CHAMPION, G.C. & LLOYD, R.W. 1909. Some interesting British insects. *Entomologist's Monthly Magazine, 45:* 196-197.

CHAMPION, G.C. & LLOYD, R.W. 1910. Some interesting British insects (II). *Entomologist's Monthly Magazine, 46:* 1-3, pl. 1: 3.

CHAMPION, H.G., CHAMPION, R.J. & MORICE, F.D. 1914. *Homonotus* (*Pompilus*) *sanguinolentus*, F., in Surrey, with notes on the characters of the male and the distribution and nomenclature of the genus. *Entomologist's Monthly Magazine, 50:* 270-273.

CHAMPION, R.J. 1915. *Homonotus sanguinolentus* F., in Surrey: a correction. *Entomologist's Monthly Magazine, 51:* 43.

CHANDLER, P.J. 1974. Additions and corrections to the British List of Platypezidae (Diptera), incorporating a revision of the Palaearctic species of *Callomyia* Meigen. *Proceedings & Transactions of the British Entomological & Natural History Society, 7:* 1-32.

CHELMICK, D.G. (ed.) 1979. *Provisional atlas of the insects of the British Isles: Part 7, Odonata: Dragonflies.* 2nd edition. Huntingdon: Biological Records Centre.

CHELMICK, D., HAMMOND, C., MOORE, N. & STUBBS, A. 1980. *The conservation of dragonflies.* London: Nature Conservancy Council. 24pp.

CHINERY, M. 1973. *A field guide to the insects of Britain and northern Europe.* London: Collins. 352pp.

CHITTY, A.J. 1903. *Nomada guttulata,* Schk., *Psen concolor,* Dalb., and other aculeates from East Kent. *Entomologist's Monthly Magazine, 39:* 282.

CHVALA, M., LYNEBORG, L. & MOUCHA, J. 1972. *The horse flies of Europe (Diptera, Tabanidae).* Copenhagen: Entomological Society of Copenhagen. 500pp., 8pls.

CLAPHAM, A.R., TUTIN, T.G. & WARBURG, E.F. 1981. *Excursion flora of the British Isles.* 3rd edition. Cambridge: University Press. 499pp.

CLARIDGE, M.F. & STADDON, B.W. 1960. *Stenelmis canaliculata* Gyll. (Col., Elmidae): A species new to the British list. *Entomologist's Monthly Magazine, 96:* 141-144.

CLAUSSEN, P.J. 1977. A revision of the Nearctic, Neotropical and Palearctic species of the genus *Ochthera,* including one Ethiopian species and one new species from India. *Transactions of the American Entomological Society, 103:* 451-530.

COE, R.L. 1953. Diptera: Syrphidae. *Handbooks for the identification of British insects, 10* (1).

COE, R.L. 1966. Diptera: Pipunculidae. *Handbooks for the identification of British insects, 10* (2c).

COE, R.L., FREEMAN, P. & MATTINGLEY, P.F. 1950. Diptera 2. Nematocera: Tipulidae to Chironomidae. *Handbooks for the identification of British insects, 9* (2).

COGAN, B.H. 1978. A revision of *Acrometopia* Schiner and closely related genera. *Beitrage zur Entomologie, 28:* 223-250.

COGAN, B.H. & DEAR, J.P. 1975. Additions and corrections to the list of British acalypterate Diptera. *Entomologist's Monthly Magazine, 110* (1974): 173-181.

COIFFAIT, H. 1960. Les *Astenus* d'Europe et de la region Mediterraneene (Coleopteres Staphylinidae). *Bulletin de la Societe d'Histoire Naturelle de Toulouse, 95:* 48-99.

COLE, J.H. 1981. *Chrysopilus erythrophthalmus* Loew (Diptera: Rhagionidae) new to Britain. *Entomologist's Gazette, 32:* 275-277.

COLLIER, R. 1986. The conservation of the chequered skipper in Britain. *Focus on Nature Conservation,* No. 16, Peterborough: Nature Conservancy Council. 16pp.

COLLIN, J.E. 1944. The British species of Anthomyzidae (Diptera). *Entomologist's Monthly Magazine, 80:* 265-272.

COLLIN, J.E. 1945. British Micropezidae (Diptera). *Entomologist's Record & Journal of Variation, 57:* 115-119.

COLLIN, J.E. 1955. Genera and species of Anthomyiidae allied to *Chirosia* (Diptera). *Journal of the Society for British Entomology, 5:* 94-100.

COLLIN, J.E. 1958. A short synopsis of the British Scatophagidae (Diptera). *Transactions of the Society for British Entomology, 13:* 37-56.

COLLIN, J.E. 1961. *British flies: Vol. 6, Empididae.* Cambridge: University Press. 782pp.

COLLIN, J.E. 1962. A species of *Xylophagus* (Diptera, Xylophagidae) new to Britain. *Entomologist, 95:* 272-274.

COLLINGWOOD, C.A. 1954. Rare ants (Hym., Formicidae) in Dorset. *Entomologist's Monthly Magazine, 90:* 43-44.

COLLINS, G.B. 1946. *Andrena vaga* Panz. (Hym., Apidae) in Kent. *Entomologist's Monthly Magazine, 82:* 245.

COLLINS, N.M. & MORRIS, M.G. 1985. *Threatened swallowtail butterflies of the world. The IUCN Red Data Book.* Gland, Switzerland: IUCN.

COLYER, C.N. & HAMMOND, C.O. 1968. *Flies of the British Isles.* 2nd edition. London: Warne. 384pp.

COOMBS, C.W. & WOODROFFE, G.E. 1955a. A revision of the British species of *Cryptophagus* (Herbst) (Coleoptera: Cryptophagidae). *Transactions of the Royal Entomological Society of London, 106:* 237-282.

COOMBS, C.W. & WOODROFFE, G.E. 1955b. An annotated check list of the British species of *Cryptophagus* (Herbst) (Col., Cryptophagidae). *Entomologist's Monthly Magazine, 91:* 249-250.

COOMBS, C.W. & WOODROFFE, G.E. 1962. A note on the nomenclature, taxonomy and distribution of certain European species of *Cryptophagus* Herbst (Coleoptera: Cryptophagidae). *Proceedings of the Royal Entomological Society of London (B), 31:* 103-106.

COOTER, J. 1970. *Platycis cosnardi* Chevr. (Col., Lycidae), the third British record. *Entomologist's Monthly Magazine, 105* (1969): 171.

COOTER, J. 1973. (Exhibit of Coleoptera). *Proceedings & Transactions of the British Entomological & Natural History Society, 6:* 26.

COOTER, J. 1976. A note on some beetles captured in Moccas Park, Herefordshire, during 1975. *Entomologist's Record & Journal of Variation, 88:* 319-320.

COOTER, J. 1981a. A further note on *Pyrrhidium sanguineum* (L.) (Col., Cerambycidae). *Entomologist's Monthly Magazine, 116* (1980): 104.

COOTER, J. 1981b. A note on *Ernoporus caucasicus* Lind. (Col., Scolytidae) in Britain. *Entomologist's Monthly Magazine, 166* (1980): 112.

COOTER, J. 1981c. (Editorial note). *Coleopterist's Newsletter,* No.5: 3.

COOTER, J. 1982. Richmond Park field meeting. *Coleopterist's Newsletter,* No.9: 4.

CORBET, P.S. 1962. *A biology of dragonflies.* London: Witherby. 247pp. (Reprinted 1983 by Classey, Faringdon).

CORBET, P.S., LONGFIELD, C. & MOORE, N.W. 1960. *Dragonflies.* London: Collins. 260pp. (Reprinted 1985).

COX, D. 1947. *Lytta vesicatoria* L. (Col., Meloidae) and *Zeugophora flavicollis* Marsh. (Col., Chrysomelidae) in Essex. *Entomologist's Monthly Magazine, 83:* 104.

CRIBB, J. 1946. *Phosphaenus hemipterus* Goeze (Col., Lampyridae) in Sussex. *Entomologist's Monthly Magazine, 82:* 254.

CROSSLEY, R. & NORRIS, A. 1976. *Bembidion humerale* Sturm (Col., Carabidae) new to Britain. *Entomologist's Monthly Magazine, 111* (1975): 59-60.

DALTRY, H.W. 1958. *Philonthus dimidiatipennis* Er. (Col., Staphylinidae) in Britain. *Entomologist's Monthly Magazine, 94:* 66.

DANDY, J.E. 1969. *Watsonian vice-counties of Great Britain.* London: Ray Society. 2 maps + booklet.

DAY, M.C. 1979. Nomenclatural studies on the British Pompilidae (Hymenoptera). *Bulletin of the British Museum (Natural History) (Entomology), 38:* 1-26.

DAY, M.C. (In preparation). Spider wasps (Hymenoptera, Pompilidae). *Handbooks for the identification of British insects, 6* (4).

DEMPSTER, J.P. & HALL, M.L. 1980. An attempt at re-establishing the swallowtail butterfly at Wicken Fen. *Ecological Entomology, 5:* 327-334.

DEMPSTER, J.P., KING, M.L. & LAKHANI, K.H. 1976. The status of the swallowtail butterfly in Britain. *Ecological Entomology, 1:* 71-84.

DICKER, G.H.L. 1979. *Passaloecus clypealis* Forster (Hym., Sphecidae) in Kent. *Entomologist's Monthly Magazine, 114* (1978): 129.

DICKSON, R. 1976. *A lepidopterist's handbook.* Hanworth, Middlesex: Amateur Entomologists' Society. 136pp.

DIECKMANN, L. 1964. Die mitteleuropaischen Arten aus der Gattung *Bagous* Germ. *Entomologische Blatter fur Biologie and Systematik der Kafer, 60:* 88-111.

DIECKMANN, L. 1971. *Ceutorhynchus* – Studien. *Beitrage zur Entomologie, 21:* 581-595.

DIECKMANN, L. 1972. Beitrage zur Insektenfauna der DDR: Coleoptera – Curculionidae: Ceutorhynchinae. *Beitrage zur Entomologie, 22:* 3-128.

DISNEY, R.H.L. 1975. A midge (Dipt., Ceratopogonidae) new to Britain that is abundant in the limestone pavement of the Yorkshire Pennines. *Entomologist's Monthly Magazine, 110* (1974): 227-228.

DOBSON, R.M. 1964. The third instar larva of *Aleochara inconspicua* Aube (Col., Staphylinidae), a parasite of the wheat bulb fly *Leptohylemyia coarctata* (Fall.) (Dipt., Muscidae). *Entomologist's Monthly Magazine, 100:* 210-211.

DOLLING, W.R. 1971. *Macroplax preyssleri* (Fieber) (Hem., Lygaeidae) new to Britain. *Entomologist's Monthly Magazine, 106* (1970): 155-156.

DONISTHORPE, H.St J. 1918. *Caenocara subglobosa* Muls., a species of Coleoptera new to Britain. *Entomologist's Monthly Magazine, 54:* 55-56.

DONISTHORPE, H.St J. 1922. A few notes on Coleoptera in 1921. Entomologist's *Monthly Magazine, 58:* 52-55.

DONISTHORPE, H.St J.1925. *Dryophthorus corticalis* Pk., a genus and species of Coleoptera new to Britain. *Entomologist's Monthly Magazine, 61:* 182.

DONISTHORPE, H.St J. 1927. *The guests of British ants.* London: Routledge. xxiii + 244pp.

DONISTHORPE, H.St J. 1928. *Dorcatoma dresdensis* Herbst and *D. serra* Pz.: two new British insects. *Entomologist's Monthly Magazine, 64:* 196-199.

DONISTHORPE, H.St J. 1931. Coleoptera, etc., in Moorhens' and Swans' nests. *Entomologist's Record & Journal of Variation, 43:* 177.

DONISTHORPE, H.St J. 1936. *Gastrallus laevigatus* Ol. (Col., Anobiidae), a genus and species of Coleoptera new to Britain. *Entomologist's Monthly Magazine, 72:* 200.

DONISTHORPE, H.St J. 1939. *A preliminary list of the Coleoptera of Windsor Forest.* London: Nathaniel Lloyd. 126pp.

DONISTHORPE, H.St J. & CHAPMAN, T.A. 1913. Notes on the capture of *Claviger longicornis,* Mull., and a description of its supposed larva. *Entomologist's Record & Journal of Variation, 25:* 290-294, pl.24.

DONISTHORPE, H.St J. & TOMLIN, J.R. le B. 1934. *Ebaeus abietinus* Abeille (Malachiidae, Col.), a beetle new to Britain. *Entomologist's Monthly Magazine, 70:* 198-199.

DONISTHORPE, H.St J. & WALKER, J.J. 1931. *An annotated list of the additions to the British coleopterous fauna.* (Reprinted from *Entomologist's Monthly Magazine.*) London: Nathaniel Lloyd. 103pp, 8pls.

DRANE, A.B. 1985. A second Northants. locality for *Ernoporus caucasicus* Lindemann (Col., Scolytidae) and notes on some other beetles. *Entomologist's Monthly Magazine, 121:* 107.

DRISCOLL, R.J. 1978. A preliminary report on the distribution of water beetles in Broadland dykes. *Balfour-Browne Club Newsletter,* No.8: 3-14.

DRUMMOND, D.C. 1956. Food plants of *Chrysolina violacea* (Mull.), *C. haemoptera* (L.), *C. crassicornis* (Hell.) and *C. polita* (L.) (Col., Chrysomelidae). *Entomologist's Monthly Magazine, 92:* 368.

DUFFY, E.A.J. 1952. Coleoptera: Cerambycidae. *Handbooks for the identification of British insects, 5*(12).

DUFFY, E.A.J. 1953. *A monograph of the immature stages of British and imported timber beetles (Cerambycidae).* London: British Museum (Natural History). 350pp.

EDINGTON, J.M. 1964. The taxonomy of British polycentropid larvae (Trichoptera). *Proceedings of the Zoological Society of London, 143:* 281-300.

EDINGTON, J.M. & HILDREW, A.G. 1981. A key to the caseless caddis larvae of the British Isles. *Scientific Publications of the Freshwater Biological Association* No. 43.

EDWARDS, F.W. 1913. Notes on British Mycetophilidae. *Transactions of the Entomological Society of London, 1913*: 334-382.

EDWARDS, F.W. 1925. British fungus-gnats (Diptera, Mycetophilidae). With a revised generic classification of the family. *Transactions of the Entomological Society of London, 1924*: 505-670.

EDWARDS, F.W. 1937. Craneflies in Mulgrave Woods. *Naturalist, Hull, 1937*: 253-254.

EDWARDS, F.W. 1938a. British short-palped craneflies. Taxonomy of adults. *Transactions of the Society for British Entomology, 5*: 1-168.

EDWARDS, F.W. 1938b. A new species of the genus *Nephrotoma* Mg., with notes on the species of the *flavescens* group. (Diptera, Tipulidae). *Encyclopedie Entomologique, ser. B2. Diptera, 9*: 97-101.

ELGAR, H. 1901a. Rare aculeate Hymenoptera at Halling, Kent. *Entomologist's Monthly Magazine, 37:* 17.

ELGAR, H. 1901b. *Andrena polita,* Smith, in Kent. *Entomologist's Monthly Magazine, 37:* 277.

ELSE, G.R. (In preparation). Bees (Hymenoptera, Apoidea). *Handbooks for the identification of British insects, 6.*

ELSE, G., FELTON, J. & STUBBS A. 1979. *The conservation of bees and wasps.* London: Nature Conservancy Council. 13pp.

van EMDEN, F.I. 1941. Larvae of British beetles. II. A key to the British Lamellicornia larvae. *Entomologist's Monthly Magazine, 77:* 117-127, 181-192.

van EMDEN, F.I. 1943. Larvae of British beetles. IV. Various small families. *Entomologist's Monthly Magazine, 79:* 209-223, 259-270.

van EMDEN, F.I. 1945. Larvae of British beetles. V. Elateridae. *Entomologist's Monthly Magazine, 81:* 13-37.

EMMET, A.M. 1976. *Phyllocnistis xenia* Hering – its foodplant and life history. *Entomologist's Record & Journal of Variation, 88:* 306.

EMMET, A.M. (ed.) 1979. *A field guide to the smaller British Lepidoptera.* London: British Entomological & Natural History Society. 271pp.

ENTWISTLE, P.F. & STUBBS, A.E. 1983. *Preliminary atlas of the hoverflies (Diptera: Syrphidae) of the British Isles.* Huntingdon: Biological Records Centre.

FARRELL, L. 1975. A survey of the status of the chequered skipper butterfly (*Carterocephalus palaemon*) (Pallas) (Lep., Hesperiidae) in Britain, 1973-1974. *Entomologist's Gazette, 26:* 148-149.

FARROW, R.A. & LEWIS, E.S. 1971. *Omophron limbatum* (F.) (Col., Carabidae) an addition (or restoration?) to the British list. *Entomologist's Monthly Magazine, 106* (1970): 219-221.

FELTON, J.C. 1963. The Hymenoptera in the Maidstone Museum Collection. *Transactions of the Kent Field Club, 1*(4): 171-190.

FISHER, D. 1977. Identification of adult females of *Tinodes* in Britain (Trichoptera: Psychomyiidae). *Systematic Entomology, 2*: 105-110.

FLETCHER, T.B. 1944. (Exhibit and note on *Cryptocephalus primarius* Harold.) *Proceedings of the Royal Entomological Society of London (C), 9*: 23-24.

FLINT, J.H. 1957. *Aphodius brevis* Er. (Col., Scarabaeidae) in Yorkshire. *Entomologist's Monthly Magazine, 93*: 12.

FONSECA, E.C.M.d'A. 1968. Diptera, Cyclorrhapha, Calyptrata: Section (b) Muscidae. *Handbooks for the identification of British insects, 10* (4b).

FONSECA, E.C.M.d'A. 1978. Diptera, Orthorrhapha, Brachycera: Dolichopodidae. *Handbooks for the identification of British insects, 9* (5).

FORD, L.T. 1946. The Psychidae. *Proceedings & Transactions of the South London Entomological & Natural History Society, 1945-46*: 103-110, pl.11.

FORSTER, H.W. 1955. *Epuraea terminalis* Man. and *Rhizophagus simplex* Reit. (Col., Nitidulidae) in Epping Forest, Essex. *Entomologist's Monthly Magazine, 91*: 6.

FORSTER, H.W. 1956. *Spercheus emarginatus* Schall. (Col., Hydrophilidae) re-discovered in Great Britain. *Entomologist's Monthly Magazine, 92*: 330.

FOSTER, A.P. 1984. Modern water beetle records from the Somerset Levels and Moors. *Balfour-Browne Club Newsletter*, No. 30: 11-23.

FOSTER, G.N. 1972. The aquatic Coleoptera of East Sussex. *Entomologist's Gazette, 23*: 25-60.

FOSTER, G.N. 1981. Atlas of British water beetles. Preliminary edition – part 1. *Balfour-Browne Club Newsletter*, No. 22: 1-18.

FOSTER, G.N. 1982. Notes on rare Dytiscidae (Coleoptera) in Norfolk. *Transactions of the Norfolk and Norwich Naturalists' Society, 26*: 3-10.

FOSTER, G.N. 1983. Atlas of British water beetles. Preliminary edition – part 2. *Balfour-Browne Club Newsletter*, No. 27: 1-23.

FOSTER, G.N. 1984. Atlas of British water beetles. Preliminary edition – part 3. *Balfour-Browne Club Newsletter*, No. 31: 1-22.

FOSTER, G.N. 1985. Atlas of British water beetles. Preliminary edition – part 4. Balfour-Browne Club Newsletter, No. 35: 1-22.

FOWLER, W.W. 1887-91. *The Coleoptera of the British islands.* 5 vols. London: Reeve.

FOWLER, W.W. & DONISTHORPE, H.St J. 1913. *The Coleoptera of the British islands.* Vol. 6. London: Reeve. xiii + 351pp.

FREUDE, H., HARDE, K.W. & LOHSE, G.A. (eds.) 1964-83. *Die Kafer Mitteleuropas.* 11 vols. Krefeld: Goecke & Evers.

FRIEDBERG, A. 1981. Taxonomy, natural history and immature stages of the bone-skipper, *Centrophlebomyia furcata* (Fabricius) (Diptera: Piophilidae, Thyreophorina). *Entomologica Scandinavica, 12*: 320-326.

FRISBY, G.E. 1928. The Hymenoptera of the Rochester District. *Rochester Naturalist, 6* (No. 131): 90-101.

FRISBY, G.E. 1934. *Andrena polita* Smith male at Halling, Kent. *Entomologist's Monthly Magazine, 70*: 136.

FRYER, J.C.F. & FRYER, H.F. 1923a. *Sitones gemellatus* Gyll. in Britain. *Entomologist's Monthly Magazine, 59*: 80-81.

FRYER, J.C.F. & FRYER, H.F. 1923b. *Dibolia cynoglossi* Koch in Cambridgeshire. *Entomologist's Monthly Magazine, 59*: 89.

GOATER, B. 1974. *The butterflies and moths of Hampshire and the Isle of Wight.* Faringdon: Classey. 439pp.

GOFFE, E.R. 1931. British Tabanidae (Diptera) with an account of the principal variation. *Transactions of the Entomological Society of the South of England, 6*: 43-114.

GORHAM, H.S. 1870. Occurrence in Britain of *Aleochara maculata* (C. Brisout). *Entomologist's Monthly Magazine, 7*: 136.

GOURREAU, J.M. 1974. Systematique de la tribu des Scymnini (Coccinellidae). *Annales de Zoologie – Ecologie Animale*, (hors serie): 1-223.

GUICHARD, K.M. 1971. A bee new to Britain from Wiltshire – *Andrena lathyri* Alfken (Hym., Apidae). *Entomologist, 104:* 40-42.

GUICHARD, K.M. 1973. *Melitta dimidiata* (Morawitz) (Hym., Melittidae) again in Wiltshire. *Entomologist's Monthly Magazine, 109:* 39.

HAES, E.C.M. (ed.) 1979. *Provisional atlas of the insects of the British Isles: Part 6, Orthoptera: Grasshoppers and crickets*. 2nd edition. Huntingdon: Biological Records Centre.

HAINES, F.H. 1934. *Odynerus (Lionotus) herrichi* Sauss. in Dorset. *Entomologist's Monthly Magazine, 70:* 117.

HALL, M.L. 1981. *Butterfly monitoring scheme*. Huntingdon: Institute of Terrestrial Ecology. 14pp.

HALLETT, H.M. 1952. The Coleoptera of Herefordshire. First supplement. *Transactions of the Woolhope Naturalists' Field Club, 1951*: 279-282.

HALL-SMITH, D.H., BRADLEY, J.D. & FLETCHER, D.S. 1983. *A recorder's log book or label list of British butterflies and moths: Index*. Leicester: Leicestershire Museums Service. 59pp.

HALSTEAD, D.G.H. 1963. Coleoptera: Histeroidea. *Handbooks for the identification of British insects, 4* (10).

HAMM, A.H. 1901. *Andrena hattorfiana*, Fab., and *Nomada armata*, H.-Schff., near Oxford. *Entomologist's Monthly Magazine, 37:* 16.

HAMM, A.H. 1903. *Nomada guttulata*, Schenck, in south Devon. *Entomologist's Monthly Magazine, 39:* 300.

HAMM, A.H. 1926. Diptera. In *The natural history of the Oxford district*: 248-279. Walker, J.J. (ed.). Oxford. 336p.

HAMM, A.H. & RICHARDS, O.W. 1926. The biology of the British Crabronidae. *Transactions of the Entomological Society of London, 74:* 297-331.

HAMM, A.H. & RICHARDS, O.W. 1930. The biology of the British fossorial wasps of the families Mellinidae, Gorytidae, Philanthidae, Oxybelidae, and Trypoxylidae. *Transactions of the Entomological Society of London, 78:* 95-131.

HAMMOND, C.O. 1983. *The dragonflies of Great Britain and Ireland*. 2nd edition, revised by R. Merritt. Colchester: Harley Books. 116pp.

HAMMOND, P.M. 1979. Beetles in Epping Forest. In: The wildlife of Epping Forest. *Essex Naturalist*, No. 4: 43-60.

HARDE, K.W. 1984. *A field guide in colour to beetles*. Ed. P.M. Hammond. London: Octopus Books. 334pp.

HARDING, P.T. 1982. A further note on *Ernoporus caucasicus* Lind. (Col., Scolytidae) in Britain. *Entomologist's Monthly Magazine, 118:* 166.

HARWOOD, P. 1918. *Scaphium immaculatum* Oliv. An additional genus and species to our list of British Coleoptera. *Entomologist's Monthly Magazine, 54:* 131-132.

HARWOOD, P. 1928. *Longitarsus nigerrimus* Gyll. in Dorset. *Entomologist's Monthly Magazine, 64:* 11.

HARWOOD, P. 1929. *Trox perlatus* Goeze in Dorset: an addition to the British coleopterous fauna. *Entomologist's Monthly Magazine, 65:* 171.

HEAL, N.F. 1984. A second British locality for *Phyllocnistis xenia* Hering. *Entomologist's Record & Journal of Variation, 96:* 98.

HEATH, J. (ed.) 1976. *The moths and butterflies of Great Britain and Ireland. Vol. 1. Micropterigidae – Heliozelidae*. London: Curwen Press (now Colchester: Harley Books). 343pp.

355

HEATH, J. 1981. *Threatened Rhopalocera (butterflies) in Europe. Nature and Environment Series* No. 23. Strasbourg: Council of Europe. 157pp.

HEATH, J. 1983. The insects of the Yellow Balsam, *Impatiens noli-tangere. Proceedings & Transactions of the British Entomological & Natural History Society, 16:* 125-131.

HEATH, J. & EMMET, A.M. (eds.). 1979. *The moths and butterflies of Great Britain and Ireland. Vol. 9. Sphingidae – Noctuidae (Noctuinae – Hadeninae).* London: Curwen Books (now Colchester: Harley Books). 288pp.

HEATH, J. & EMMET, A.M. (eds.). 1983. *The moths and butterflies of Great Britain and Ireland. Vol. 10. Noctuidae (Cuculliinae – Hypeninae) - Agaristidae.* Colchester: Harley Books. 459pp.

HEATH, J. & EMMET, A.M. (eds.) 1985. *The moths and butterflies of Great Britain and Ireland. Vol. 2. Cossidae-Heliozelidae.* Colchester: Harley Books. 460pp.

HEATH, J. & LECLERCQ, J. (eds.) 1981. *Provisional atlas of the invertebrates of Europe. Maps 1-27.* Huntingdon: Biological Records Centre, & Gembloux: Faculte des Sciences Agronomiques.

HEATH, J., POLLARD, E. & THOMAS, J.A. 1984. *Atlas of butterflies in Britain and Ireland.* Harmondsworth, Middlesex: Viking. 162pp.

HENNING, W. 1969. In *Die Fliegen der Palaearktischen Region, 63a.* Lindner, E. (ed.).

HICKIN, N.E. 1953. *Tinodes pallidula* McLachlan (Trichoptera, Psychomyidae). A second British station. *Entomologist, 86:* 113.

HICKIN, N.E. 1967. *Caddis larvae: Larvae of the British Trichoptera.* London: Hutchinson. 476pp.

HILDREW, A.G. & MORGAN, J.C. 1974. The taxonomy of the British Hydropsychidae (Trichoptera). *Journal of Entomology (B), 43:* 217-229.

HILEY, P.D. 1976. The identification of British limnephilid larvae (Trichoptera). *Systematic Entomology, 1:* 147-167.

HODGE, P.J. 1978. Two rare water beetles on the Lewes Levels, East Sussex. *Balfour-Browne Club Newsletter,* No. 7: 3.

HODGE, P.J. 1979. *Graptodytes flavipes* (Ol.) (Col., Dytiscidae) in East Sussex. *Entomologist's Monthly Magazine, 113* (1977): 242.

HOLLAND, D.G. 1972. A key to the larvae, pupae and adults of the British species of Elminthidae. *Scientific Publications of the Freshwater Biological Association,* No. 26.

HOLLAND, D.G. 1980. Distribution of Elmidae/Elminthidae. *Balfour-Browne Club Newsletter,* No. 16: 1-12.

HOLMEN, M. 1981. Status over Danmarks Haliplidae (Coleoptera) med bemaerkninger om zoogeografi og autoekologi. *Entomologiske Meddelelser, 49:* 1-14.

HOLMES, P.F. 1963. Trichoptera. *Proceedings of the Leeds Philosophical & Literary Society (Scientific Section), 9:* 31-35.

HORION, A. 1961. Clavicornia 2, Teredilia, Coccinellidae. *Faunistik der Mitteleuropaischen Kafer.* Vol. 8. Uberlingen. xv + 375pp.

HORSFIELD, D. & FOSTER, G.N. 1982. *Hydroporus scalesianus* Stephens and *Laccornis oblongus* (Stephens) (Col. Dytiscidae) in Hart Bog, County Durham. *Entomologist's Monthly Magazine, 119:* 62.

HORTON, G.A.N. 1980. *Pyrrhidium sanguineum* L. and *Criocephalus rusticus* L. (Col.: Longicornia) in Monmouthshire. *Entomologist's Record & Journal of Variation, 92:* 52.

HOWARTH, T.G. 1973a. *South's British butterflies.* London: Warne. 210pp, 48 pls. (Abridged edition reprinted 1984 as *Colour identification guide to butterflies of the British Isles* by Viking, Harmondsworth, Middlesex.)

HOWARTH, T.G. 1973b. The conservation of the Large Blue butterfly (*Maculinea arion* L.) in West Devon and Cornwall. *Proceedings and Transactions of the British Entomological and Natural History Society, 5:* 121-126.

HUGGINS, H.C. 1962. *Emus hirtus* L. in the Southend district. *Entomologist's Record & Journal of Variation, 74:* 279.

HUNT, O.D. 1965. Status and conservation of the large blue butterfly, *Maculinea arion* L. In *Symposium on the conservation of invertebrates*: 35-44. Huntingdon: Nature Conservancy.

HUNTER, F.A. 1977. Ecology of pinewood beetles. In *Native pinewoods of Scotland*: 42-55. Bunce, R.G.H. & Jeffers, J.N.R. (eds.) Cambridge: Institute of Terrestrial Ecology.

HUTSON, A.M., ACKLAND, D.M. & KIDD, L.N. 1980. Diptera, Nematocera: Mycetophilidae (Bolitophilinae to Manotinae). *Handbooks for the identification of British insects, 9* (3).

HUTSON, A.M. & STUBBS, A.E. 1974. *Limonia* (*Dicranomyia*) *omissinervis* de Meijere (Diptera: Tipulidae) new to Britain, and the identity of *L.* (*D.*) *patens* in Britain. *Entomologist's Gazette, 25:* 297-301.

HUTSON, A.M. & VANE-WRIGHT, R.I. 1969. Corrections and additions to the list of British Nematocera (Diptera) since Kloet and Hincks' 'A check list of British insects' (1945). Part 1. *Entomologist's Gazette, 20:* 231-256.

ISMAY, J.W. 1981. Some Diptera from Wytham Wood. *Entomologist's Monthly Magazine, 117:* 26.

JACKSON, P.H. 1907. Coleoptera in North Wales. *Entomologist's Monthly Magazine, 43:* 251.

JACOBS, S.N.A. 1951. The British Oecophoridae (Part 2). *Proceedings & Transactions of the South London Entomological & Natural History Society, 1949-50:* 187-203, pl.19.

JENKINSON, P.J. 1908. Notes on certain Mycetophilidae, including several species new to the British list. *Entomologist's Monthly Magazine, 44:* 129-133, 151-154.

JOHNSON, C. 1962a. The deletion of the Herefordshire record for *Aphodius niger* (Col., Scarabaeidae). *Entomologist's Monthly Magazine, 98:* 88.

JOHNSON, C. 1962b. The scarabaeoid (Coleoptera) fauna of Lancashire and Cheshire and its apparent changes over the last 100 years. *Entomologist, 95:* 153-165.

JOHNSON, C. 1967. Taxonomic notes on British Coleoptera. No.6 *Stenus glacialis* Heer (Staphylinidae). *Entomologist, 100:* 22-24.

JOHNSON, C. 1974. Studies on the genus *Corticaria* Marsham (Col., Lathridiidae). Part 1. *Annales Entomologici Fennici, 40:* 97-107.

JOHNSON, C. 1975. Five species of Ptiliidae (Col.) new to Britain, and corrections to the British list of the family. *Entomologist's Gazette, 26:* 211-223.

JOHNSON, C. 1976a. The identity of the British *Prionychus fairmairei* Reiche (Col., Alleculidae). *Entomologist's Gazette, 27:* 112.

JOHNSON, C. 1976b. Synonymic and other notes on British Coleoptera. *Entomologist's Monthly Magazine, 111* (1975): 111-113.

JOHNSON, C. 1978. Notes on Byrrhidae (Col.): with special reference to, and a species new to, the British fauna. *Entomologist's Record & Journal of Variation, 90:* 141-147.

JOINT COMMITTEE FOR THE CONSERVATION OF BRITISH INSECTS. 1973a. British Macrolepidoptera: rare and endangered species and forms. *Entomologist's Monthly Magazine, 108* (1972): 179-180.

JOINT COMMITTEE FOR THE CONSERVATION OF BRITISH INSECTS. 1973b. British Odonata and Orthoptera: rare and endangered species. *Entomologist's Monthly Magazine, 109:* 50.

JOINT COMMITTEE FOR THE CONSERVATION OF BRITISH INSECTS. 1974. Rare and endangered species – general list. *Entomologist's Monthly Magazine, 109* (1973): 250-251.

JONES, H.P. 1925-26. The Hymenoptera – Aculeata of Hampshire. *Entomologist's Record & Journal of Variation, 37-38,* Supplement. 14pp.

JONES, H.P. 1932. The Aculeate Hymenoptera of Hampshire: supplementary list. *Transactions of the Entomological Society of the South of England, 8:* 108-116.

JOY, N.H. 1930. Coleoptera in birds' nests, including a species of *Microglossa* new to Britain. *Entomologist's Monthly Magazine, 66:* 41-42.

JOY, N.H. 1932. *A practical handbook of British beetles.* 2 vols. London: Witherby. (Reprinted 1976 by Classey, Faringdon).

KAUFMANN, R.R.U. 1948. Notes on the distribution of the British longicorn Coleoptera. *Entomologist's Monthly Magazine, 84:* 66-85.

KEEN, D. 1977. *Collecting and studying dragonflies (Odonata).* AES leaflet No.12. 24pp.

KENDALL, P. 1982. *Bromius obscurus* (L.) in Britain (Col., Chrysomelidae). *Entomologist's Monthly Magazine, 117* (1981): 233-234.

KEVAN, D.K. 1959. The British species of the genus *Sitona* Germar (Col., Curculionidae). *Entomologist's Monthly Magazine, 95:* 251-261.

KEVAN, D.K. 1967. The British species of the genus *Longitarsus* Latreille (Col., Chrysomelidae). *Entomologist's Monthly Magazine, 103:* 83-110.

KEYS, J.H. 1916. *Anchonidium unguiculare* Aube: a genus and species of Coleoptera new to the British list. *Entomologist's Monthly Magazine, 52:* 112-113.

KEYS, J.H. 1921. *Cathormiocerus attaphilus* Bris.: an addition to the British Coleoptera. *Entomologist's Monthly Magazine, 57:* 100-102, pl. 1.

KIMMINS, D.E. 1942. *Cyrnus insolutus* McL. (Trichoptera), new to Britain. *Entomologist, 75:* 66-68.

KIMMINS, D.E. 1952. *Agrypnetes crassicornis* McLachlan (Fam. Phryganeidae), a caddis fly new to Britain. *Annals & Magazine of Natural History, 12th ser., 5:* 1039-1043.

KIMMINS, D.E. 1957. Notes on some British species of the genus *Hydropsyche* (Trichoptera). *Entomologist's Gazette, 8:* 199-210.

KIRBY, W. 1802. *Monographia Apum Angliae.* Vol. 2. Ipswich: J. Raw. xxii + 388pp.

KLEMPERER, H.G. 1982a. Normal and atypical nesting behaviour of *Copris lunaris* (L.): comparison with related species (Coleoptera, Scarabaeidae). *Ecological Entomology, 7:* 69-83.

KLEMPERER, H.G. 1982b. Parental behaviour in *Copris lunaris* (Coleoptera, Scarabaeidae): care and defence of brood balls and nest. *Ecological Entomology, 7:* 155-167.

KLOET, G.S. & HINCKS, W.D. 1964-78. A check list of British insects. 2nd edition. 5 parts. *Handbooks for the identification of British insects, 11.*

KNUTSON, L.V. & LYNEBORG, L. 1965. Danish acalypterate flies. 3. Sciomyzidae (Diptera). *Entomologiske Meddelelser, 34:* 61-101.

KNUTSON, L.V., STEPHENSON, J.W. & BERG, C.O. 1970. Biosystematic studies of *Salticella fasciata* (Meigen), a snail-killing fly (Diptera: Sciomyzidae). *Transactions of the Royal Entomological Society of London, 122:* 81-100.

KULLENBERG, B. 1944. Studien uber die Biologie der Capsiden. *Zoologiska Bidrag fran Uppsala, 23* (Suppl.). 522pp.

LAST, H.R. 1963. Notes on *Quedius molochinus* Gravenhorst (Col., Staphylinidae) with the addition of two species new to the British list. *Entomologist's Monthly Magazine, 99:* 43-45.

LEAR, N.W. 1986. The capture of *Emus hirtus* (Linn.) (Col.: Staphylinidae) in West Gloucestershire (Vice County 34). *Entomologist's Record & Journal of Variation, 98:* 135-136.

LEFKOVITCH, L.P. 1959. A revision of the European Laemophloeinae (Coleoptera: Cucujidae). *Transactions of the Royal Entomological Society of London, 111:* 95-118.

LEPNEVA, S.G. 1971. *Fauna of the USSR. Trichoptera Vol. 2 No. 2. Larvae and pupae of Integripalpia.* Jerusalem: Israel Program for Scientific Translations.

LEVEY, B. 1977. Coleoptera: Buprestidae. *Handbooks for the identification of British insects, 5* (1b).

LEYS, R. 1978. On the biology of *Andrena ferox* Smith (Hymenoptera, Aculeata: Andrenidae). *Entomologische Berichten, 38:* 58-60.

LINDROTH, C.H. 1960. On *Agonum sahlbergi* Chd. (Col., Carabidae). *Entomologist's Monthly Magazine, 96:* 44-47.

LINDROTH, C.H. 1972. Taxonomic notes on certain British groundbeetles (Col., Carabidae). *Entomologist's Monthly Magazine, 107* (1971): 209-223.

LINDROTH, C.H. 1974. Coleoptera: Carabidae. *Handbooks for the identification of British insects, 4* (2).

LINSSEN, E. 1959. *Beetles of the British Isles.* 2 vols. London: Warne.

LLOYD, R.W. 1953. *Ostoma ferrugineum* L. (Col., Clavicornia, Ostomidae) new to Britain. *Entomologist's Monthly Magazine, 89:* 251.

LUFF, M.L. 1982. *Preliminary atlas of British Carabidae (Coleoptera).* Huntingdon: Biological Records Centre.

LUMHOLDT, O. 1975-76. The Sphecidae (Hymenoptera) of Fennoscandia and Denmark. 2 parts. *Fauna Entomologica Scandinavica, 4.* 452pp.

MACAN, T.T. 1965. A key to British water bugs (Hemiptera – Heteroptera). 2nd edition. *Scientific Publications of the Freshwater Biological Association,* No.16.

MACAN, T.T. 1973. A key to the adults of the British Trichoptera. *Scientific Publications of the Freshwater Biological Association,* No.28.

MACAN, T.T 1982. *The study of stoneflies, mayflies and caddis flies.* Hanworth, Middlesex: Amateur Entomologists' Society. 44pp.

MacNULTY, B.J. 1971. An introduction of the study of Acari – Insecta associations. *Proceedings & Transactions of the British Entomological & Natural History Society, 4:* 46-70.

MAILLARD, Y.-P. 1970. Etude comparee de la construction du cocon de ponte chez *Hydrophilus piceus* L. et *Hydrochara caraboides* L. (insecte Coleopt. Hydrophilidae). *Bulletin de la Societe Zoologique de France, 95:* 71-84.

MAITLAND, P.S. 1963. *Ecological studies on the fauna of the River Endrick.* PhD thesis, University of Glasgow.

MALICKY, H. 1983. *Atlas of European Trichoptera.* The Hague: Junk. 298pp.

MALICKY, H. 1984. The distribution of *Hydropsyche guttata* Pictet and *H. bulgaromanorum* Malicky (Trichoptera: Hydropsychidae), with notes on their bionomics. *Entomologist's Gazette, 35:* 257-264.

MALLOCH, J.R. 1904. Some rare aculeates at Rochester. *Entomologist's Monthly Magazine, 40:* 87.

MANEVAL, H. 1936. Nouvelles notes sur divers hymenopteres et leurs larves. *Revue Francaise d'Entomologie, 3:* 18-32.

MARSHALL, J.E. 1978a. Trichoptera: Hydroptilidae. *Handbooks for the identification of British insects, 1* (14a).

MARSHALL, J.E. (ed.) 1978b. Provisional atlas of the insects of the British Isles: *Part 8, Trichoptera, Hydroptilidae: Caddisflies (part 1).* Huntingdon: Biological Records Centre.

MASSEE, A.M. 1945. Abundance of *Labidostomis tridentata* L. (Col., Chrysomelidae) in Kent. *Entomologist's Monthly Magazine, 81:* 164-165.

MASSEE, A.M. 1964. *Some of the more interesting Coleoptera (beetles) and Hemiptera – Heteroptera (plant bugs) recorded at Moccas Deer Park, Moccas, Herefordshire.* Manuscript report to Nature Conservancy. 8pp.

MATTHEWS, A. 1868. On some species of Trichopterygia new to the British list. *Entomologist's Monthly Magazine, 5:* 9-13.

McALPINE, J.F. 1977. A revised classification of the Piophilidae, including 'Neottiophilidae' and 'Thyreophoridae' (Diptera: Schizophora). *Memoirs of the Entomological Society of Canada* No.103. 66pp.

MENDEL, H. 1979. *Prionychus melanarius* (Germ.) (Col., Tenebrionidae) in Staverton Park, Suffolk, a third British locality. *Entomologist's Monthly Magazine, 114* (1978): 190.

MEYRICK, E. 1928. *A revised handbook of British Lepidoptera.* London: Watkins & Doncaster. 914pp. (Reprinted 1968 and 1970 by Classey, Hampton, Middlesex).

MILLS, N.J. 1981. Essential and alternative foods for British Coccinellidae (Coleoptera). *Entomologist's Gazette, 32:* 197-202.

MOORE, N.W. 1980. *Lestes dryas* Kirby – a declining species of dragonfly (Odonata) in need of conservation: notes on its status and habitat in England and Ireland. *Biological Conservation, 17:* 143-148.

MORGAN, D. 1984. Cuckoo-wasps. Hymenoptera, Chrysididae. *Handbooks for the identification of British insects, 6* (5).

MORICE, F.D. 1901. Hymenopterological notes. *Entomologist's Monthly Magazine, 37:* 96-98.

MORICE, F.D. 1906. Nidification of *Odynerus reniformis*, Gmel., near Chobham. *Entomologist's Monthly Magazine, 42:* 216-220.

MORLEY, C. 1897. *Nomada guttulata*, Schenck, at Ipswich. *Entomologist's Monthly Magazine, 33:* 280.

MORLEY, C. 1920. Collecting fungus-gnats. *Entomologist, 53:* 83-89.

MORRIS, M.G. 1963. Two rare scarabaeid beetles rediscovered in the Suffolk Breckland. *Transactions of the Suffolk Naturalists' Society, 12:* 245-247.

MORTIMER, C.H. 1908a. *Nomada guttulata* at Swanage, Dorset. *Entomologist's Monthly Magazine, 44:* 186.

MORTIMER, C.H. 1908b. *Odynerus basalis* in Dorset. *Entomologist's Monthly Magazine, 44:* 236.

MORTIMER, C.H. 1913. *Dufourea halictula* (Nyl.) at Byfleet, Surrey. *Entomologist's Monthly Magazine, 49:* 214-215.

NASH, D.R. 1975. *Silpha carinata* Herbst – a remarkable re-discovery in the British Coleoptera. *Entomologist's Record & Journal of Variation, 87:* 285-288.

NASH, D.R. 1977. *Silpha carinata* Herbst (Col.: Silphidae) confirmed as a British breeding species. *Entomologist's Record & Journal of Variation, 89:* 305-308.

NASH, D.R. 1979. *Agabus brunneus* (F.) (Col., Dytiscidae) in Wiltshire. *Entomologist's Monthly Magazine, 114* (1978): 30.

NASH, D.R. 1980. *Leptophloeus clematidis* (Erichson) (Col., Cucujidae) discovered in Suffolk. *Entomologist's Record & Journal of Variation, 92:* 120-121.

NASH, D.R. 1982. *Prionychus ater* (Germ.) (Col., Tenebrionidae) in Suffolk – a further record. *Entomologist's Monthly Magazine, 118:* 144.

NAU, B.S. 1979. Two plant bugs new to Britain, *Placochilus seladonicus* (Fall.) and *Campylomma annulicornis* (Sig.) (Heteroptera, Miridae). *Entomologist's Monthly Magazine, 114* (1978): 157-159.

NAU, B.S. 1980. *Tuponia carayoni* Wagner (Hem., Miridae) new to Britain. *Entomologist's Monthly Magazine, 116:* 83-84.

NEVINSON, E.B. 1904. Aculeate Hymenoptera at Lyme Regis. *Entomologist's Monthly Magazine, 40:* 13-14.

NEVINSON, E.B. 1916. Aculeate Hymenoptera and Chrysididae at Wicken. *Entomologist's Monthly Magazine, 52:* 90-91.

NEWBERY, E.A. 1902. A revision of the British species of *Bagous*, Schoen. *Entomologist's Record & Journal of Variation, 14:* 149-156.

NEWTON, H.C.F. 1934. On the biology of *Psylliodes hyoscyami* Linn. (Chrysomelidae, Coleoptera), the henbane flea-beetle, with descriptions of the larval stages. *Annals of Applied Biology, 21:* 153-161.

NICHOLSON, G.W. 1921. *Cryptocephalus biguttatus* Scop. on *Erica tetralix. Entomologist's Monthly Magazine, 57:* 36-37.

NURSE, C.G. 1913. Two species of aculeate Hymenoptera new to Britain. *Entomologist's Monthly Magazine, 49:* 83-84.

O'CONNOR, J.P. 1980. *Limnephilus pati* sp. n. (Trichoptera: Limnephilidae), a caddisfly new to Great Britain and Ireland. *Irish Naturalists' Journal, 20:* 129-133.

O'CONNOR, J.P. & BARNARD, P.C. 1981. *Limnephilus tauricus* Schmid (Trichoptera: Limnephilidae) new to Great Britain, with a key to the *L. hirsutus* (Pictet) group in the British Isles. *Entomologist's Gazette, 32:* 115-119.

OLBERG, G. 1959. *Das Verhalten der Solitaren Wespen Mitteleuropas (Vespidae, Pompilidae, Sphecidae).* Berlin: Veb Deutscher Verlag der Wissenschaften. xiii + 402pp.

OLDROYD, H. 1969. Diptera, Brachycera: Tabanoidea and Asiloidea. *Handbooks for the identification of British insects, 9* (4).

OLDROYD, H. 1970. Diptera 1. Introduction and key to families. 3rd edition. *Handbooks for the identification of British insects, 9* (1).

OMER-COOPER, J., PERKINS, M.G.L. & TOTTENHAM, C.E. 1928. The Coleoptera of Wicken Fen. II. Geodephaga. In *The natural history of Wicken Fen, 4:* 277-297. Gardiner, J.S. (ed.). Cambridge: Bowes & Bowes.

OMER-COOPER, J. & TOTTENHAM, C.E. 1932. The Coleoptera of Wicken Fen. V. Staphylinidae – Ipidae. In *The natural history of Wicken Fen, 6:* 516-538. Gardiner, J.S. (ed.). Cambridge: Bowes & Bowes.

d'ORCHYMONT, A. 1952. *Bulletin du Musee Royale d'Histoire Naturelle de Belgique, 18* (39): 1-16.

OWEN, J.A. 1981. Six beetles apparently new to Windsor Forest, Berkshire. *Entomologist's Monthly Magazine, 117:* 96.

OWEN, J.A. 1982a *Cryptophagus falcozi* Roubal (Col., Cryptophagidae) in Windsor Forest. *Entomologist's Monthly Magazine, 118:* 22.

OWEN, J.A. 1982b. *Anaspis schilskyana* Csiki (Col., Scraptiidae) at Moccas Park, Hereford. *Entomologist's Monthly Magazine, 118:* 68.

OWEN, J.A. 1984. *Bembidion virens* Gyll. (Col., Carabidae) in Easter Ross. *Entomologist's Monthly Magazine, 120:* 258.

PACKER, L. 1983. The nesting biology and social organisation of *Lasioglossum (Evylaeus) laticeps* (Hymenoptera, Halictidae) in England. *Insectes Sociaux, 30:* 367-375.

PALM, T. 1951. Die Holz- und Rindenkafer der norschwedischen Laubbaume. *Meddelanden fran Statens Skogsforskningsinstitut, 5:* 40.

PALM, T. 1959. Die Holz- und Rindenkafer der Sud- und Mittelschwedischen Laubbaume. *Opuscula Entomologica,* Supplementum *16.*

PALMER, M. 1981. Relationship between species richness of macrophytes and insects in some water bodies in the Norfolk Breckland. *Entomologist's Monthly Magazine, 117:* 35-46.

PARRY, J. 1979. *Emus hirtus* Linnaeus (Col.: Staphylinidae) at Canterbury in 1950. *Entomologist's Record & Journal of Variation, 91:* 102.

PEACOCK, E.R. 1977. Coleoptera: Rhizophagidae. *Handbooks for the identification of British insects, 5* (5a).

PEARCE, E.J. 1926. A list of the Coleoptera of Dorset. *Proceedings of the Dorset Natural History & Antiquarian Field Club, 47:* 51-128.

PEARCE, E.J. 1957. Coleoptera: Pselaphidae. *Handbooks for the identification of British insects, 4* (9).

PEARCE, E.J. 1971. *Bibloplectus tenebrosus* (Reitter) in Yorkshire (Col., Pselaphidae). *Entomologist's Monthly Magazine, 106* (1970): 173.

PELHAM-CLINTON, E.C. 1966. *Nemotaulius punctatolineatus* (Retzius), a caddis-fly new to the British Isles (Trichoptera, Limnephilidae). *Entomologist's Gazette, 17:* 5-8.

PELHAM-CLINTON, E.C. 1976. *Phyllocnistis xenia* Hering, 1936, a recent addition to the British list of Lepidoptera. *Entomologist's Record & Journal of Variation, 88:* 161-164.

PERKINS, R.C.L. 1917. Note on an old specimen of *Andrena vaga* Panz. (*ovina* Kl.), a species not recorded as British. *Entomologist's Monthly Magazine, 53:* 236-237.

PERKINS, R.C.L. 1919a. Note on a peculiarity in the burrows of *Halictus maculatus* Sm. *Entomologist's Monthly Magazine, 55:* 160-161.

PERKINS, R.C.L. 1919b. The British species of *Andrena* and *Nomada*. *Transactions of the Entomological Society of London, 1919:* 218-319, pls 11-15.

PERKINS, R.C.L. 1923. The Aculeate Hymenoptera of Devon. *Transactions of the Devonshire Association for the Advancement of Science, Literature and Art, 55:* 188-241.

PERKINS, R.C.L. 1924. The Aculeate Hymenoptera of Gloucestershire and Somerset. *Proceedings of the Bristol Naturalists' Society*, 4th ser., *6:* 133-160.

PERRING, F.H. & FARRELL, L. 1983. *British Red Data Books: 1. Vascular plants.* 2nd edition. Lincoln: Royal Society for Nature Conservation. 99pp.

PHILP, E.G. 1973. *Omophron limbatum* F. and other Coleoptera new to Kent. *Entomologist's Monthly Magazine, 108* (1972): 211.

POPE, R.D. 1953. Coleoptera: Coccinellidae & Sphindidae. *Handbooks for the identification of British insects, 5* (7).

POPE, R.D. 1973. The species of *Scymnus* (s. str.), *Scymnus* (*Pullus*) and *Nephus* (Col., Coccinellidae) occurring in the British Isles. *Entomologist's Monthly Magazine, 109:* 3-39.

PORTEVIN, G. 1934. Histoire naturelle des Coleopteres de France. 3. Polyphaga: Heteromera, Phytophaga. *Encyclopedie Entomologique, 17.*

RAGGE, D.R. 1965. *Grasshoppers, crickets and cockroaches of the British Isles.* London: Warne. 299pp.

RATCLIFFE, D. (ed.) 1977. *A nature conservation review.* 2 vols. Cambridge: University Press.

REID, C. 1982. Rediscovery of *Stenus fossulatus* Er. (Col., Staphylinidae) in Durham. *Entomologist's Monthly Magazine, 118:* 246.

REITTER, E. 1911. *Fauna Germanica. Die Kafer des Deutschen Reiches.* Vol. 3. Stuttgart: Lutz. 436pp.

RICHARDS, O.W. 1977. Hymenoptera: Introduction and key to families. 2nd edition. *Handbooks for the identification of British insects, 6* (1).

RICHARDS, O.W. 1980. Scolioidea, Vespoidea and Sphecoidea. Hymenoptera, Aculeata. *Handbooks for the identification of British insects, 6* (3b).

RICHARDS, O.W. & HAMM, A.H. 1939. The biology of the British Pompilidae (Hymenoptera). *Transactions of the Society for British Entomology, 6* (4): 51-114.

ROBERT, P.-A. 1958. *Les Libellules (Odonates).* Neuchatel: Delachaux & Niestle. 364pp.

ROCHE, P.J.L. 1964a. (Exhibit of *Lymexylon navale* L.). *Proceedings & Transactions of the South London Entomological & Natural History Society, 1963*(1): 15.

ROCHE, P.J.L. 1964b. (Exhibit of Coleoptera from Hatfield, Herts.). *Proceedings & Transactions of the South London Entomological & Natural History Society, 1963*(1): 18.

ROZKOSNY, R. 1973. The Stratiomyoidea (Diptera) of Fennoscandia and Denmark. *Fauna Entomologica Scandinavica, 1.* 152pp.

ROZKOSNY, R. 1983. *A biosystematic study of the European Stratiomyidae (Diptera).* Vol.2. The Hague: Junk.

SANKEY, J.H.P. 1956. *Diaperis boleti* (L.) (Col., Tenebrionidae) in Hants. *Entomologist's Monthly Magazine, 92:* 405.

SAUNDERS, E. 1876. Captures of rare Coleoptera, Hemiptera, and Hymenoptera, at Chobham: including an *Odynerus* new to Britain. *Entomologist's Monthly Magazine, 13:* 113-114.

SAUNDERS, E. 1887. *Odynerus reniformis,* Gmel., at Chobham, Surrey. *Entomologist's Monthly Magazine, 24:* 68.

SAUNDERS, E. 1896. *The Hymenoptera Aculeata of the British Islands.* London: Reeve. xii + 391pp., 52pls.

SAUNDERS, E. 1900. *Pompilus (Wesmaelinius) sanguinolentus,* F.: an addition to the British list. *Entomologist's Monthly Magazine, 36:* 206-207.

SAUNDERS, E. 1903. *Odynerus (Hoplopus) simillimus,* Mor., a wasp new to the British list. *Entomologist's Monthly Magazine, 39:* 6-7.

SAUNDERS, E. 1904. Two new species of British aculeate Hymenoptera. *Entomologist's Monthly Magazine, 40:* 10-12.

SAUNDERS, E. 1909. *Osmia xanthomelana* and other aculeates at Shanklin, Isle of Wight. *Entomologist's Monthly Magazine, 45:* 237-238.

SAUNDERS, E. 1910. On four additions to the list of British Hymenoptera. *Entomologist's Monthly Magazine, 46:* 10-12.

SAUNDERS, S.S. 1880. Capture of a *Dufourea* in Hants, a genus of Hymenoptera new to Britain. *Entomologist's Monthly Magazine, 16:* 181.

SAUNDERS, S.S. 1881. Capture of rare Hymenoptera on the south coast of England. *Entomologist's Monthly Magazine, 18:* 160-161.

SCHMIEDEKNECHT, O. 1930. *Die Hymenopteren Nord- und Mitteleuropas.* Jena: Verlag von Gustav Fischer. x + 1062pp.

SEGUY, E. 1934. Dipteres (Brachyceres). Muscidae Acalypterae et Scathophagidae. *Faune de France, 28.* 832pp., 27pls.

SHARPE, D. 1917. Studies in Rhynchophora. 2 – The British Bagoini. *Entomologist's Monthly Magazine, 53:* 100-108.

SHEPHARD, G. 1970. *Dyschirius obscurus* Gyll. (Col., Carabidae) in Sussex, and a key to the British species of the genus. *Entomologist's Monthly Magazine, 106:* 91-94.

SHUTE, S.L. 1975. The specific status of *Psylliodes luridipennis* Kuts. *Entomologist's Monthly Magazine, 111:* 123-127.

SITWELL, N. 1984. *The Shell guide to Britain's threatened wildlife.* London: Collins. 208pp.

SKIDMORE, P. 1973. *Chrysanthia nigricornis* Westh. (Col., Oedemeridae) in Scotland, a genus and species new to the British list. *Entomologist, 106:* 234-237.

SKIDMORE, P. & HUNTER, F.A. 1981. *Ischnomera cinerascens* Pand. (Col., Oedemeridae) new to Britain. *Entomologist's Monthly Magazine, 116* (1980): 129-132.

SKINNER, B. 1984. *Colour identification guide to the moths of the British Isles.* Harmondsworth, Middlesex: Viking. 267pp.

SLADEN, F.W.L. 1897. *Cilissa melanura,* Nyl., a species new to the British list, and other bees at St Margaret's Bay. *Entomologist's Monthly Magazine, 33:* 229.

SLADEN, F.W.L. 1900. Aculeate Hymenoptera on the coast of Kent. *Entomologist's Monthly Magazine, 36:* 265.

SMITH, F.D. 1851a. Notes on the Hymenoptera of the Undercliff, Isle of Wight. *Zoologist, 9:* 3248-3253.

SMITH, F.D. 1851b. On the habits of *Osmia parietina. Zoologist, 9:* 3253-3255.

SMITH, F.D. 1855. *Catalogue of the British Hymenoptera in the collection of the British Museum.* London: British Museum. 252pp.

SMITH, F.D. 1858. *Catalogue of British fossorial Hymenoptera, Formicidae and Vespidae in the collection of the British Museum.* London: British Museum. 236pp.

SMITH, F.D. 1876. *Catalogue of British Hymenoptera in the British Museum. Pt.1 Andrenidae and Apidae.* 2nd edition. London: British Museum. xi + 236pp.

SMITH, K.G.V. 1957. Some miscellaneous records of bred Diptera. *Entomologist's Record & Journal of Variation, 69:* 214-216.

SOKOLOFF, P. 1980. *Practical hints for collecting and studying the Microlepidoptera.* Hanworth, Middlesex: Amateur Entomologists' Society. 40pp.

SOMMERVILLE, A. 1984. The ecology of the chequered skipper in Scotland. *British Ecological Society. Bulletin, 15:* 143-145.

SOUTH, R. 1961. *Moths of the British Isles.* Revised edition. 2 vols. London: Warne.

SOUTHWOOD, T.R.E. & LESTON, D. 1959. *Land and water bugs of the British Isles.* London: Warne. 436pp.

SPOONER, G.M. 1934. Observations on *Odynerus* (*Lionotus*) *herrichi* Sauss. in Dorset. *Entomologist's Monthly Magazine, 70:* 46-54.

SPOONER, G.M. 1937. *Psammochares rufus* Haupt, a wasp new to Britain. *Entomologist's Monthly Magazine, 73:* 220-224.

SPOONER, G.M. 1946. *Nomada errans* Lep., a bee new to Britain. *Entomologist's Monthly Magazine, 82:* 105-106.

SPOONER, G.M. 1954. Notes on species of *Omalus* (Hym., Chrysididae) including one new to the British list. *Entomologist's Monthly Magazine, 90:* 135-138.

SPOONER, G.M. 1963. On causes of the decline of *Maculinea arion* L. (Lep. Lycaenidae) in Britain. *Entomologist, 96:* 199-120.

SPRADBERY, J.P. 1973. *Wasps.* London: Sidgwick & Jackson. xvi + 408pp.

STEPHENS, J.F. 1827-35. *Illustrations of British entomology. Mandibulata.* 7 vols. London.

STEPHENS, J.F. 1839. *A manual of British Coleoptera.* London. 443pp.

STEVENS, S. 1877. Capture of *Teretrius picipes. Entomologist's Monthly Magazine, 14:* 70.

STICHEL, W. 1955-62. *Illustrierte Bestimmungstabellen der Wanzen. II. Europa (Hemiptera – Heteroptera Europae).* 4 vols. Berlin: Hermsdorf.

STOECKHERT, F.K. 1933. Die Bienen Frankens (Hym. Apid.). *Deutsche Entomologische Zeitschrift, 1932* (Supplement). viii + 294pp.

STRENZKE, K. 1951. *Dasyhelea lithotelmatica* n. sp. Appendix to Thienemann, A. Lunzer Chironomiden uber Hochalpine Diamesa – Formen. *Archiv fur Hydrobiologie*, Supplement, *18:* 1-202.

STUBBS, A.E. 1976. Craneflies of Seabrook Valley and Holy Well, Cheriton, Kent. *Transactions of the Kent Field Club, 6* (1): 43-51.

STUBBS, A.E. 1980. The largest pipunculid in the land: *Nephrocerus scutellata* (Macquart, 1834) (Diptera, Pipunculidae) new to Britain, with observations on its behaviour in Greece. *Proceedings & Transactions of the British Entomological & Natural History Society, 13:* 46-48.

STUBBS, A.E. & CHANDLER, P.J. 1978. *A dipterist's handbook.* Hanworth, Middlesex: Amateur Entomologists' Society. 255pp.

STUBBS, A.E. & FALK, S.J. 1983. *British hoverflies. An illustrated identification guide.* London: British Entomological & Natural History Society. 253pp., 12pls.

THIRION, C. 1976. Les Ichneumoninae "Amblypygi" sensu Wesmael, en Belgique. *Bulletin et Annales de la Societe Royale Entomologique de Belgique, 112:* 29-69.

THIRION, C. 1981. Les Ichneumoninae (Hymenoptera Ichneumonidae) en Belgique (2eme partie). *Bulletin et Annales de la Societe Royale Entomologique de Belgique, 117:* 229-254.

THOMAS, J.A. 1975. *The Black Hairstreak: Conservation Report.* Cambridge: Institute of Terrestrial Ecology.

THOMAS, J.A. 1980a. Why did the Large Blue become extinct in Britain? *Oryx, 15:* 243-247.

THOMAS, J.A. 1980b. The extinction of the large blue and the conservation of the black hairstreak butterflies (a contrast of failure and success). *Institute of Terrestrial Ecology Annual Report 1979:* 19-23.

THOMSON, G. 1980. *Butterflies of Scotland. A natural history.* London: Croom Helm. xvii + 267pp.

TINBERGEN, N. 1951. *The study of instinct.* Oxford: University Press.

TOBIAS, W. 1972. Zur kenntnis europaischer Hydropsychidae (Insecta: Trichoptera). *Senckenbergiana Biologica, 53:* 58-89, 245-268.

TOMLIN, J.R.le B. & JOY, N.H. 1908. Two new British beetles. *Entomologist's Monthly Magazine, 44:* 104.

TOMLIN, J.R.le B. & SHARP, W.E. 1912. Supplementary note on *Longitarsus nigerrimus,* Gyll. *Entomologist's Monthly Magazine, 48:* 284-286.

TOTTENHAM, C.E. 1954. Coleoptera: Staphylinidae, section (a) Piestinae to Euaesthetinae. *Handbooks for the identification of British insects, 4* (8a).

TOZER, D. 1947. *Hypulus quercinus* Quens. (Col., Melandryidae) in Hunts. *Entomologist's Monthly Magazine, 83:* 111-112.

TOZER, E.R. 1973. On *Rhizophagus simplex* Reitter and *R. oblongicollis* Blatch & Horner sp. rev. (Col., Rhizophagidae). *Entomologist's Monthly Magazine, 108* (1972): 219-221.

UNWIN, D.M. 1981. *A key to the families of British Diptera.* Taunton: Field Studies Council. 41pp.

UNWIN, D.M. 1984. *A key to the families of British Coleoptera (and Strepsiptera).* Taunton: Field Studies Council. 49pp.

VERDCOURT, B. 1983. Persistence of *Elater* (=*Ludius*) *ferrugineus* L. (Col., Elateridae) in a suburban garden in Windsor. *Entomologist's Monthly Magazine, 119:* 210.

VERRALL, G.H. 1909. *British Flies. 5. Stratiomyidae and succeeding families of the Diptera Brachycera of Great Britain.* London: Gurney & Jackson. 780pp.

VIEDMA, M.G. & GOMEZ-BUSTILLO, M.R. 1976. *Libro rojo de los lepidopteros ibericos.* Madrid.

WAGNER, E. 1973. Die Miridae Hahn, 1831, des Mittelmeerraumes und der Makaronesischen Inseln (Hemiptera, Heteroptera). Part 1. *Entomologische Abhandlungen und Berichte aus dem Staatlichen Museum fur Tierkunde in Dresden, 37* (Suppl.). 484pp.

WAKELY, S. 1955. Notes on collecting in the Isle of Wight. *Entomologist's Record & Journal of Variation, 67:* 79-82.

WALLACE, I.D. 1976. *The taxonomy of larvae of the British species of the family Leptoceridae (Trichoptera), with notes on their general biology.* PhD thesis, University of Newcastle-upon-Tyne.

WALLACE, I.D. 1981. A key to larvae of the family Leptoceridae (Trichoptera) in Great Britain and Ireland. *Freshwater Biology, 11:* 273-297.

WALLACE, I.D. & WIGGINS, G.B. 1978. Observations on the larva and pupa of the caddisfly genus *Hagenella* (Trichoptera: Phryganeidae). In *Proceedings 2nd International Symposium on Trichoptera:* 207-214. Crichton, M.I. (ed.). The Hague: Junk. 359pp.

WALSH, G.B. & DIBB, J.R. (eds.) 1974. *A coleopterist's handbook.* 2nd edition, revised by J. Cooter & P.W. Cribb. Hanworth, Middlesex: Amateur Entomologists' Society. 142pp.

WARREN, M.S., THOMAS, C.D. & THOMAS, J.A. 1980. Preliminary reports of the 1980 Heath Fritillary Survey to the Joint Committee for the Conservation of British Insects.

WARREN, M.S., THOMAS, C.D. & THOMAS, J.A. 1984. The status of the Heath Fritillary Butterfly *Mellicta athalia* Rott. in Britain. *Biological Conservation, 29:* 287-305.

WATERHOUSE, G.R. 1844. Notes on the habits of *Osmia atricapilla. Zoologist, 2:* 403-404.

WELCH, R.C. 1963. *Uleiota planata* (L.) (Col., Cucujidae) breeding in Berkshire. *Entomologist's Monthly Magazine, 99:* 213-214.

WELCH, R.C. 1965. *The biology of the genus* Aleochara *Grav. (Coleoptera, Staphylinidae).* PhD thesis, University of London.

WELCH, R.C. 1972. *Windsor Forest Study.* Duplicated report to Nature Conservancy, Huntingdon.

WELCH, R.C. 1977. Recent Coleoptera records from Huntingdonshire with particular reference to Monks Wood and Woodwalton Fen National Nature Reserves. *Report of the Huntingdonshire Fauna & Flora Society,* No. 29 (1976): 15-18.

WELCH, R.C. 1979a. *Haploglossa picipennis* (Gyll.) (Col., Staphylinidae), *Cryptophagus badius* Sturm and *C. lapponicus* Gyll. (Col., Cryptophagidae) from a sparrow hawk's nest near Aviemore, Inverness. *Entomologist's Monthly Magazine, 114* (1978): 240.

WELCH, R.C. 1979b. New Coleoptera records for Huntingdonshire, with particular reference to Woodwalton Fen National Nature Reserve. *Report of the Huntingdon Fauna & Flora Society,* No. 31 (1978): 20-29.

WELCH, R.C. 1982. *Aleochara villosa* Man. (Col., Staphylinidae) and other Coleoptera from a dovecote at Wytham, Oxford. *Entomologist's Monthly Magazine, 117* (1981): 197.

WELCH, R.C. 1983a. *Bibloplectus tenebrosus* (Reitt.) (Col., Pselaphidae) in East Norfolk and the Huntingdonshire fens. *Entomologist's Monthly Magazine, 119:* 38.

WELCH, R.C. 1983b. *Aleochara inconspicua* Aube (Col., Staphylinidae) in Northumberland and Hertfordshire. *Entomologist's Monthly Magazine, 119:* 197.

WELCH, R.C. 1984. *Stichoglossa semirufa* Er. (Col., Staphylinidae) in Cambridgeshire. *Entomologist's Monthly Magazine, 120:* 98.

WELCH, R.C. & COOTER, J. 1981. *The Coleoptera of Moccas Park, Herefordshire.* Duplicated report. 9pp. + Appendix 27pp.

WELLS, S.M., PYLE, R.M. & COLLINS, N.M. 1983. *The IUCN Invertebrate Red Data Book.* Gland, Switzerland: IUCN. 632pp.

WHICHER, L.S. 1952. *Hister quadrimaculatus* L. (Col., Histeridae) in N. Kent. *Entomologist's Monthly Magazine, 88:* 208.

WHITE, G. 1789. *The natural history of Selborne.* (Many editions).

WILLIAMS, S.A. 1969. *Aegialia rufa* (F.) (Col., Scarabaeidae) in Lancashire. *Entomologist's Monthly Magazine, 104* (1968): 277.

WILLMER, P. 1985. *Bees, ants and wasps. The British aculeates.* Taunton: Field Studies Council. 28pp.

WOLF, H. 1972. Hymenoptera: Pompilidae. *Insecta helvetica, 5.* 176pp.

WOOD, J.H. 1890. *Nepticula torminalis*, a species new to science. *Entomologist's Monthly Magazine, 26:* 209-210.

WOOD, J.H. 1908. Lepidoptera. *Victoria County History of Herefordshire, 1:* 110-168.

WOODROFFE, G.E. 1956a. Some Hemiptera – Heteroptera from Virginia Water, Surrey, including *Pilophorus confusus* (Kb.) (Miridae) new to Britain. *Entomologist, 89:* 84-87.

WOODROFFE, G.E. 1956b. A further note on *Pilophorus confusus* (Kb.) (Hem., Miridae). *Entomologist's Monthly Magazine, 92:* 341.

WOODROFFE, G.E. 1958. A note on *Pilophorus confusus* (Kb.), *Globiceps cruciatus* Reut. and *Adelphocoris ticinensis* (Mey-Duer) (Hem., Miridae) at Virginia Water and *Acompus rufipes* Wolff (Hem., Lygaeidae) at Chobham, Surrey. *Entomologist's Monthly Magazine, 94:* 64.

WOODROFFE, G.E. 1961. Insects on the Oar Stone rock, Tor Bay, S. Devon. *Entomologist's Monthly Magazine, 97:* 96.

WOODROFFE, G.E. 1962. *Pterotmetus staphyliniformis* (Schill.) (Hem., Lygaeidae) – a genus and species new to Britain. *Entomologist's Monthly Magazine, 98:* 214-215.

WOODROFFE, G.E. 1963. The identity of the British *Eremocoris* Fieber (Hem., Lygaeidae). *Entomologist's Monthly Magazine, 98* (1962): 262-263.

WOODROFFE, G.E. 1971. *Globicornis nigripes* F. (Col., Dermestidae) in Buckinghamshire. *Entomologist's Monthly Magazine, 106* (1970): 148.

YARROW, I.H.H. 1954. Some observations on the genus *Bombus*, with special reference to *Bombus cullumanus* (Kirby) (Hym. Apidae). *Journal of the Society for British Entomology, 5:* 34-39.

YARROW, I.H.H. 1955. *Andrena combinata* Christ (Hym., Apidae): a bee new to Britain. *Entomologist's Monthly Magazine, 91:* 234-235.

YARROW, I.H.H. 1968. Recent additions to the British bee-fauna, with comments and corrections. *Entomologist's Monthly Magazine, 104:* 60-64.

YARROW, I.H.H. 1970. Some nomenclatorial problems in the genus *Passaloecus* Shuckard and two species not before recognised as British (Hym. Sphecidae). *Entomologist's Gazette, 21:* 167-189.

YARROW, I.H.H. & GUICHARD, K.M. 1941. Some rare Hymenoptera Aculeata, with two species new to Britain. *Entomologist's Monthly Magazine, 77:* 2-13.

YEO, P.F. & CORBET, S.A. 1983. *Solitary wasps. Naturalists' Handbooks* No. 3. Cambridge: University Press. 65pp.

INDEX

This index includes all the scientific and vernacular names and synonyms of insects mentioned in the species accounts and lists. Species accounts are indexed in bold.

Designed by Lesniak Jones Liddell Ltd. Printed by Crewe Colour Printers 2M.